About the authors...

ALEXANDER S. LEVENS is Professor of Mechanical Engineering at the University of California at Berkeley.

Educated at the University of Minnesota, he received his B.S. in 1922 and did graduate work in Civil Engineering, earning his M.S. in 1924 and his C.E. in 1927. He has worked as draftsman, designer, and engineer consultant with some of America's largest industrial organizations, and has held a number of government appointments, both state and federal.

As a teacher, he has been a member of the faculties of the University of Minnesota and the University of California. He has given several special courses in nomography for engineers and scientists of the U. S. Navy and of the Boeing Airplane Company. He is author of a number of books in the field of graphics, notably GRAPHICS IN ENGINEERING AND SCIENCE, published by Wiley in 1954 and reprinted in 1957.

Professor Levens has acted as a consultant in the preparation of the Aeronautical Drafting Manual of the Society of Automotive Engineers. He is a member of the A.S.A. Committee on Preferred Practice for the Preparation of Graphs, Charts, and other Technical Illustrations. He served on the A.S.E.E. Drawing Division Committee on Advanced Graphics, and as Chairman of the Committee on Nomography.

Nomography

A . S . L E V E N S , M . S . , C . E .

Professor of Mechanical Engineering

University of California at Berkeley

New York • **John Wiley & Sons, Inc.**

Nomography

2ND EDITION

London • Chapman & Hall, Limited

Preface

During the last decade there has been an ever-increasing use of nomography. Many technical journals and books include nomograms that are very useful and time-saving in repetitive solutions of mathematical formulas. Moreover, nomograms are most helpful in showing the inter-relationship among the variables.

A more recent development, which is presented in this book, deals with the application of nomographic methods to test the validity of experimental data curves that are assumed to be consistent with the relationship among the variables.

The fields to which nomography can be applied are many. Among these are the following: statistics, electronics, ballistics, heat transfer, radioactivity, medicine, biomechanics, food technology, the various branches of engineering, physical and biological sciences, and business.

This second edition, as in the first edition of *Nomography,* emphasizes "the geometric method" in the development of the basic theory which is used for the design of alignment charts that may involve three or more variables. The treatment of the "determinant method" has been expanded considerably over that of the first edition.

The simple approach to projective transformations will encourage the reader to use the determinant method wherever appropriate.

Another feature of this edition is the introduction of the Duality Principle and its application to the transformation of families of experimental data curves from the Cartesian coordinate system (concurrency charts) to the parallel coordinate system (alignment charts). This is quite important when a high degree of accuracy is needed for interpolation between curves. In this connection the alignment chart increases the accuracy of interpolation and in addition simplifies the reading of values of the variables.

Acknowledgments are due graduate students of my classes in Nomography, especially John Bentsen, James Haughian, Robert Lawton, and Professor Perlito Reyes of the University of the Philippines for valuable suggestions; to Charles Trilling of the United States Naval Radiological Defense Laboratory, San Francisco, for critical review of the text material; to Sanford Baum, Senior Scientist, also of the United States Naval Radiological Defense Laboratory, for his cooperation in obtaining certain nomograms on radioactivity; to A. D. MacLellan, Senior Dynamics Engineer of Convair for his fine cooperation; to E. C. Varnum,

Head, Operations Research, Barber-Colman Company, who provided several circular nomograms; to Professor C. W. Shilbury, Head, Department of Engineering, Perth Technical College, Perth, West Australia, for helpful advice; and to the following publications, companies, and agencies that granted permission to reproduce certain nomograms that appear in the Appendix: Barber-Colman Company; Civil Aeronautics Administration; Crane Company; Crobalt Inc. *Design News; Electronics; Food Engineering;* Globe Valve and Regulator Company; Handy and Harman Company; Lincoln Electric Company; *Petroleum Refiner; Product Engineering; Radiological Health Handbook;* and United States Radiological Defense Laboratory.

I am grateful to the many users of the first edition for valuable suggestions that have been incorporated in this book.

A. S. LEVENS

University of California
Berkeley 4, California
August, 1959

Contents

1

Introduction

It has often been stated that "one picture is worth a thousand words." Graphical representation has proved to be an effective method for conveying technical and nontechnical information to both professional and business persons; to production personnel; to research, development, and design engineers; and to scientists.

Business magazines, newspapers, industrial brochures, technical journals, etc., usually contain charts and graphs which present information in a simple, easy-to-understand manner. Typical forms of such charts and graphs are shown in Figures 1, 2, 3, and 4.

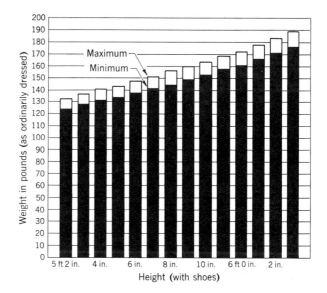

Figure 1. Column chart, showing ideal weights of men, ages 25 and over, medium frame. (Courtesy Metropolitan Life Insurance Co., Statistical Bureau.)

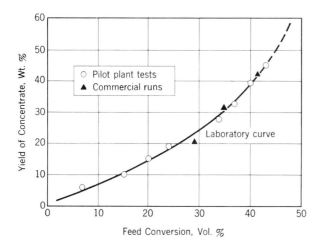

◄ **Figure 2.** Rectangular Cartesian chart. (From *ASA Standard Y-15.1,* 1958.)

Figure 3. Pie chart showing the composition of copper-base alloys for sand casting. Leaded nickel bronze. (From *ASTM Specification 11A.*) ▶

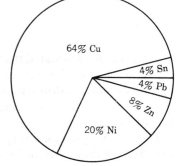

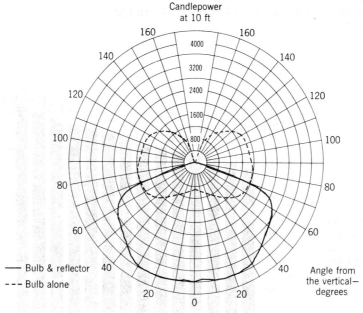

▲

Figure 4. Polar coordinate chart for the intensity distribution for a standard industrial reflector.

Cartesian Coordinate System

In technology frequent use is made of the Cartesian coordinate system for the graphical representation and solution of relationships among several variables.

Example 1

The relation between two variables may be expressed by the equation $y = 3x + 5$; another by the relation $y = x^2 + 3$ or by $y = -3x + 12$, etc. These three expressions are shown graphically in Figure 5. The x and y coordinates of points which lie on the curve and on each of the straight lines satisfy the respective equations.

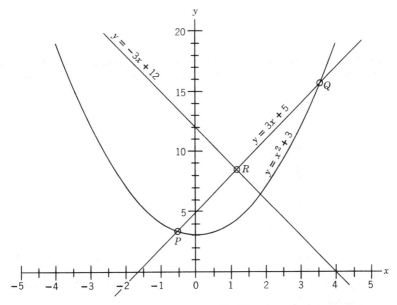

Figure 5. Cartesian coordinate representation of equations: $y = x^2 + 3$; $y = 3x + 5$; and $y = -3x + 12$.

It should also be noted that the abscissa values of points P and Q are the values of x which satisfy both equations $y = 3x + 5$ and $y = x^2 + 3$, since points P and Q are common to both the straight line and the parabola. Similarly, the abscissa value of point R is the x value which satisfies both equations $y = 3x + 5$ and $y = -3x + 12$. Each of the above equations deals with two variables. Now let us consider an equation of three variables.

Example 2

Suppose the given equation is of the form $y = mx + b$. Specifically, let us assume that the equation is $y = 3x + b$ and that b varies from 0 to 10, with intervals of 1.

In effect, this really means that we are dealing with a family of straight lines whose equations are:

$$y = 3x$$
$$y = 3x + 1$$
$$y = 3x + 2$$
$$y = 3x + 3$$
$$y = 3x + 4$$
$$y = 3x + 5$$
$$y = 3x + 6$$
$$y = 3x + 7$$
$$y = 3x + 8$$
$$y = 3x + 9$$
$$y = 3x + 10$$

Since the slope of each line is 3, the family consists of a set of parallel lines. This is shown in Figure 6. The completed chart now serves to solve the equation $y = 3x + b$ within the limits shown.

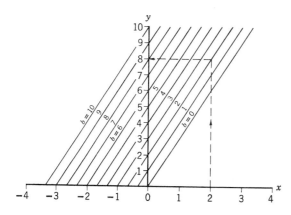

Figure 6. Family of parallel lines for $y = 3x + b$. Example: When $x = 2$ and $b = 2$, $y = 8$ (follow the arrows shown in the chart).

Example 3

Equations of the form $f_1(u) + f_2(v) + f_3(w) = f_4(q)$ may be represented by a combination of Cartesian coordinate charts.

Let us consider the relation:

$$u + v + w = q \tag{1}$$

This equation can be written as two equations:

$$u + v = T \tag{2}$$

and

$$T + w = q \tag{3}$$

These two equations are of the straight-line form $y = mx + b$. In this form the equations are:

$$T = u + v \tag{4}$$

and

$$T = q - w \tag{5}$$

It should be carefully noted that the latter two equations provide for a common axis, T. This is necessary if Figures 7 and 8, which represent equations (4) and (5), are to be conveniently combined to form the single chart, Figure 9, for the representation of the given relation stated in equation (1).

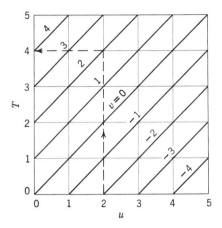

Figure 7. Cartesian coordinate representation of the equation $T = u + v$.

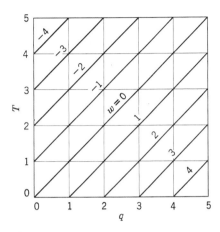

Figure 8. Cartesian coordinate representation of the equation $T = q - w$.

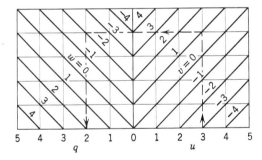

Figure 9. Cartesian coordinate representation of the equation $u + v + w = q$. Example: When $u = 3$, $v = 1$, and $w = -2$, then $q = 2$.

Example 4

When the given equation is of the form $f_1(u)f_2(v) = f_3(w)$, it can be expressed logarithmically as $\log f_1(u) + \log f_2(v) = \log f_3(w)$ and shown graphically as a straight line.

Let us consider the simple relation:

$$uv = w \tag{1}$$

which expressed logarithmically is

$$\log u + \log v = \log w \tag{2}$$

When $y = \log w$, $x = \log u$, and $b = \log v$, then $y = x + b$ (straight line).

Figure 10 shows the graphical solution of equation (1) for various values of the variables. Note that the u- and w-scales are logarithmic.

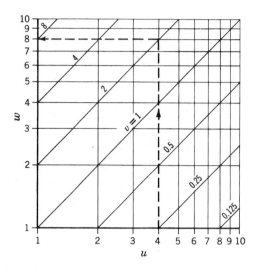

Figure 10. Representation of the equation $uv = w$. Example: When $u = 4$ and $v = 2$, $w = 8$.

Now suppose the given equation is $uvw = q$. A Cartesian chart for this equation can be designed in the following manner:

Let
$$uv = T \tag{1}$$
and
$$Tw = q \tag{2}$$
Each of these equations is of the form $f_1(u)f_2(v) = f_3(w)$.

Equation (1) can be expressed logarithmically as
$$\log u + \log v = \log T \tag{3}$$
The graphical representation of this equation (similar to Figure 10) is shown in Figure 11.

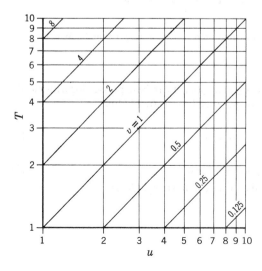

Figure 11. Cartesian coordinate representation of the equation $uv = T$.

In a similar manner:

$$\log T + \log w = \log q \tag{4}$$

or
$$\log T = \log q - \log w \tag{5}$$

Figure 12 shows the graphical representation of equation (2).
The combination of Figures 11 and 12 is shown in Figure 13.

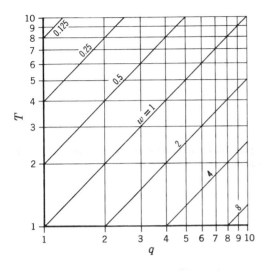

Figure 12. Cartesian coordinate representation of the equation $Tw = q$.

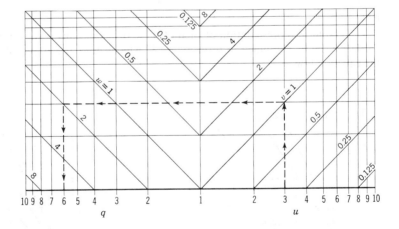

Figure 13. Cartesian coordinate representation of the equation $uvw = q$. Example: When $u = 3$, $v = 1$, and $w = 2$, then $q = 6$.

Example 5

Logarithmic scales may be eliminated by treating the equation $uv = w$ in the following manner:

Let $y = w$ and $x = u$; then $y = vx$. This equation represents a family of straight lines with the slopes equal to values of v and the y-intercept equal to 0. Figure 14 shows the family of lines for various values of v.

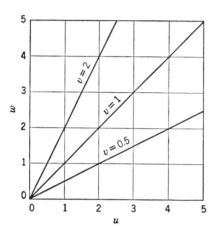

Figure 14. Cartesian coordinate representation of the equation $uv = w$.

When the given equation is $uvw = q$, then we can proceed as follows:

Let
$$uv = T \tag{1}$$
and
$$Tw = q \tag{2}$$

The graphical representation of each of these two equations is shown in Figures 15 and 16. These can be combined to form Figure 17 which shows the graphical representation of the equation $uvw = q$.

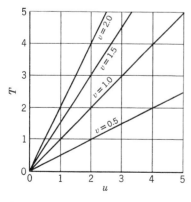

Figure 15. Cartesian coordinate representation of the equation $uv = T$.

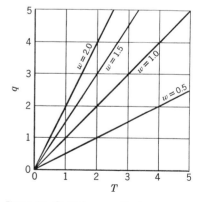

Figure 16. Cartesian coordinate representation of the equation $Tw = q$.

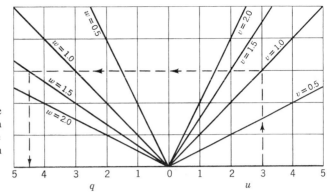

Figure 17. Cartesian coordinate representation of the equation $uvw = q$. Example: When $u = 3$, $v = 1.0$, and $w = 1.5$, then $q = 4.5$.

Alignment Charts

The simplest type of alignment chart consists of three parallel scales so graduated that a straight line which joins values on two of the scales will intersect the third scale at a value which satisfies the relation among the variables.

Example

The expression $x^2 + y^2 = r^2$ can be represented by an alignment chart consisting of three parallel scales as shown in Figure 18. A straight edge which joins values on two of the scales will intersect the third scale in a value which satisfies the given equation, i.e., a straight edge (isopleth) joining $x = 3$ with $y = 4$ intersects the r scale at $r = 5$.

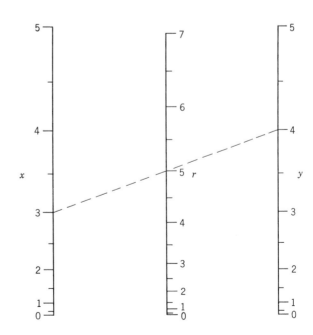

Figure 18. Alignment chart representation of the equation $x^2 + y^2 = r^2$. Example: When $x = 3$ and $y = 4$, then $r = 5$.

Alignment charts are advantageous in solving equations of three, four, five, or more variables, especially where repeated use is made of the equations. The particular form of the chart will depend upon the given expression. In many cases straight-line scales will be found quite satisfactory. In others, especially those equations which contain more than one function of the variables, curved scales will be necessary. Then, too, the alignment chart representation of some equations may well require combinations of straight-line and curved-line charts.

An example of a combination of straight line and curved scales is shown in Figure 19.

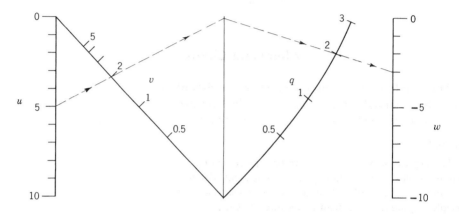

Figure 19. Combination nomogram—straight line and curved scales. Equation: $uv + wq = q^2$. Example: When $u = 5$, $v = 2$, and $q = 2$, then $w = -3$.

A variety of alignment charts can be developed once the fundamentals are well understood. The only real limitation is the degree of ingenuity of the designer.

The Basic Relationship Between Cartesian
Charts and Alignment Charts

Let us consider Figure 20, which shows a Cartesian chart of the equation $u + v = w$, and Figure 21, which shows an alignment chart of the same equation.

Any point, such as A in Figure 20, is the common point (point of concurrency) of three lines, i.e., $u = 3$, $v = 3$, and $w = 6$. These values satisfy the given equation $u + v = w$.

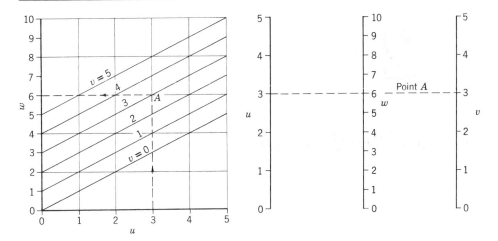

Figure 20. Cartesian chart of the equation $u + v = w$.

Figure 21. Alignment chart of the equation $u + v = w$.

In Figure 21, however, these three lines $u = 3$, $v = 3$, and $w = 6$ are represented by points (the graduation 3 on the u scale, the graduation 3 on the v scale, and the graduation 6 on the w scale, respectively).

Now it should be observed that in Figure 20 three lines pass through point A, whereas in Figure 21 the "corresponding" lines lie on a line which "corresponds" to point A of Figure 20.

The relationship "For every line in the Cartesian chart there is a corresponding point in the alignment chart (for the same equation)" will be most useful, later, when we discuss transformations from a rectangular Cartesian coordinate system to a parallel coordinate system, Chapter 16.

The introductory material that has been presented discloses the fact that nomograms may be of the *concurrency* (Cartesian coordinate) type, or of the *alignment* form, or of combinations of both. In addition, the basic relationship between the Cartesian coordinate system and the parallel coordinate system has been observed.

The major portion of the material covered in this book deals with the theory and design of alignment charts involving straight-line scales, curved scales (including circular), and combinations of both. Primary use will be made of the "geometric method" in the development of the theory for the design of alignment charts involving straight-line scales and curved scales. The advantages in using the "method of determinants" will be pointed out in connection with the design of alignment charts involving two or three curves.

The application of the basic relationship between the Cartesian coordinate and parallel coordinate systems will be emphasized in Chapter 16.

Examples of nomograms which may prove useful in the fields of research, development, and design; production, statistics, and business are included in the Appendix.

2

Functional Scales

The first step necessary in the design of alignment charts is a thorough under-standing of the use of functional scales.

A *graphical scale* is a curved or straight line carrying graduations which corre-spond to a set of numbers arranged in order of magnitude. If the distances be-tween successive points on the scale are equal for equal increments of the vari-able, the scale is said to be uniform; if not, the scale is nonuniform.

A *functional scale* is one on which the graduations are marked with the "values of the variable" and on which the distances to the graduations are laid off in pro-portion to the corresponding values of the *"function of the variable."* The dis-tances are laid off from an initial point of the scale, not necessarily the zero point.

Example 1

Suppose the function of u, $f(u)$, is u^3 (Figure 22). Let u vary from 0 to 5. Form the following table:

u	0	1	2	3	4	5
$f(u) = u^3$	0	1	8	27	64	125
$X = u^3$	0	1	8	27	64	125

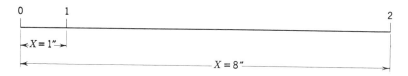

Figure 22.

We can readily understand that the above scale would be 125 in. long if the inch is used as the unit of measure. Obviously this is not a convenient length. In order to have a scale of a more practical length, a **scale modulus** or scale multiplier is introduced, i.e., $X = mu^3$ or $m = X/u^3$, where m is the scale modulus. The expression $X = mf(u)$ is called the **scale equation.**

Figure 23. Functional scale for $f(u) = u^3$.

Now suppose that the scale is to be approximately 6 in. long (Figure 23). Then $m = X/u^3 = 6/125 = 0.048$. To simplify the computational work, $m = 0.05$ will be used. This means that the scale length will be 6.25 in. instead of 6 in. The new table then is:

u	0	1	2	3	4	5
$f(u) = u^3$	0	1	8	27	64	125
$X = 0.05u^3$	0	0.05	0.40	1.35	3.20	6.25

Figure 24. Functional scale for $f(u) = u^3$.

In the practical use of functional scales further subdivision of the scale into fifths or tenths may be advisable. Suppose that the range of the variable is from 2 to 4 and that the scale length is approximately 6 in. (Figure 24). In this case $X = m[f(u_2) - f(u_1)] = m(4^3 - 2^3) = 56m$ or $m = 6/56 = 0.107$. For convenience we shall use 0.1. Then we have the table:

u	2	3	4
$f(u) = u^3$	8	27	64
$X = 0.1(u^3 - 2^3)$	0	1.9	5.6

It should be noted that in this case the initial point of the scale is 2, not 0.

The distance between any two graduations, u_1 and u_2, is equal to $X = m[f(u_2) - f(u_1)]$.

Any unit of length other than inches could be adopted as the unit of measure. It is most important to observe (1) that the distance between any two points on the scale is equal to the product of the modulus and the difference in the **values of the function** for the two points, **not** the **values of the variables**; and (2) that the points are marked with the value of the variable.

Suppose that the $f(u)$ is $2u^3$. The scale equation is $X = m(2u^3)$. If u varies from 0 to 4, and the scale length is to be approximately 6 in., then

$$m = \frac{6}{2(4^3)} = \frac{6}{128} = 0.047$$

For convenience, $m = 0.05$ will be used. This lengthens the scale to 6.4 in.

Hence, $X = 0.05(2u^3)$ or $X = 0.1u^3$. It is important to note that 0.1 is the **effective modulus,** whereas 0.05 is the **actual modulus** of the scale. *The effective modulus is used in graduating the scale. The "actual modulus" is necessary in the location of scales that occur in alignment chart design.* This distinction will be evident later when the design and construction of alignment charts are considered.

If the function of u is $(u + 2)$ (Figure 25), then the scale equation is $X = m(u + 2)$. If u varies from 0 to 12, and the scale is 6 in. long, then

$$m = \frac{6 \text{ in.}}{[(12 + 2) - (0 + 2)]} = \frac{6}{12} = \frac{1}{2} \text{ in.}$$

or
$$X = \tfrac{1}{2}(u + 2)$$

u	0	1	2	. .	12
$f(u) = (u + 2)$	2	3	4	. .	14
$X = \tfrac{1}{2}(u + 2)$	1	1.5	2	. .	7

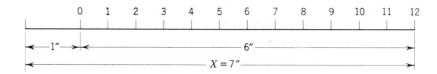

Figure 25. Scale for $f(u) = (u + 2)$.

In this case, the constant 2 merely shifts the zero point of the scale a distance from the reference point of the scale equal to $\tfrac{1}{2}(0 + 2) = 1$ in. Except for the shift of the zero point, the scale is the same as though the $f(u)$ were u, because the total length of the scale is $X = \tfrac{1}{2} \times 12 = 6$ in., which is the same as $X = \tfrac{1}{2}[(12 + 2) - (0 + 2)] = 6$ in.

Example 2

$$f(u) = \sqrt{u}$$

where u varies from 0 to 100, scale length approximately 6 in. (Figure 26).

$$m = \frac{6}{\sqrt{100} - \sqrt{0}} = \frac{6}{10}; \qquad X = 0.6\sqrt{u}$$

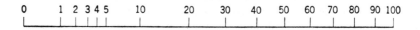

Figure 26. Functional scale for $f(u) = \sqrt{u}$.

Example 3

$$f(u) = \frac{1}{u^2}$$

where u varies from 1 to 3, scale length 6 in. (Figure 27).

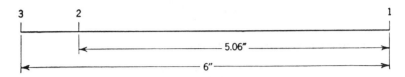

Figure 27. Functional scale for $f(u) = 1/u^2$.

$$m = \frac{6}{\left(\frac{1}{1^2} - \frac{1}{3^2}\right)} = 6.75; \qquad X = 6.75\left(\frac{1}{u^2} - \frac{1}{1^2}\right)$$

u	1	2	3
$f(u) = \dfrac{1}{u^2}$	1	$\frac{1}{4}$	$\frac{1}{9}$
$X = 6.75\left(\dfrac{1}{u^2} - \dfrac{1}{1^2}\right)$	0	$-\frac{81}{16}$	-6

Note that the negative distances, X, are laid off to the left of point 1, since distances laid off to the right have been regarded as positive. Note: The scale could be graduated with respect to $u = 3$ as the initial point.

Example 4

$$f(u) = \log u$$

where u varies from 2 to 10, scale length 7 in. (Figure 28).

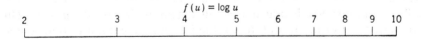

Figure 28. Functional scale for $f(u) = \log u$.

$$m = \frac{7}{\log 10 - \log 2} = \frac{7}{\log 5} = 10; \qquad X = 10(\log u - \log 2)$$

A few points are tabulated below:

u	2	4	8	10
$\log u$	0.301	0.602	0.903	1.000
$X = 10(\log u - \log 2)$	0	3.01	6.02	6.99

We should note that (1) powers *greater* than 1 "stretch out" the *upper* end of the scale and (2) powers *less* than 1 "stretch out" the *lower* end of the scale. This is clearly seen in Figures 23 and 26 respectively.

Example 5

Now let us consider

$$f(u) = \frac{2u + 3}{u + 5}$$

Suppose *u* varies from 0 to 10, and *m* = 4; then the scale equation is

$$X = 4\left(\frac{2u + 3}{u + 5}\right)$$

Corresponding values of *u* and *X* are shown in the table below.

u	0	1	2	3	4	5	6	7	8	9	10
X	2.40	3.33	4.00	4.50	4.89	5.20	5.45	5.67	5.85	6.00	6.13

The functional scale is shown in Figure 29.

Figure 29. Scale for $f(u) = \dfrac{2u + 3}{u + 5}$.

Projection Method

It is only necessary to establish two graduations on the scale, e.g. *u* = 0 and *u* = 10, and then locate the center of projection through which a family of lines can be drawn to intersect the *u*-scale in points that correspond to the other values of *u*. In Figure 30 the graduations for *u* = 0 and *u* = 10 are first established, either by calculations as shown in the above table, or by an arbitrary length. Through *u* = 0 a temporary line is drawn at a convenient angle with the *u*-scale. This line is graduated uniformly from 0 to 10, the 0's being common to both the *u*-scale and the temporary scale. Now a line is drawn through the 10's of both scales. This line is intersected by another line which passes through the graduation − 5 on the temporary scale, parallel to the *u*-scale. The point of intersection is the center of projection, *P*. The family of lines drawn through point *P* and the graduations on the temporary scale intersects the *u*-scale in corresponding values of *u*, as shown in Figure 30.

It should be carefully noted that when *u* = − 5, *X* = ∞; hence the parallel to the *u*-scale was drawn. Of course, point *P* could be located by drawing (instead of the parallel) a line through any two pairs of corresponding values on the *u*- and temporary scales. This means, however, that the location of the values of *u* would have to be computed. The advantage in using the first approach is self-evident, since we can assign any length to the *u*-scale.

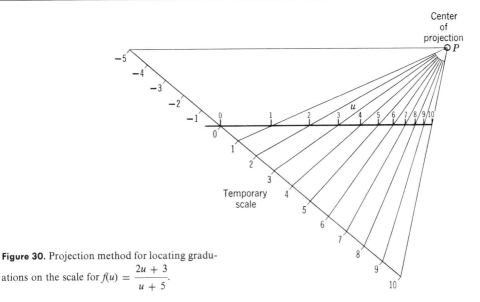

Figure 30. Projection method for locating graduations on the scale for $f(u) = \dfrac{2u + 3}{u + 5}$.

Now suppose that the values of u vary from 1 to 10. In this case we draw the temporary scale through the value $u = 1$ and lay off a uniform scale from 1 to 10. See Figure 31. The center of projection, point P, is located in the same manner as shown in Figure 30.

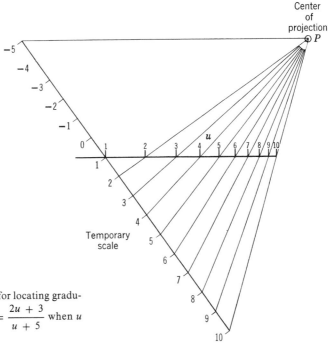

Figure 31. Projection method for locating graduations on the scale for $f(u) = \dfrac{2u + 3}{u + 5}$ when u
varies from 1 to 10.

The projection method is a convenience in locating graduations. In some cases the intersections of the projection lines (rays through point P) with the scale bearer may not be dependable when the angle between the rays and the scale is small. In such cases it is better to draw the temporary scale through a different value of the scale. For a high degree of accuracy it would be best to compute the locations of those graduations about which there may be some doubt.

Subdivision of Nonuniform Scales

Subdivision of nonuniform scales can, of course, be made by computing distances from the scale equation. If the scale is logarithmic, subdivisions can easily be projected from reliable printed log scales, employing the methods shown in Figures 32 and 33.

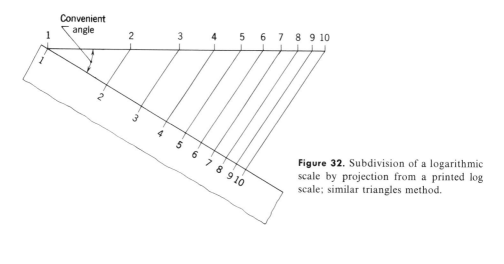

Figure 32. Subdivision of a logarithmic scale by projection from a printed log scale; similar triangles method.

Figure 33. Use of the projection method to subdivide a log scale from a printed log scale.

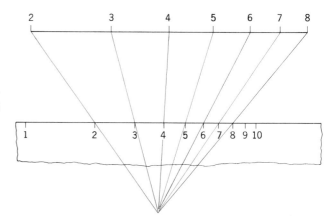

In a number of cases however, subdividing a nonuniform scale can be accomplished, reasonably well, by using the projective-ray method. First let us prepare a "projective pencil" (concurrent rays) as shown in Figure 34. This should be done on a transparent sheet.

Now suppose we wish to subdivide the scale shown in Figure 35 to include all

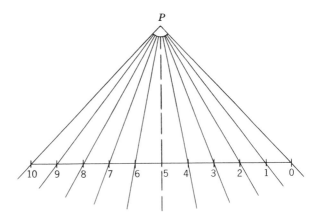

Figure 34. Projective pencil.

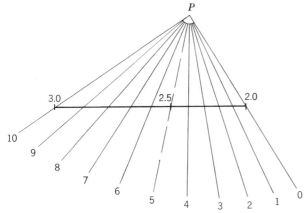

Figure 35. Subdivision of scale using the projective pencil method.

of the tenths graduations between 2.0 and 3.0. Place the projective pencil over the scale so that rays *P*-0, *P*-5, *P*-10 pass through 2.0, 2.5, and 3.0 respectively. Now, locate the intersections of the other rays with the scale (use a needle point or compass point to prick through the overlay). This method is based on the assumption that the scale is homographic.* If it is, the locations of the subdivisions are quite accurate; if not, they are close approximations.

* A homographic function is of the form $y = \dfrac{A \cdot f(x) + B}{C \cdot f(x) + D}$, where $AD - BC \neq 0$. The distances to

the scale graduations (from an initial point) are proportional to $\dfrac{A \cdot f(x) + B}{C \cdot f(x) + D}$.

Adjacent Scales for Equations of the Form

$$f_1(u) = f_2(v)$$

Equations of the above form may be solved by graduating both sides of one line in such a manner that a point on the scale will give values which satisfy the given equation. The scale equations are:

$$X_u = m_u f_1(u) \qquad \text{and} \qquad X_v = m_v f_2(v)$$

Since $f_1(u) = f_2(v)$ and $X_u = X_v$, i.e., for any point on the scale, then $m_u = m_v$.

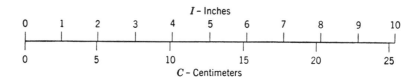

Figure 36. Adjacent scales for the equation $2.54I = C$.

Example 1

Consider the relation $2.54I = C$ (Figure 36), where I represents inches and C represents centimeters. Let I vary from 0 to 10; scale length 6 in. If we rewrite the given equation so that

$$I = \frac{C}{2.54}$$

then $X_I = m_I I$,   or $6 = m_I 10$

from which $m_I = 0.6$

Thus, the scale equation is $X_I = 0.6I$. The scale equation for C is $X_c = 0.6(C/2.54) = 0.236C$.

Note: Having computed the scale modulus for I, the *same* modulus must be used for C. If the scale modulus for C had been computed first, then this modulus would apply to I.

Example 2

$C = \pi D$ (Figure 37). $C = $ circumference of a circle, with diameter D. Let D vary from 2 to 10 in. Scale length 6 in.

The scale equations are:

$$X_c = m_c \left(\frac{C}{\pi} \right)$$

and $X_D = m_D D;$ or $6 = m_D(10 - 2);$ $m_D = \frac{3}{4}$

hence $X_D = \frac{3}{4}(D - 2)$

and $X_c = \frac{3}{4}\frac{C}{\pi} = \frac{3C}{4\pi} = 0.239C$

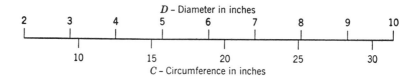

Figure 37. Adjacent scales for the equation $C = \pi D$.

To locate a point on the scale C, e.g., $C = 10$, proceed as follows: Point 10 on the C-scale is 2.39 in. from the zero point of that scale $[X_c = 0.239(10)]$. Since point 2 of the D-scale is $1\frac{1}{2}$ in., $(X = \frac{3}{4} \times 2)$ from the zero point of the D-scale, point 10 is $(2.39 - 1.50) = 0.89$ in. to right of point 2. (It should be observed that $C = 0$ when $D = 0$.) Point 20 of the C-scale is 2.39 in. to the right of point 10 $[X_c = 0.239 \times (20 - 10) = 2.39 \text{ in.}]$. Points between 10 and 20 can easily be located by subdivision. Points beyond 20 can be located in a similar manner. Of course, a point of the C-scale could be located by solving C from a specific value of D. The scale could then be graduated from the scale equation,

$$X_c = 0.239(C_2 - C_1)$$

Example 3

$U = \sin V$ (Figure 38). Let V vary from $0°$ to $90°$; scale length 6 in.
The scale equations are:

$$X_u = m_u U \tag{1}$$

and
$$X_v = m_v \sin V \tag{2}$$

From equation (2), $6 = m_v(\sin 90° - \sin 0°)$; $m_v = 6$. Hence the scale equations are:

$$X_u = 6U$$

and
$$X_v = 6 \sin V$$

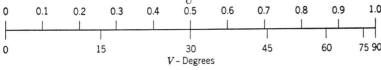

Figure 38. Adjacent scales for the equation $U = \sin V$.

Alternative Solution (Figure 39)

Let $U^2 = \sin^2 V$. Now

$$X_U = m_U U^2 \tag{1}$$

and
$$X_V = m_V \sin^2 V \tag{2}$$

From equation (2) $$m_V = \frac{6}{\sin^2 90° - \sin^2 0°}$$

Therefore $X_V = 6 \sin^2 V$ and $X_U = 6U^2$

This solution is included to show another approach to the problem if it is desired to make the V-scale more nearly uniform.

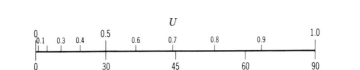

Figure 39. Adjacent scales for the equation $U = \sin V$ (alternative solution).

Example 4

$V = \frac{4}{3}\pi r^3$ (Figure 40). $V =$ the volume of a sphere of radius r. Let r vary from 0 to 5 in.; length of scale to be approximately 6 in. Then

$$X_r = m_r r^3 \qquad \text{and} \qquad X_v = m_v \frac{3V}{4\pi}$$

$$m_r = \tfrac{6}{125} = 0.048$$

For convenience, use $m_r = 0.05$. Then

$$X_r = 0.05 r^3 \qquad \text{and} \qquad X_v = 0.05 \times \frac{3V}{4\pi} = 0.0119 V$$

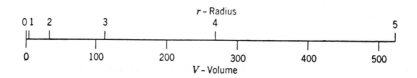

Figure 40. Adjacent scales for the equation $V = \frac{4}{3}\pi r^3$.

Alternative Solution (Figure 41)

The given equation is written as $r = \left(\dfrac{3V}{4\pi}\right)^{\frac{1}{3}}$. The scale for the variable, r, will be uniform; and the lower end of the V-scale will be "stretched out" (recall Example 2, page 14).

Now $\qquad\qquad X_r = m_r r$ (1)

and $\qquad\qquad X_V = m_V \left(\dfrac{3V}{4\pi}\right)^{\frac{1}{3}}$ (2)

From equation (1) $\qquad m_r = \dfrac{X_r}{r} = \dfrac{6}{5} = 1.2$

or $\qquad\qquad X_r = 1.2r$

and $\qquad\qquad X_V = 1.2 \left(\dfrac{3V}{4\pi}\right)^{\frac{1}{3}} = 0.745\ V^{\frac{1}{3}}$

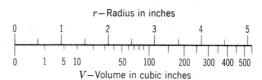

Figure 41. Adjacent scales for the equation $V = \frac{4}{3}\pi r^3$ (alternative solution).

This solution provides for "stretch out" of the lower end of the V-scale while the r-scale is uniform. This arrangement is desirable because the *per cent* reading error is more uniform throughout the scale.

Nonadjacent Scales for Equations of the Form

$$f_1(u) = f_2(v)$$

In the foregoing material it was pointed out that the *same* modulus was used in each scale equation. It may be desirable to use two different moduli. This can be done by separating the scales in the following manner. (See Figure 42.)

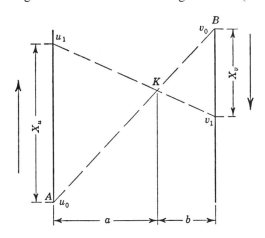

Figure 42.

Let $X_u = m_u f_1(u)$ (1)

and $X_v = m_v f_2(v)$ (2)

u_0 and v_0 are zero values of the functions of u and v; and K is a point located on line AB so that any line passing through K and a selected point on the u- or v-scale will cut the other scale in a value which satisfies the equation.

From the similar triangles $A u_1 K$ and $B v_1 K$,

$$\frac{X_u}{X_v} = \frac{AK}{KB} = \frac{a}{b}$$

Therefore $\dfrac{m_u f_1(u)}{m_v f_2(v)} = \dfrac{a}{b}$ [from equations (1) and (2)]

Since $f_1(u) = f_2(v)$,

$$\frac{a}{b} = \frac{m_u}{m_v}$$

Hence point K can be located on the diagonal AB by dividing it into the ratio

$$\frac{AK}{KB} = \frac{a}{b} = \frac{m_u}{m_v}$$

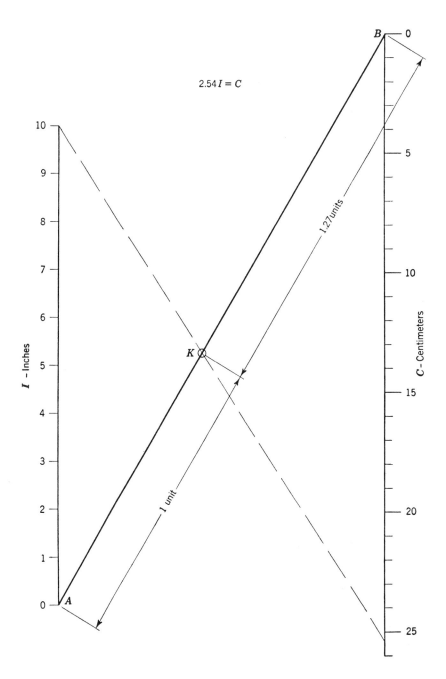

Figure 43. Separated scales for the relation $2.54I = C$.

Example

Again consider the equation $2.54I = C$ (Figure 43).

Let
$$X_I = \tfrac{1}{2}I; \qquad X_c = \left(\frac{2.54}{4}\right)\left(\frac{C}{2.54}\right) = \frac{C}{4}$$

It should be observed that by choosing the constant $2.54/4$, we obtain a convenient *effective* modulus for the C-scale.

$$\frac{AK}{KB} = \frac{m_I}{m_C} = \frac{\tfrac{1}{2}}{\frac{2.54}{4}} = \frac{1}{1.27}$$

EXERCISES

Functional Scales*

2.1   Construct a scale for the function $f(u) = (u^2 + 2u)$. u varies from -10 to $+10$. Scale length about 8 in.

2.2   Construct a scale for the function $f(u) = 3 \log u$. u varies from 10 to 250. Scale length about 6 in.

2.3   Construct a scale for the function $f(u) = u^{5/2}$. u varies from 5 to 9. Scale length about 8 in.

2.4   Construct a scale for the function $f(u) = 1/u$. u varies from 1 to 8. Scale length about 6 in.

2.5   Construct a scale for the function $f(u) = \sin u$. u varies from $0°$ to $180°$. Select suitable scale length.

2.6   Construct a scale for the function $f(u) = \cos u$. u varies from $0°$ to $90°$. Select suitable scale length.

2.7   Construct a scale for the function $f(u) = (u^2 + 3)$. u varies from 0 to 7. Select suitable scale length.

2.8   Construct a scale for the function $f(u) = \log u$. u varies from 1 to 9. Select suitable scale length.

2.9   Construct a scale for the function $f(u) = \dfrac{u^2 + 5}{2u^2 + 3}$. u varies from 5 to 10. Select suitable scale length.

* *Suggestions for Drawing Scales:*

1. Make the shortest strokes $\tfrac{1}{10}$ in.
2. Make the intermediate strokes $\tfrac{3}{20}$ in.
3. Make the longest strokes $\tfrac{3}{16}$ in.
4. Adjacent strokes should not be less than $\tfrac{1}{20}$ in. apart, nor more than $\tfrac{1}{2}$ in.
5. The distance between labeled strokes should not be less than $\tfrac{1}{4}$ in.
6. The interval between units should be divided into fifths or tenths, if necessary.

Suggestions for Graphic Precision:

1. Layout lines should be sharp and light.
2. Finish lines should be sharp and dark.
3. Use as large a scale as possible.
4. If the chart is to be reduced, use a reducing glass to determine the relative weights of lines required in the original drawing.

2.10 Construct a scale for the function $f(u) = \dfrac{u}{u+2}$. u varies from -10 to $+10$. Select suitable scale length.

2.11 Construct a scale for the function $f(t)$ given by the following table, where $f(t)$ is the vapor pressure in air corresponding to t, the air temperature, in degrees Fahrenheit:

t	$f(t)$	t	$f(t)$
0	0.0383	55	0.432
5	0.0491	60	0.517
10	0.0631	65	0.616
15	0.0810	70	0.732
20	0.1026	75	0.866
25	0.130	80	1.022
30	0.164	85	1.201
35	0.203	90	1.408
40	0.247	95	1.645
45	0.298	100	1.916
50	0.360		

2.12 Given the following experimental data:

u	$f(u)$	u	$f(u)$
0	0.05	26	0.12
11	0.065	32	0.17
18	0.085	40	0.33

Draw a smooth curve through the points and construct a functional scale for $f(u)$ from the curve.

Adjacent and Nonadjacent Scales

2.13 Construct adjacent scales for the expression $A = \dfrac{\pi d^2}{576}$

where A = area of circle in square feet;
         d varies from 2 to 10 in.

2.14 Construct adjacent scales for the expression $h = \dfrac{v^2}{2g}$

where h (3 to 15 ft) = velocity head in feet;
         v = velocity in feet per second;
         g = 32.2 ft/sec².

2.15 Construct adjacent scales for the expression $F = \frac{9}{5}C + 32$

where F varies from $-40°$ to $212°$.

2.16 Construct adjacent scales for the expression $L = \dfrac{gt^2}{4\pi^2}$

where L varies from 2 to 8 ft;
         g = 32.2 ft/sec².

2.17 Construct adjacent scales for the expression $H = 2.3P$

where P varies from 25 to 350 psi.

2.18 Construct adjacent scales for the expression $hp = 0.001818F$

where hp = horsepower;
         F = foot-pounds per second (500 to 500,000).

2.19 Construct nonadjacent scales for the expression $C = \frac{5}{9}(F - 32)$

where C varies from $-40°$ to $100°$. (Select moduli so that the same degree of reading accuracy is maintained for both variables.)

2.20 Construct nonadjacent scales for the expression $P = A(1 + R)^n$

where $P =$ principal sum in dollars;
       $R =$ rate of interest;
       $n =$ number of times compounded.
  Let $A = \$100; R = 6\%; n$ (0 to 10).

2.21 Construct nonadjacent scales for the expression $H = 2.3P$

where $H =$ pressure head in feet.
       $P =$ pressure in pounds per square
             inch (10 to 120).

2.22 Construct nonadjacent scales for the expression $V = \frac{4}{3}\pi R^3$

where $V =$ volume of sphere;
       $R =$ radius of sphere (10 to 20 in.).

2.23 Construct nonadjacent scales for the expression $S = 4\pi R^2$

where $S =$ area of sphere;
       $R =$ radius of sphere (10 to 20 in.).

2.24 Construct nonadjacent scales for the expression $A = \frac{S^2}{4}\sqrt{3}$

where $A =$ area of an equilateral triangle;
       $S =$ length of a side (5 to 15 in.).

2.25 Construct nonadjacent scales for the expression in Problem 2.14.

3

Alignment Charts—Parallel Scales for the Form

$$f_1(u) + f_2(v) = f_3(w)$$

An alignment chart in its simplest form consists of three parallel scales so graduated that a straight line cutting the scales will determine three points whose values satisfy the given equation.

In general, alignment charts may consist of three or more straight-line scales, of curved scales, or of combinations of both.

Suppose we have three parallel scales (Figure 44), A, B, and C, so graduated that lines (isopleths) 1 and 2 cut the scales in values which satisfy the equation $f_1(u) + f_2(v) = f_3(w)$. Now,

$$X_u = m_u[f_1(u_1) - f_1(u_0)]$$
$$X_v = m_v[f_2(v_1) - f_2(v_0)]$$
$$X_w = m_w[f_3(w_1) - f_3(w_0)]$$

If u_0, v_0, and w_0 represent zero values of the functions, and if line 2 is any line, we may drop the subscripts and write simply

$$X_u = m_u f_1(u) \tag{1}$$
$$X_v = m_v f_2(v) \tag{2}$$
$$X_w = m_w f_3(w) \tag{3}$$

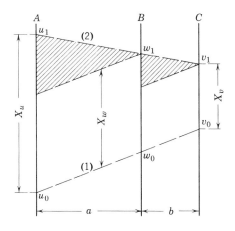

Figure 44.

Let us agree further that the spacing of the scales is in the ratio a/b. If we graduate the scales for $f_1(u)$ and $f_2(v)$ in accordance with their scale equations (1) and (2), respectively, what will be the modulus for the scale equation of $f_3(w)$ and what will the ratio a/b equal if the chart satisfies this relation $f_1(u) + f_2(v) = f_3(w)$?

In Figure 44 draw lines through points w_1 and v_1 parallel to line $u_0 v_0$. The shaded triangles are similar by construction; hence

$$\frac{X_u - X_w}{X_w - X_v} = \frac{a}{b}$$

Cross-multiplying, we obtain

$$X_u b + X_v a = X_w(a + b)$$

Dividing through by ab,

$$\frac{X_u}{a} + \frac{X_v}{b} = \frac{X_w}{\dfrac{ab}{a+b}}$$

Since
$$X_u = m_u f_1(u) \tag{1}$$
$$X_v = m_v f_2(v) \tag{2}$$
$$X_w = m_w f_3(w) \tag{3}$$

Then
$$\frac{m_u f_1(u)}{a} + \frac{m_v f_2(v)}{b} = \frac{m_w f_3(w)}{\dfrac{ab}{a+b}}$$

This equation can be made identical to the desired form
$$f_1(u) + f_2(v) = f_3(w)$$

when we set
$$\frac{a}{b} = \frac{m_u}{m_v} \quad \text{and} \quad m_w = \frac{ab}{a+b} = \frac{m_u m_v{}^*}{m_u + m_v}$$

Design Summary

Thus, to construct an alignment chart for an equation of the form $f_1(u) + f_2(v) = f_3(w)$:

1. Place the parallel scales for u and v a convenient distance apart.
2. Graduate them in accordance with their scale equations $X_u = m_u f_1(u)$ and $X_v = m_v f_2(v)$.
3. Locate the scale for w so that its distance from the u-scale is to its distance from the v-scale as $m_u / m_v = a/b$.
4. Graduate the w-scale from its scale equation $X_w = \dfrac{m_u m_v}{m_u + m_v} f_3(w)$.

Example 1

$u + v = w$ (Figure 45). Let u vary from 0 to 10, and v vary from 0 to 15. Suppose that the scale lengths are to be 6 in.

Now
$$m_u = \tfrac{6}{10} = 0.6; \qquad\qquad X_u = 0.6u$$
and
$$m_v = \tfrac{6}{15} = 0.4; \qquad\qquad X_v = 0.4v$$
and
$$m_w = \frac{0.6 \times 0.4}{0.6 + 0.4} = 0.24; \qquad X_w = 0.24w$$

$$\frac{m_u}{m_v} = \frac{0.6}{0.4} = \frac{3}{2} = \frac{a}{b}$$

* If we let
$$r = \frac{m_u}{m_v} = \frac{a}{b} = \frac{p}{q}$$

where p and q are small whole integers in which r can sometimes be expressed, then we have the following useful relations:

$$\frac{a}{a+b} = \frac{m_u}{m_u + m_v} = \frac{p}{p+q} = \frac{r}{r+1}$$

$$\frac{b}{a+b} = \frac{m_v}{m_u + m_v} = \frac{q}{p+q} = \frac{1}{r+1}$$

The distance $(a + b)$ is usually selected first to suit the width of paper used. The above relations, then, determine a and b.

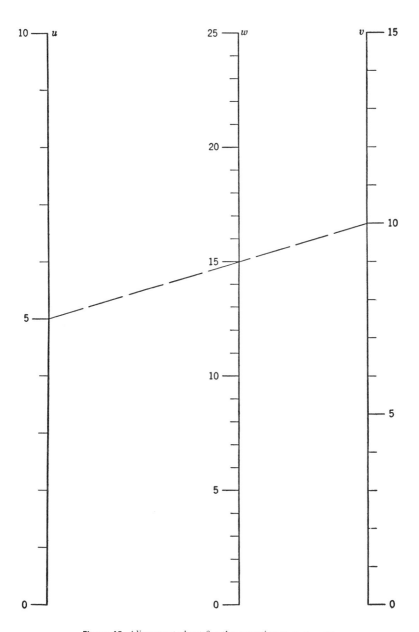

Figure 45. Alignment chart for the equation $u + v = w$.

Now suppose that it is desirable to cut off the chart at the line 1 (Figure 46), eliminating the portion below line 1. The scale equations will then be (using line 1 as the base line):

$$X_u = m_u[f_1(u_2) - f_1(u_1)]$$
$$X_v = m_v[f_2(v_2) - f_2(v_1)]$$
$$X_w = m_w[f_3(w_2) - f_3(w_1)]$$

where u_1, v_1, and w_1 satisfy the equation $f_1(u) + f_2(v) = f_3(w)$.

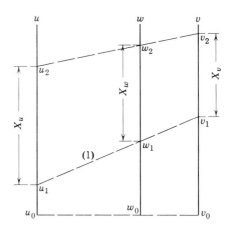

Figure 46.

Example 2

$u + v = w$ (Figure 47). Let u vary from 2 to 6, and v vary from 3 to 8. Length of scales 6 in.

Now
$$m_u{}^* = \frac{6}{6-2} = \frac{3}{2}; \qquad X_u = \frac{3}{2}(u-2)$$

$$m_v = \frac{6}{8-3} = \frac{6}{5}; \qquad X_v = \frac{6}{5}(v-3)$$

Since
$$m_w = \frac{m_u m_v}{m_u + m_v}$$

$$m_w = \frac{\frac{3}{2} \times \frac{6}{5}}{\frac{3}{2} + \frac{6}{5}} = \frac{\frac{18}{10}}{\frac{27}{10}} = \frac{2}{3}$$

Since $u_1 = 2$ and $v_1 = 3$, therefore $w_1 = 5$ (from the original equation $u + v = w$). Hence,

$$X_w = \tfrac{2}{3}(w - 5)$$

$$\frac{a}{b} = \frac{m_u}{m_v} = \frac{\frac{3}{2}}{\frac{6}{5}} = \frac{5}{4}$$

Form the following tables:

u	2	3	4	5	6
$f_1(u) = u$	2	3	4	5	6
$X_u = \tfrac{3}{2}(u-2)$	0	1.5 in.	3.0 in.	4.5 in.	6.0 in.

* Remember $X_u = m_u f(u)$. Therefore $m_u = \dfrac{X_u}{f_1(u_2) - f_1(u_1)}$. In this case $X_u = 6$ in. and $[f_1(u_2)] - f_1(u_1)] = (6 - 2)$.

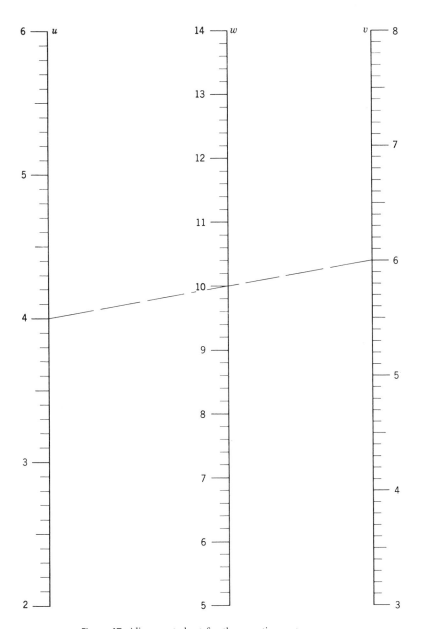

Figure 47. Alignment chart for the equation $u + v = w$.

v	3	4	5	6	7	8
$f_2(v) = v$	3	4	5	6	7	8
$X_v = \frac{6}{5}(v - 3)$	0	1.2 in.	2.4 in.	3.6 in.	4.8 in.	6.0 in.

w	5	6	7	. . .	14
$f_3(w) = w$	5	6	7	. . .	14
$X_w = \frac{2}{3}(w - 5)$	0	$\frac{2}{3}$ in.	$\frac{4}{3}$ in.	. . .	6 in.

Much of the calculations set forth in the above tables can be eliminated if we compute the location of the end points for each scale, and then project the other points geometrically.

Example 3

$I = \frac{1}{12}bd^3$ (Figure 48), where I is the moment of inertia of a rectangle about its axis parallel to b, where b is the width, and d is the height of the rectangle.

Let b vary from 1 to 10 in., d from 1 to 10 in. Length of scales 6 in. The equation, which may be written $bd^3 = 12I$, is put in the type form by taking logarithms; thus we obtain

$$\log b + 3 \log d = \log I + \log 12$$

Now the moduli m_b and m_d are computed as follows:

$$m_b = \frac{6}{\log 10 - \log 1} = 6; \qquad X_b = 6 \log b$$

$$m_d = \frac{6}{3 \log 10 - 3 \log 1} = 2; \qquad X_d = 2(3 \log d) = 6 \log d$$

It should be pointed out that the function of d is $3 \log d$, the modulus 2 is the "actual modulus" which is used in locating the I-scale, and the coefficient 6 is the *effective modulus* which is used in graduating the d-scale.

$$m_I = \frac{6 \times 2}{6 + 2} = \frac{12}{8} = \frac{3}{2}; \qquad X_I = \frac{3}{2}(\log I + \log 12)$$

Note carefully that the actual moduli of b and d are used in computing m_I. Form the following table:

b	1	2	3	. . .	10
$f(b) = \log b$	0	0.301	0.477	. . .	1.000
$X_b = 6 \log b$	0	0.81	2.86	. . .	6.00

The table for d will be the same as the above since $m_d = 6$ (effective modulus).

Now we can graduate the scales for b and d in accordance with the scale equations $X_b = 6 \log b$ and $X_d = 2(3 \log d)$. The scales are placed a convenient distance apart. The position of the I-scale is determined from the ratio $m_b/m_d = \frac{6}{2} = \frac{3}{1}$. Our next step is to locate one point on the I-scale, i.e., point 1. Suppose we let $d = 2$. Then $b = 12I/d^3$ or $b = (12 \times 1)/8 = 1.5$. The line joining $b = 1.5$ and $d = 2$ cuts the I-scale at point 1. Now we can locate other points on the I-scale from the scale equation:

$$X_I = \frac{6 \times 2}{6 + 2}(\log I - \log 1) \qquad \text{or} \qquad X_I = 1.5(\log I)$$

This means that points on the I-scale are laid off from point 1. If the selected point on the I-scale were 10, then graduations would be laid off from this point in accordance with the scale equation:

$$X_I = 1.5(\log I - \log 10) \qquad \text{or} \qquad X_I = 1.5(\log I - 1)$$

If the equation were $f_1(u) - f_2(v) = f_3(w)$, the scale equations would be:

$$X_u = m_u f_1(u) \tag{1}$$
$$X_v = m_v[-f_2(v)] \tag{2}$$
$$X_w = \frac{m_u m_v}{m_u + m_v} f_3(w) \tag{3}$$

The negative sign in equation (2) implies that positive values of $f_2(v)$ are laid off downwardly if we agree to lay off positive values of $f_1(u)$ upwardly.

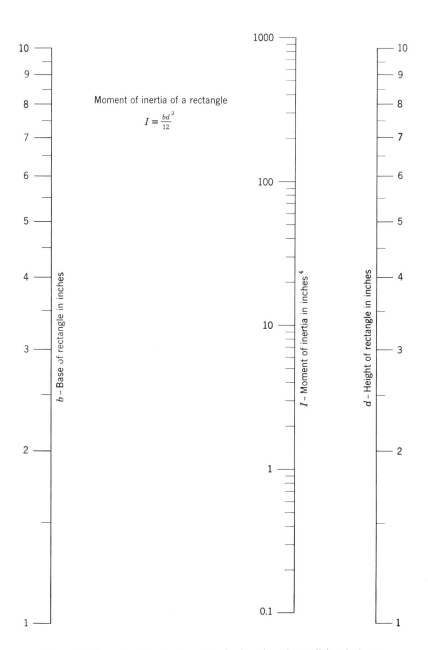

Figure 48. Moment of inertia of a rectangle about its axis parallel to the base.

Example 4

$u - v = w$ (Figure 49). Suppose u varies from 0 to 5, and v varies from 2 to 6. Scale lengths, 6 units (inches, centimeters, or any convenient length).

$$m_u = \tfrac{6}{5}; \qquad\qquad\qquad X_u = \tfrac{6}{5}u$$

$$m_v = \tfrac{6}{4} = \tfrac{3}{2}; \qquad\qquad X_v = \tfrac{3}{2}(-v) = -\tfrac{3}{2}v$$

$$m_w = \frac{\tfrac{6}{5} \times \tfrac{3}{2}}{\tfrac{6}{5} + \tfrac{3}{2}} = \frac{\tfrac{9}{5}}{\tfrac{27}{10}} = \frac{2}{3}; \qquad X_w = \frac{2}{3}w$$

$$\frac{m_u}{m_v} = \frac{\tfrac{6}{5}}{\tfrac{3}{2}} = \frac{4}{5}$$

Scales u and v are placed a convenient distance apart. Scale u is graduated in accordance with the scale equation $X_u = \tfrac{6}{5}u$. Scale v is graduated from the equation $X_v = \tfrac{3}{2}v$. This is done by locating point 2 on the upper end of the v-scale, and laying off distances equal to $\tfrac{3}{2}$ units for each point 3, 4, 5, and 6.

NOTE: POSITIVE VALUES OF 'V' ARE LAID OFF DOWNWARDLY!

A point on the w-scale can be located by solving the original equation, $u - v = w$.

Example: Let $u = 3$ and $v = 4$; then $w = -1$ (of course, in this case it might have been simpler to locate the zero point on the w-scale by letting u and v equal the same value). Having located one point on w, other points can be located from the scale equation $X_w = \tfrac{2}{3}(w - w_1)$ where w_1 is the value of the located point.

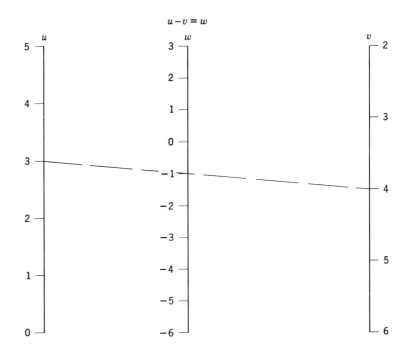

Figure 49. Alignment chart for the equation $u - v = w$.

Practical Short-Cut Method

If the designer is thoroughly grounded in the theory of alignment charts and fully understands the mathematical methods employed in changing a given equation to a type form, it is frequently possible to short-cut the actual construction of the chart.

Example

Suppose that the given equation is $M = wl^2/8$ (bending moment in foot-pounds, simple beam, uniform load), where the ranges are w (10 to 300 lb/ft) and l (5 to 30 ft).

If a chart consisting of parallel scales is desired, the designer recognizes the fact that the equation can be converted to the form:

$$\log w + 2 \log l = \log M + \log 8$$

The chart can now be constructed without making any further calculations. The following procedure is suggested:

1. Draw two parallel lines any convenient distance apart.
2. Graduate the left-hand scale for w by simply marking the lower point 10 and the upper point 300. Other points on the scale may be located by projecting from a log scale (two-cycle slide-rule scale or commercial log sheets having two cycles).
3. Mark the lower point of the l-scale 5 and the upper point 30. Again, locate additional graduations by projecting from a log scale.
4. Now calculate two points for M, i.e.:
   (a) Let $w = 40$ and $l = 10$.   This yields $M = 500$.
   (b) Let $w = 160$ and $l = 5$.   This yields $M = 500$.

The point in which the line joining 40 and 10 intersects the line joining 160 and 5 is point $M = 500$. The vertical line through this point locates the M-scale. A second point on this scale can be now located by letting $w = 40$ and $l = 30$, which yield $M = 4500$. The line joining $w = 40$ with $l = 30$ then cuts the M-scale in point 4500. Other points may be obtained by projecting from a log scale. The completed chart is shown in Figure 50.

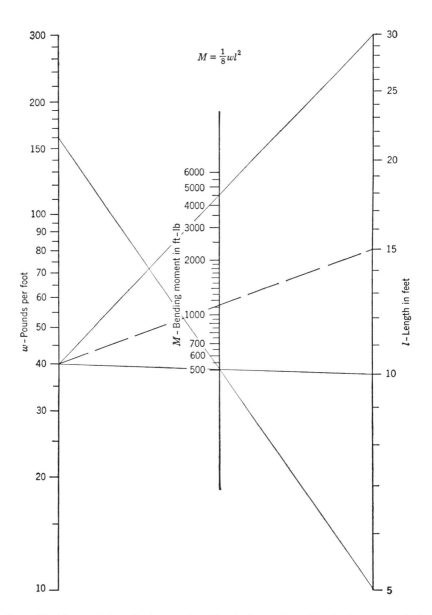

Figure 50. Alignment chart for the equation $M = \frac{1}{8}wl^2$, constructed by the short-cut method.

EXERCISES

Hydraulics

3.1　$H = \dfrac{P}{W}$ (head in feet of a liquid equivalent to the pressure, P, in pounds per square foot)

where W = weight per cubic foot of the liquid. If P is in pounds per square inch, $H = 144P/W$. Let P vary from 5 to 300 psi. For W use the common fluids such as water and kerosene.

3.2　$h = \dfrac{aV_0}{g}$ (maximum surge pressure due to instantaneous valve shutoff)

where h = maximum surge pressure rise in feet of water;
　　　a = pressure wave velocity (2000 to 4000 ft/sec);
　　　V_0 = initial velocity of water flow in pipeline (1.0 to 10 ft/sec);
　　　g = 32.2 ft/sec².

3.3　$V = C\sqrt{2gH}$ (velocity of water, in feet per second, through an orifice due to a head of water, H)

where g = 32.2 ft/sec²;
　　　C = a coefficient for the orifice depending on shape, etc. (0.6 to 1);
　　　H = head of water (1 to 15 ft).

3.4　The horsepower of a jet of water is given by the equation

$$hp = \frac{Wv^2}{2g \times 550}$$

where W = weight of water per second (1 to 100 lb);
　　　v = velocity of water in feet per second (1 to 50).
　　If desired, since 1 cu ft of water is 62.4 lb, the formula may be converted to

$$hp = \frac{Qv^2 \times 62.4}{2g \times 550}$$

where Q = quantity in cubic feet per second;
　　　g = 32.2 ft/sec².

3.5　$Q = 3.33bH^{3/2}$ (Francis' weir formula for a rectangular weir)

where Q = discharge in cubic feet per second;
　　　b = width of weir (3 to 20 ft);
　　　H = head above crest (0.5 to 1.5 ft).
　　Use a double graduation of the Q-scale to indicate gallons per minute.

3.6　$Q = 2.5H^{2.5} \tan\dfrac{\Theta}{2}$ (triangular weir formula for water, V-notch)

where Q = discharge over the weir in cubic feet per second;
　　　H = head of water above apex of the notch (0.1 to 1.0 ft);
　　　Θ = angle of notch (30° to 120°).

3.7　NPSH $= 6.3 \cdot 10^{-6} N_s{}^{3/4} \cdot H$ (net positive suction head)

where NPSH = net positive suction head in feet;
　　　N_s = specific speed (0 to 10,000) at maximum efficiency;
　　　H = head (0 to 200 ft).

3.8 $H = 0.38 \dfrac{V^{1.86}}{D^{1.25}}$ (friction head for water flowing in 1000 ft of pipe)

where V = velocity of flow in feet per second (2 to 15);
D = diameter of pipe in feet (1 to 6).

Strength of Materials

3.9 $S = \dfrac{12wV^2}{32.2}$ (maximum tensile hoop stress in a free rotating ring)

where S = maximum tensile hoop stress in pounds per square inch;
w = density in pounds per cubic inch (0.09 to 0.35);
V = mean rim velocity in feet per second (10 to 1000).

3.10 $V = \dfrac{P}{0.5393d^2}$ (Vicker's formula for hardness testing)

where V = Vicker's hardness number;
P = applied load (5 to 120 kg);
d = the diagonal of indentation (0 to 2 mm).

3.11 $F_b = \left(1.35 - 0.01\dfrac{d}{t}\right) \cdot$ (ult. T.S.) allowable stress in bending in a chrome molybde-

num steel tube)

where d/t = diameter/thickness of wall = thickness ratio (10 to 30);
ult. T.S. = ultimate tensile strength of material (90,000 to 180,000 psi).

3.12 $R_s = \dfrac{\pi}{4} d^2 f_s$ (allowable strength of a rivet)

where d = diameter of rivet ($\frac{1}{8}$ to 1 in.);
f_s = allowable unit shearing stress of material (3000 to 15,000 psi).

3.13 $\rho^2 = \dfrac{I}{A}$ (radius of gyration of a section)

where I = moment of inertia (1 to 1000 in.^{4});
A = area of section (1 to 100 sq in.).

3.14 $f = \dfrac{C\pi E}{\dfrac{L^2}{(P)}}$ (critical stress in a long column)

where C = 1, fixity coefficient for pin ended column;
E = modulus of elasticity ($10 \cdot 10^6$ to $30 \cdot 10^6$ psi);
(L/P) = slenderness ratio (70 to 200).

3.15 $E = 2G(1 + \mu)$; $K = \dfrac{E}{3(1 - 2\mu)}$

where E = modulus of elasticity in tension or compression ($10 \cdot 10^6$ to $30 \cdot 10^6$ psi);
G = modulus of elasticity in shear ($4 \cdot 10^6$ to $12 \cdot 10^6$ psi);
K = bulk modulus of elasticity ($8 \cdot 10^6$ to $20 \cdot 10^6$ psi);
μ = Poisson's ratio (0.21 to 0.36).

3.16 $e = \dfrac{f_x}{E} - \dfrac{mf_y}{E}$ (unit elongation in the x direction)

where f_x = unit stress in x direction (0 to 50,000 psi);
f_y = unit stress in y direction (0 to 50,000 psi);
m = 0.3;
E = 30×10^6 psi for structural steel.

Mechanical

3.17 $hp = \dfrac{4.71\,T}{cop}$ (refrigeration compressor horsepower requirement)

where hp = horsepower required;
   T = tons of refrigeration required (10 to 100);
   cop = coefficient of performance (1 to 6).

3.18 $T = 0.049\,\dfrac{V}{a}$

where T = reverberation time in seconds;
   V = volume of enclosure (1000 to 10,000 cf);
   a = number of absorption units = $\alpha_1 S_1 + \alpha_2 S_2 + \alpha_3 S_3 + \ldots$ where α_1 is the acoustic absorptivity of the surface of area S_1 sq ft, etc. (10 to 5000 sq ft).

3.19 $bhp = \dfrac{d^2 n}{2.5}$ (Association of Automobile Manufacturers formula)

where d = diameter of cylinders ($1\frac{3}{4}$ in. to 5 in.);
   n = number of cylinders (2, 4, 6, 8, 12);
   bhp = brake horsepower.

3.20 $d = 2.87\,\sqrt[3]{\dfrac{hp}{rpm}}$ (diameter in inches of a spur gear steel shaft)

where hp = horsepower (100 to 2000);
   rpm = revolutions per minute (100 to 1000).

3.21 $S = \dfrac{\pi D N}{12}$

where S = cutting speed in feet per minute in lathe or boring mill;
   D = diameter of work (0.35 to 15 in.);
   N = (10 to 1000 rpm).

3.22 $P = C F^{3/4} D^{14/15}$ (pressure in pounds on tool when cutting cast iron)

where F = feed (0.01 to 0.20 in.);
   D = depth of cut ($\frac{1}{8}$ to 1 in.);
   C = 45,000 for soft cast iron and 69,000 for hard cast iron.

3.23 $F = \dfrac{P^{0.97} A_0}{60}$ (flow of steam through a steam nozzle in pounds per second)

where P = absolute initial pressure (5 to 300 psi);
   A_0 = area at throat (1 to 30 sq in.).

3.24 $P_m = \dfrac{(1 + \log_e R)}{R} P_1$ (absolute mean pressure of expanded steam)

where P_1 = absolute initial pressure (50 to 350 psi);
   R = ratio of expansion = V/V_1 (1 to 10).

3.25 $N_N(\text{max}) = N_R \sec \alpha$ } maximum and minimum
   $N_N(\text{min}) = N_R \cos \alpha$ } velocities of universal joints

where N_N = angular speed of *driven* shaft (100 to 1000 rpm);
   N_R = angular speed of *driver* shaft (100 to 1000 rpm);
   α = angle between shafts (0° to 70°).

Civil

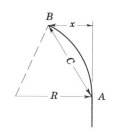

3.26 $x = \dfrac{C^2}{2R}$

where x = offset distance as shown in the figure;
    C = chord distance (10 to 100 ft);
    R = radius of curve (100 to 6000 ft).

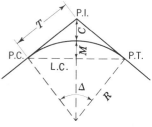

3.27   For the simple curve, $T = R \tan \Delta/2$, where R is usually obtained from the degree of curvature and is equal to

$$R = \frac{5729.65}{(\text{degree of curv.})} = \frac{5729.65}{D}$$

where D, the degree of curvature, varies (1° to 30°) and Δ varies (10° to 150°).

3.28   L.C. $= 2R \sin \dfrac{\Delta}{2}$ (long chord as shown in figure of Problem 3.27)

Use limits of Problem 3.27.

3.29 $C = R \operatorname{exsec} \dfrac{\Delta}{2}$ (external distance of a curve)

See figure of Problem 3.27. Use same limits.

3.30 $M = R \operatorname{vers} \dfrac{\Delta}{2}$ (mid-ordinate of a curve)

See figure of Problem 3.27. Use same limits.

3.31 $V = \dfrac{1.486}{n} R^{\frac{2}{3}} S^{\frac{1}{2}}$ (Manning's formula)

where V = velocity in feet per second;
    n = 0.015, the coefficient of roughness;
    R = the hydraulic radius (0 to 25 ft);
    S = slope of channel (0 to 0.01).

3.32 $C_L = \dfrac{LA}{R}$ (formula for correction, C_L, to be subtracted from the actual length of a base line for equivalent length at mean sea level)

where L = length of base line (200 to 1500 ft);
    A = mean altitude above sea level (500 to 5000 ft);
    R = radius of the earth = 20,889,000 ft.

3.33 $V = \dfrac{D}{54}(A_1 + A_2)$.

where V = volume in cubic yards between two adjacent sections;
D = distance between the sections = 100 ft;
A_1 = area of one cross section (200 to 2000 sq ft);
A_2 = area of the adjacent cross section (200 to 2000 sq ft).

3.34 $E = 0.67\dfrac{V^2}{R}$

where E = maximum superelevation in feet per foot of width of roadway;
V = velocity of vehicles (15 to 65 mph);
R = radius of curve (100 to 6000 ft).

3.35 $e = 0.0000572DV^2$ (superelevation of outer rail)

where e = superelevation in feet;
D = degree of curve (1° to 10°);
V = velocity (10 to 100 mph).

Electrical

3.36 $\mu = g_m r_p$

where μ = amplification factor;
g_m = transconductance (1000 to 5000 micromhos);
r_p = plate resistance (10,000 to 50,000 ohms).

3.37 $\Delta f = \dfrac{f_r}{Q}$

where Δf = bandwidth, or frequency range over which the gain does not fall below 70.7% of maximum, in cycles per second;
f_r = resonant frequency of parallel resonant circuit (10^6 to $30 \cdot 10^6$ cps);
Q = figure of merit of coil of resonant circuit (100 to 300).

3.38 $T = \dfrac{7.05P}{N}$

where T = starting torque in foot-pounds;
P = rotor input (5000 to 25,000 watts);
N = rotor synchronous speed (600 to 1800 rpm).

3.39 $P = \dfrac{E^2}{R}$ (power in watts used in passing an electric current through a resistance, R)

where E = voltage (10 to 220 volts);
R = resistance (10 to 1000 ohms).

3.40 $X = \dfrac{1,000,000}{2\pi f C}$ (reactance of a coil)

where f = frequency in cycles per second (30 to 3000);
C = (1 to 100) capacitance of condenser in microfarads.

3.41 $(db) = 20\log\dfrac{E_2}{E_1}$

where (db) = amplifier gain in decibels;
E_2 = output signal voltage (10 to 100 volts);
E_1 = input signal voltage (1 to 10 volts).

3.42 $E = 0.232 \log \dfrac{d}{0.78r}$ (inductive volts per ampere per mile of line with two wires for a
25-cycle current)

where $r =$ the radius of the wire in inches;
      $d =$ the spacing in inches (4 to 100).
Express r in B and S gage numbers, which vary from (0000 to 10).

3.43   Double-graduate the E-scale of Problem 3.42 to solve the formula, when using a 60-cycle current:

$$E = (0.232 \times 3.4) \log \frac{d}{0.78r}$$

3.44 $W = \eta(B_m)^{1.6}$ (Steinmetz's law)

where $W =$ ergs per cubic centimeter $=$ energy loss per cycle due to hysteresis;
     $B_m =$ maximum value of flux density (0 to 10 kilogausses);
     $\eta =$ Steinmetz coefficient (values in Mark's *Handbook**).

* 5th ed., McGraw-Hill, New York, 1951, p. 1946.

3.45 $A = \dfrac{4}{\pi} WD$ (equivalent cross-sectional area of rectangular conductor in circular mils)

where $W =$ width of bar (0.1 to 3.0 in.);
     $D =$ depth of bar (0.1 to 3.0 in.).

Aeronautical

3.46 $R = \dfrac{S^2}{A}$ (aspect ratio of wing)

where $S =$ span of airplane wing in feet (20 to 100);
     $A =$ area of airplane wing in square feet;
     $R =$ aspect ratio (4 to 7).

3.47 $q = \dfrac{\rho V^2}{2}$ (dynamic pressure of air moving at velocity V)

where $\rho =$ air density slugs per cubic foot (0.0010 to 0.0025);
     $V =$ velocity of air in feet per second (30 to 300).

3.48 $V_s = 29 \left(\dfrac{S}{C_{L_{(max)}}}\right)^{1/2}$ (stalling speed of an airplane in feet per second)

where $S =$ wing loading in pounds per square foot (5 to 40);
     $C_{L_{(max)}} =$ maximum lift coefficient (1.1 to 2.5).

3.49 $m = m_6 \dfrac{4}{3 + \dfrac{6}{R}}$ (slope of lift curve for aspect ratio, R)

where $m_6 =$ slope dC_L/d at aspect ratio 6, range (4 to 7);
     $R =$ aspect ratio (4 to 7).

3.50   When the equation of Problem 3.49 is constructed as a Z type, it is possible by the proper selection of moduli to make all scales uniform. Show how this can be done.

3.51   Since $V_{mph} = \frac{30}{44} V_{fps}$ and 1 slug $= 32.2$ lb, double-graduate the ρ- and V-scales of Problem 3.47 to increase the usefulness of the chart by eliminating the conversion of units.

3.52 $R = 9354Vl$ (Reynold's number)

where $V =$ velocity (100 to 500 mph);
     $l =$ chord length (1.0 to 10 ft).

3.53 $\dfrac{a}{c} = 0.25 - 0.40 \left(\dfrac{t}{c}\right)^2$ (location of aerodynamic center of an airfoil)

where $a =$ distance from leading edge to aerodynamic center;
$c =$ chord length (25 to 100 in.);
$t =$ airfoil thickness (2 to 20 in.).

Chemical

3.54 $V = 174.24 \sqrt{t + 459.6} \sqrt{H}$ (velocity of air at or near atmospheric pressure)

where $V = $ (300 to 15,000 ft/min);
$t = $ temperature in degrees Fahrenheit—range ($0°$ to $1000°$);
$H = $ velocity head in inches (0 to 5).

3.55 $V_1 = V \sqrt{\dfrac{P}{P_1}}$ (corrected velocity of Problem 3.54 for pressures considerably above

atmospheric)

where $V_1 = $ (100 to 10,000 ft/min);
$V = $ as before, Problem 3.54;
$P = $ (14.7 to 100 psi);
$P_1 = $ 14.7 psi.

3.56 $V_2 = V_1 \sqrt{\dfrac{1}{S}}$ (correction of V_1 of Problem 3.55 for specific gravity)

where $V_2 = $ (100 to 20,000 ft/min);
$V_1 = $ as before;
$S = $ (0.2 to 1.6), relative to air.

3.57 $P = M\left(10.82 - \dfrac{4425}{T}\right)$ (partial pressure of ammonia in atmosphere over a solution of

M gram-*moles* of ammonia per 1000 grams of water; T is the temperature in degrees absolute)

where $P = $ (0 to 1000 mm);
$M = $ (0 to 100 grams);
$T = $ ($10°$ to $40°C$).
Note that the limits of P, M, and T are not given in the units to be used in the equation. Therefore revise the equation, noting that 1 atm $=$ 760 mm, molecular weight of $NH_3 = $ 17.0, and $0°A = -273°C$.

3.58 $\mu = \mu_1{}^n$ (specific viscosity referred to water with the same temperature of a salt solution whose normality is n)

where μ_1 is the specific viscosity of a normal solution and may be determined from the values shown below for various salt solutions and acids at $25°C$, n varies (0.1 to 1.0), and μ varies (0.95 to 1.45).

Dissolved Salt	μ_1
Aluminum sulfate	1.406
Calcium chloride	1.156
Cadmium chloride	1.134
Barium chloride	1.123
Potassium nitrate	0.975
Potassium sulfate	1.105

3.59 $p_r = \dfrac{p}{p_c}$ (reduced pressure for use with the compressibility form of the equation of
state)

where p = given pressure (1 to 1000 atm);
     p_c = critical pressure (see the table in Problem 3.60).

3.60 $T_r = \dfrac{T}{T_c}$ (reduced temperature)

where T = given temperature (40 to 4000°R);
     T_c = critical temperature (see table below).

		p_c (Atm)	T_c (°R)
Air	—	37.2	238.4
Ammonia	NH_3	111.5	730.0
Butane	C_4H_{10}	36.0	766.8
Carbon monoxide	CO	34.6	241.5
Carbon dioxide	CO_2	73.0	547.6
Hydrogen	H_2	12.8	59.9
Methane	CH_4	45.8	343.9
Water	H_2O	218.2	1165.1

3.61 $A_E = A_B \dfrac{(A_T + 1)}{(A_B + 1)}$ (effective absorption factor for use in Kremsen's equation for computing the efficiency of an absorption column)

where A_B = absorption factor at base of column (0.1 to 2.0);
     A_T = absorption factor at top of column (0.1 to 2.0).

3.62 Ultimate % $CO_2 = \dfrac{\% \ CO_2 \text{ in flue gas sample} \times 100}{100 - \dfrac{\% \ O_2 \text{ in same sample}}{0.209}}$

where % O_2 varies from 1.0 to 15%;
     % CO_2 varies from 1.0 to 20%.

Statistics

3.63 $\sigma_y = \sqrt{\dfrac{\Sigma y^2}{N}}$

where σ_y = standard deviation from mean (0.05 to 1000);
     Σy^2 = sum of deviations squared (1 to 10^6);
     N = number of cases in sample (1 to 1000).

3.64 $\sigma_{est} \ \sigma_y \sqrt{1 - r_{xy}{}^2}$ (standard error of estimate in predicting y scores from x)

where σ_y = standard deviation of y scores (1 to 20);
     r_{xy} = correlation of x and y scores (0.50 to 0.99);
     σ_{est} = standard error of estimate (1 to 20).

3.65 $\sigma_\sigma = \dfrac{\sigma^1}{\sqrt{2n}}$ (standard deviation of the sample)

where σ^1 = "true" standard deviation of the lot from which the sample was drawn (0.05 to
     1.00)
   n = sample size (10 to 1000).

3.66 $\sigma_{\bar{x}} = \dfrac{\sigma^1}{\sqrt{n}}$ (standard deviation of the sample average)

where σ^1 and n are the same as in Problem 3.65.

3.67 $3\sigma = \dfrac{3}{d}\bar{R}$ (3-sigma limits for quality control charts, as a guide for determining eco-

nomically satisfactory limits)

where $\bar{R}$ = average range (0.05 to 1000);

d = conversion factor, based on Am. War Stds. for quality control, based on no. of readings in samples (see table below).

n	d	n	d
2	1.128	9	2.970
3	1.693	10	3.078
4	2.059	11	3.173
5	2.326	12	3.258
6	2.534	13	3.336
7	2.704	14	3.407
8	2.847	15	3.472

General

3.68 $I = \dfrac{bd^3}{12}$ (moment of inertia of rectangle)

where I = moment of intertia in inches^4;

b = width of rectangle (2 to 16 in.);

d = depth of rectangle (4 to 24 in.).

3.69 $I = \frac{1}{2}Wr^2$ (moment of inertia of a right circular cylinder about its axis)

where W = total weight in pounds (1 to 25,000);

r = radius in inches (1 to 25).

3.70 $V = 2.467Dd^2$ (volume of a torus)

where D = large diameter of torus (1 to 10);

d = small diameter of torus (1 to 10).

3.71 $r = \sqrt{x^2 + y^2}$ (vector r whose coordinates are x and y)

where x varies (0 to 10), y varies (0 to 10).

3.72 $I_x = \dfrac{\pi}{64}ab^3$ (moment of inertia of elliptical area about major axis in inches^4)

where a = major axis (1.0 to 10 in.);

b = minor axis (1.0 to 10 in.).

3.73 $A = \dfrac{Pn}{365}$

where P = annual insurance premium ($20 to $500);

n = number of days prior to expiration of policy (1 to 365);

A = amount of premium returnable.

3.74 $P = \dfrac{w^2 h^2}{4}$ ("product of inertia" of rectangle about axes coincident with adjacent sides)

where w = width of rectangle (0 to 10 in.);
$\quad\quad\ h$ = height of rectangle (0 to 20 in.).

3.75 $I = k^2 m$ (mass moment of inertia in inch-pound-seconds^2)

where k = radius of gyration (0 to 12 in.);
$\quad\quad\ m$ = mass of body (0 to 20 lb-sec^2/in.).

3.76 $P = A(1 + R)^n$ (principal P after n compoundings of the amount A at the rate of interest, R)

where A = \$1.00;
$\quad\quad\ R$ = interest rate in per cent (1 to 8);
$\quad\quad\ n$ = number of times compounded (1 to 20).

3.77 $I = \dfrac{M}{(1 - r)}$

where M = yield on tax-exempt investment (2% to 8%);
$\quad\quad\ r$ = marginal income tax rate (20% to 90%);
$\quad\quad\ I$ = yield on ordinary investment (3% to 50%).

3.78 $D = \dfrac{2.2 W^{0.45}}{\rho}$ (economic inside pipe diameter in inches)

where W = mass flow rate, 1000 lb-mass/hr (0.01 to 100);
$\quad\quad\ \rho$ = fluid density in pounds-mass per foot^3 (0.01 to 10).

3.79 $D = \dfrac{0.42 W^{0.462}}{C^{0.163}}$

where W and D are the same as in Problem 3.78;
$\quad\quad\ C$ = annual cost for assembly, including fittings, in dollars per foot (\$50 to \$5000).

4

Alignment Charts—
Z Charts for the Form

$$f_1(u) = f_2(v) \cdot f_3(w)$$

Suppose that the parallel scales (Figure 51), A and B, are graduated in accordance with their scale equations $X_u = m_u f_1(u)$ and $X_v = m_v f_2(v)$, respectively. **The diagonal scale for $f_3(w)$ joins $f_1(u_0)$ and $f_2(v_0)$, i.e., the zero values of the functions of u and v.**

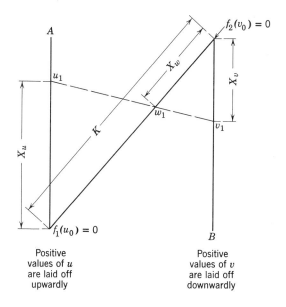

Figure 51.

Let us suppose further that a straight line joining points u_1 and v_1 cuts the diagonal scale in point w_1 so that the equation $f_1(u) = f_2(v) \cdot f_3(w)$ is satisfied. What will be the scale equation for $f_3(w)$?

From the similar triangles $u_0u_1w_1$ and $v_0v_1w_1$,

$$\frac{X_u}{X_v} = \frac{K - X_w}{X_w} \quad \text{or} \quad X_u = X_v \frac{(K - X_w)}{X_w}$$

since $\qquad\qquad X_u = m_u f_1(u) \qquad \text{and} \qquad X_v = m_v f_2(v)$

Then $\qquad\qquad m_u f_1(u) = m_v f_2(v) \dfrac{(K - X_w)}{X_w}$

When $\qquad\qquad\qquad f_1(u) = f_2(v) \cdot f_3(w)$

then $\qquad\qquad\qquad \dfrac{K - X_w}{X_w} = \dfrac{m_u}{m_v} f_3(w)$

from which $\qquad\qquad X_w = \dfrac{K m_v}{m_u f_3(w) + m_v}$

or $\qquad\qquad X_w = \dfrac{K}{\dfrac{m_u}{m_v} f_3(w) + 1} = \dfrac{K}{r f_3(w) + 1}$

where $\qquad\qquad\qquad r = \dfrac{m_u}{m_v}$

If it is desired to graduate the w-scale from u_0 instead of v_0, it can be shown that the distance from u_0 to w_1 is equal to $\dfrac{K m_u f_3(w)}{m_u f_3(w) + m_v}$. (This should be verified by the reader.)

Design Summary

From the above one can construct this type of chart in the following manner:

1. Draw scales for the variables, u and v, parallel to each other.
2. Graduate the u-scale in accordance with its scale equation $X_u = m_u f_1(u)$.
3. Graduate the v-scale in accordance with its scale equation $X_v = m_v f_2(v)$ (plotting positive values of v downwardly if positive values of u were plotted upwardly).
4. Graduate the w-scale from the upper end of the scale in accordance with its scale equation

$X_w = \dfrac{K}{\dfrac{m_u}{m_v} f_3(w) + 1}$, or from the lower end in accordance with the scale equation

$X_w = \dfrac{K m_u f_3(w)}{m_u f_3(w) + m_v} .$

Example 1

Consider the equation $u + 2 = v^2w$ (Figure 52). Suppose that u varies from 0 to 10, and v from 0 to 5. The scale lengths are to be approximately 6 in.

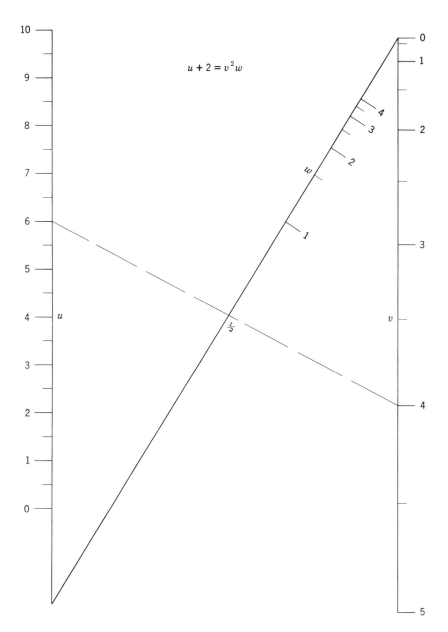

Figure 52. Z-type chart for the equation $u + 2 = v^2w$.

$$m_u = \frac{6}{(10+2)-(0+2)} = 0.6$$

$m_v = \frac{6}{25} = 0.24$. (We shall use 0.25, which merely lengthens the scale from 6 to 6.25 in.) Hence $X_u = 0.6(u+2)$; $X_v = 0.25v^2$

and
$$X_w = \frac{10}{\dfrac{0.6w}{0.25}+1} = \frac{10}{\dfrac{12w}{5}+1}$$

where $K = 10$ (ten of any convenient unit).

Form the following table:

w	0	0.5	1	2	3
X_w	10	$\frac{50}{11}$	$\frac{50}{17}$	$\frac{50}{29}$	$\frac{50}{41}$

Example 2

Let us consider the equation for the volume of a right circular cylinder, $V = \pi r^2 h/144$, where V is the volume in cubic feet, r is the radius of the base circle, in inches (4 to 12), and h is the height of the cylinder in feet (4 to 15). We may write the equation,

$$KV = r^2 h, \qquad \text{where } K = 144/\pi$$

The range of V is determined from the ranges of r and h. Simple calculations will show that V varies from 1.40 (or $4\pi/9$) cu ft to 47.15 (or 15π) cu ft.

Now
$$m_V = \frac{10\pm}{\dfrac{144}{\pi}\left(15\pi - \dfrac{4\pi}{9}\right)} = 0.005$$

and
$$X_V = 0.005\left[\frac{144}{\pi}\left(V - \frac{4\pi}{9}\right)\right]$$

$$m_r = \frac{10\pm}{144 - 16} = 0.08$$

$$X_r = 0.08(r^2 - 4^2)$$

From the above scale equations, we can graduate the V- and r-scales. It will be observed that it is necessary only to compute the total length of the V-scale; i.e., $X_V = 0.005\left[\dfrac{144}{\pi}\left(15\pi - \dfrac{4\pi}{9}\right)\right]$

$= 10.48$. Then we know that the lower point of the scale will be marked 1.40 and the upper point will be marked 47.15. Additional graduations can be obtained by proportion. Since the function is linear, the scale is uniform.

In the case of the r-scale, it should be noted that the function is r^2, and therefore distances between consecutive points are proportional to the square of r.

The location of the diagonal scale must be determined next. Many students make the typical error of connecting point 4 on the r-scale with point 1.40 on the V-scale. Remember that *the diagonal line joins the zero value of the function of r with the zero value of the function of V.* These points would be zero on the r-scale and zero on the V-scale. In this case, it would be possible to include these points on the respective scales. However, often the zero values of the functions are not accessible within the limits of the drawing. Let us assume this to be the case in our problem.

The position of the h-scale can be established by a very simple method. Let us locate points 6 and 12 on the h-scale. If we let $r = 10$, then $V = 13.1$ when $h = 6$. The line joining $r = 10$ with $V = 13.1$ contains $h = 6$. Again, if we let $r = 12$, then $V = 18.9$ when $h = 6$. The line joining $r = 12$ with $V = 18.9$ contains $h = 6$. Therefore, the intersection of these two lines is $h = 6$ and, in addition, is a point on the diagonal. This method can be repeated for another point such as $h = 12$. Other points on the h-scale can then be located from point 12, by properly using the scale equation

$$X_h = \frac{K}{\frac{m_V}{m_r}h + 1} = \frac{K}{\frac{0.005}{0.08}h + 1}$$

It is evident that K must be determined. This can be done, since the distance between points 6 and 12 can be measured. Hence,

$$\frac{K}{\frac{0.005}{0.08} \times 6 + 1} - \frac{K}{\frac{0.005}{0.08} \times 12 + 1} = 2.37$$

from which $K = 15.23$.

The distances from $r = 0$, along the diagonal, can now be computed from

$$X_h = \frac{15.23}{\frac{0.005}{0.08}h + 1} = \frac{243.68}{h + 16}$$

h	4	5	6	7	8	9	10	11	12	13	14	15
X_h	12.18	11.59	11.07	10.58	10.13	9.73	9.36	9.01	8.70	8.40	8.12	7.86
X_h from $h = 12$	3.48	2.89	2.37	1.88	1.43	1.03	0.66	0.31	0	0.30	0.58	0.84

$\longleftarrow$ Distances below $h = 12$ $\longrightarrow$ $\quad$ $\longleftarrow$ Above $h = 12$ $\longrightarrow$

The alignment chart is shown in Figure 53.

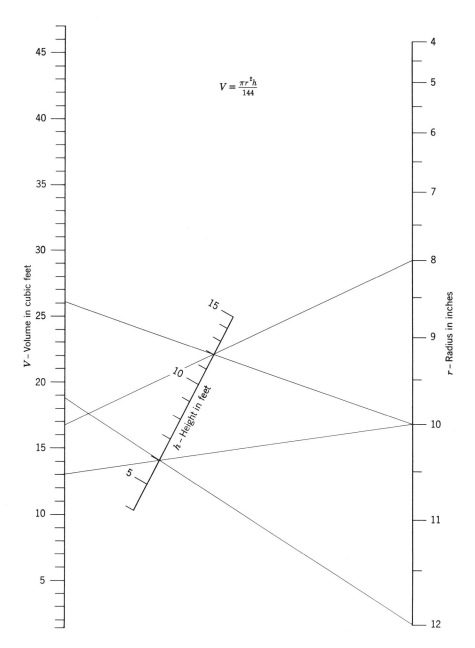

Figure 53. Z-type chart for the relation $V = \dfrac{\pi r^2 h}{144}$.

Simplified Method

A method which may simplify the work of graduating the diagonal scale can be developed in the following manner (Figure 54). Let F be a fixed point on the right vertical scale. Let the distance from point A to the fixed point be L (inches, centimeters, or any other convenient number of units). Suppose that the *right-hand* side of the left vertical scale carries a temporary w-scale. From the similar triangles, BDE and AFE,

$$\frac{X_w'}{L} = \frac{K - X_w}{X_w}$$

$$X_w' = L\left(\frac{K - X_w}{X_w}\right)$$

Previously it had been shown that

$$\frac{K - X_w}{X_w} = \frac{m_u}{m_v}[f_3(w)]$$

Hence
$$X_w' = L\,\frac{m_u}{m_v}[f_3(w)]$$

This equation enables us to graduate the temporary w-scale. Lines joining the fixed point, F, with the graduations on the temporary scale will intersect the diagonal in points having the same values of w.

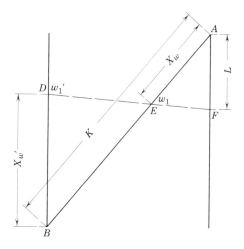

Figure 54.

This method has two advantages over the one of locating points on the diagonal from the equation, $X_w = \dfrac{K}{\dfrac{m_u}{m_v}f_3(w) + 1}$.

First, if the function of w is linear, a uniform scale can be graduated on the temporary scale; second, the length, K, of the diagonal scale need not be known.

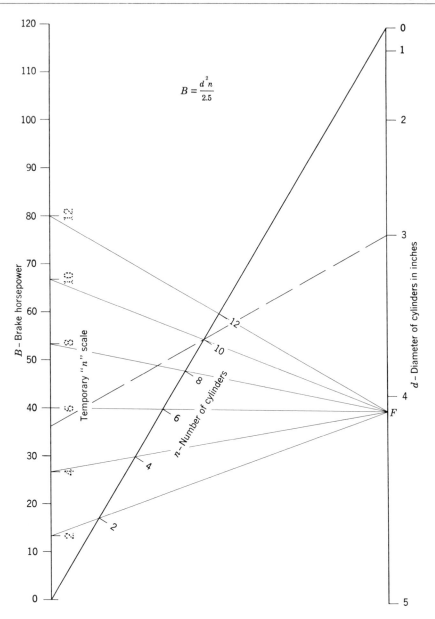

Figure 55. Z-type chart, employing the simplified method, for the expression $B = \dfrac{d^2 n}{2.5}$.

Example 1

$B = \dfrac{d^2 n}{2.5}$ (formula taken from the Association of Automobile Manufacturing)

where B represents brake horsepower, d (0 to 5 in.) the diameter of the cylinder in inches, and n (2, 4, 6, 8, 10, 12) the number of cylinders. The maximum value of $B = 120$. Suppose that the lengths of the parallel scales, B and d, are 7.5 in. The scale equations will be:

$$X_B = m_B(2.5B); \qquad 7.5 = m_B(300); \qquad m_B = \frac{7.5}{300} = 0.025$$

$$X_d = m_d(d^2); \qquad 7.5 = m_d(25); \qquad m_d = \frac{7.5}{25} = 0.3$$

(a) Applying the first method, $K = 9$ in., we have

$$X_n = \frac{9}{\dfrac{0.025}{0.3}n + 1} = \frac{9}{\dfrac{n}{12} + 1} = \frac{108}{n + 12}$$

Form the following table. (Plot n from these values.)

n	2	4	6	8	10	12
X_n	7.71	6.75	6.00	5.40	4.91	4.50

(b) Applying the second method, we obtain

$$X_n' = L\frac{m_B}{m_d}n; \qquad X_n' = 5 \times \frac{0.025}{0.3}n = \frac{5n}{12}$$

Points on temporary scale $X_n' = \frac{5}{12}n$ are located on the right-hand side of the B-scale. These points are connected with the fixed point, F. The intersection of these lines with the diagonal locate the points on the n-scale. In this example, $L = 5$ in. (See Figure 55 for completed chart.)

Example 2

Let us consider the equation $Q = 3.33bH$ (Francis' weir formula). The ranges of the variables are : b (3 ft to 20 ft); and H (0.5 ft to 1.5 ft). Scale lengths for Q and H are approximately 6 in. The preliminary design of the Z chart will be as shown in Figure 56.

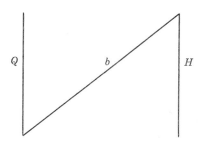

Figure 56.

Note carefully that by placing the b variable on the diagonal scale, the *temporary b-scale will be uniform*. This is a definite advantage over the placement of the H variable on the diagonal since the temporary scale for H would not be uniform.

Calculations of the scale moduli are:

$$m_Q = \frac{6\pm}{120} = 0.05 \qquad (Q_{max} = 120+)$$

$$m_H = \frac{6\pm}{3.33(1.5\% - 0.5\%)} = \frac{6\pm}{4.94} = 1.2$$

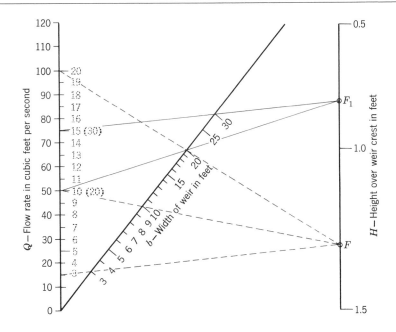

Figure 57. $Q = 3.33bH^{3/2}$ (simplified method used).

The scale equations are:

$$X_Q = 0.05Q \quad \text{(graduated from } Q = 0\text{)}$$
$$X_H = 1.2(3.33H^{3/2}) = 4H^{3/2} \quad \text{(graduated from } H = 0\text{)}$$
or
$$X_H = 4(H^{3/2} - 0.5^{3/2}) \quad \textit{(graduated from } H = 0.5\text{)}$$
$$X_b' = L\,\frac{0.05}{1.2}\ b\ =\frac{5}{120}\,Lb\ =\frac{1}{24}\,Lb$$

Let $L = 6$; then $X_b' = b/4$. The completed nomogram is shown in Figure 57.

Now suppose that b has a maximum value of 30. It is clearly seen that the location of $b = 30$ *on the temporary scale* would fall beyond the maximum length of the present scale. In order to locate $b = 30$ on a temporary scale we shall shift the location of the fixed point F to F_1 which can be determined in the following manner:

Since $X_b' = (1/24) Lb$, let us choose $L = 3$. Then $X_b' = b/8$. When $b = 30$, $X_b' = 30/8 = 3.75$ in. [Note $b = 30$ is shown as (30) on the new temporary scale, $X_b' = b/8$.] The line connecting F_1 and (30) intersects the diagonal scale at $b = 30$.

Locating the Diagonal Scale

A little reflection on the use of two F positions should lead us to conclude that the location of the diagonal scale can be fixed very simply.

The diagonal scale passes through the zero values of the functions of Q and H. This means that the diagonal scale passes through $Q = 0$ and $H = 0$. The value $Q = 0$ is available; however, $H = 0$ is not. Therefore, it is only necessary to locate one point on the diagonal, i.e. $b = 20$.

Using F. The line joining F and 20 on the temporary b-scale contains $b = 20$.
Using F_1. The line joining F_1 and (20) also contains $b = 20$.

Therefore, the intersection of the two lines, described above, is $b = 20$. The line joining this point with $Q = 0$ is the diagonal line which carries the graduations of b.

EXERCISES

Many problems of Chapter 3 are suitable for Z-type nomograms. The reader should select those problems that can be represented more advantageously as Z charts.

5

Alignment Charts— Z Charts for the Form

$$f_1(u) + f_2(v) = \frac{f_2(v)}{f_3(w)}$$

Let us consider Figure 58 which is a typical Z chart. We will assume that the u- and v-scales have been graduated respectively in accordance with the scale equations:

$$X_u = m_u f_1(u) \tag{1}$$

and

$$X_v = m_v f_2(v) \tag{2}$$

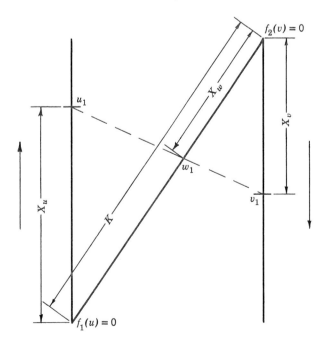

Figure 58.

It should be noted that positive values of the variable u are plotted upwardly and those of v downwardly. The diagonal which carries the graduations for the function of w joins *the zero values* of the functions of u and v.

Now we shall determine the scale equation for the function of w so that co-linear values on the u-, v-, and w-scales satisfy the form:

$$f_1(u) + f_2(v) = \frac{f_2(v)}{f_3(w)}$$

From similar triangles (easily identified)

$$\frac{X_u}{X_v} = \frac{K - X_w}{X_w}$$

Now, substituting $X_u = m_u f_1(u)$, $X_v = m_v f_2(v)$, and $X_w = m_w f_3(w)$, we get

$$\frac{m_u f_1(u)}{m_v f_2(v)} = \frac{K - m_w f_3(w)}{m_w f_3(w)}$$

Now, by adding 1 to each side of the equation we obtain,

$$\frac{m_u f_1(u) + m_v f_2(v)}{m_v f_2(v)} = \frac{K}{m_w f_3(w)}$$

or

$$m_u f_1(u) + m_v f_2(v) = \frac{K m_v f_2(v)}{m_w f_3(w)}$$

When $m_u = m_v$ and $K = m_w$, then

$$f_1(u) + f_2(v) = \frac{f_2(v)}{f_3(w)}$$

Therefore to construct a Z chart for this form, graduate the scales in accordance with the following scale equations:

$$X_u = m_u f_1(u)$$

$$X_v = m_u f_2(v)$$

$$X_w = K f_3(w)$$

Example

$$f = \frac{20,000}{1 + \dfrac{144 L^2}{9000 r^2}} \qquad \text{(Gordon column formula)}$$

L (0 to 50 ft), r (0 to 10 in.), and f (3000 to 20,000 psi). The equation can easily be reduced to the form

$$0.016 L^2 + r^2 = \frac{r^2}{\dfrac{f}{20,000}}$$

The scale equations are:

$$X_L = m_L(0.016 L^2) \qquad \text{and} \qquad X_r = m_L r^2$$

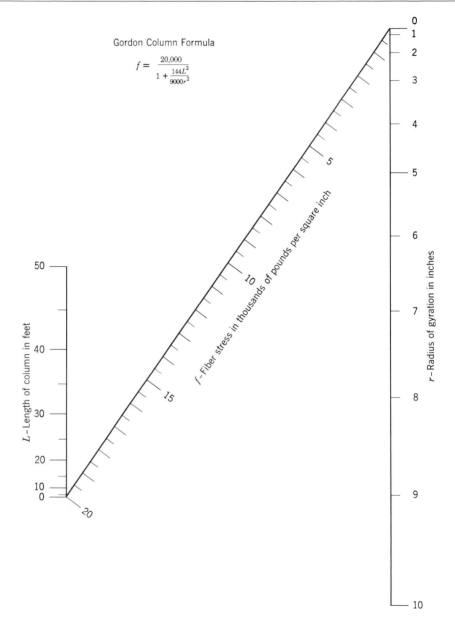

Gordon Column Formula

$$f = \frac{20{,}000}{1 + \frac{144L^2}{9000r^2}}$$

Figure 59. Gordon column formula.

(Remember that the moduli for the parallel scales must be the same.)

If the length of the r-scale is 7.5 in., then

$$m_r = m_L = \frac{7.5}{10^2} = 0.075$$

or $X_r = 0.075r^2$ and $X_L = 0.075(0.016L^2) = 0.0012L^2$

Now, when $K = 8$,

$$X_f = 8\left(\frac{f}{20,000}\right) = 0.0004f$$

The completed nomogram is shown in Figure 59.

When the equation is of the form,

$$f_1(u) - f_2(v) = \frac{f_2(v)}{f_3(w)}$$

the scales for u and v will be graduated in the same direction as shown in Figure 60.

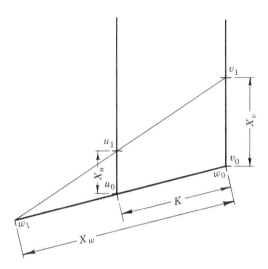

Figure 60.

EXERCISES

5.1 $C = \dfrac{87}{0.552 + \dfrac{m}{\sqrt{R}}}$ (Bazin's coefficient for velocity in open channel flow)

where m = coefficient of roughness (0.05 to 2);
       R = hydraulic radius (0.5 to 30 ft).

5.2 $f = \dfrac{18,000}{1 + \dfrac{1}{18,000}\left(\dfrac{l}{r}\right)^2}$ (steel column formula)

where f = fiber stress (6000 to 10,000 psi);
       l/r = slenderness ratio (125 to 200).

5.3 $W = S_G(W - W')$

where W = weight of body in air (0 to 12 kg);
       W' = weight of body in water (0 to 10 kg);
       S_G = specific gravity (1 to 12).

5.4 $T = \dfrac{1}{1 - \dfrac{N^2}{N_n{}^2}}$ (vibration isolation without damping)

where $T =$ ratio of transmitted force to impressed force;
$N =$ frequency of forcing function (1000 to 2000 rpm);
$N_n =$ natural frequency of system (1000 to 2000 rpm).

5.5 $\text{pf} = \dfrac{P_A}{\sqrt{P_A{}^2 + P_R{}^2}}$

where pf $=$ power factor;
$P_A =$ active power (1 to 10 va) (10 to 100), etc.;
$P_R =$ reactive power (1 to 10 va) (10 to 100), etc.

5.6 $V_R = \dfrac{E_{NL} - E_{FL}}{E_{FL}} \cdot 100$

where $V_R =$ voltage regulation in per cent;
$E_{NL} =$ no-load voltage (1 to 10); (10 to 100); (100 to 1000);
$E_{FL} =$ full-load voltage (1 to 10); (10 to 100); (100 to 1000).

5.7 $S = \dfrac{N_S - N_R}{N_S} \cdot 100$ (induction motor slip)

where $S =$ per cent slip;
$N_S =$ synchronous speed (0 to 1800 rpm);
$N_R =$ rotor speed (0 to 1800 rpm).

Alignment Charts for the Form

$$\frac{1}{f_1(u)} + \frac{1}{f_2(v)} = \frac{1}{f_3(w)}$$

Suppose that the intersecting scales, A and B, are graduated in accordance with the scale equations (Figure 61):

$$X_u = m_u f_1(u) \qquad \text{and} \qquad X_v = m_v f_2(v)$$

If a straight line joining points u_1 and v_1 intersects scale C in a point w_1 so that the given equation is satisfied, how should the w-scale be graduated and how is it located?

Through w_1 draw parallels to scales A and B. From similar triangles

$$\frac{R}{X_u} = \frac{X_v - S}{X_v}$$

Dividing the numerator and denominator of the right-hand side of the equation by X_v, we get

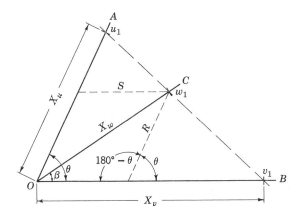

Figure 61.

$$\frac{R}{X_u} = 1 - \frac{S}{X_v} \qquad \text{or} \qquad \frac{R}{X_u} + \frac{S}{X_v} = 1^*$$

Substituting $\qquad X_u = m_u f_1(u) \qquad$ and $\qquad X_v = m_v f_2(u)$

we obtain

$$\frac{R}{m_u f_1(u)} + \frac{S}{m_v f_2(v)} = 1$$

Now if we set $\qquad R = m_u f_3(w) \qquad$ and $\qquad S = m_v f_3(w)$

we get

$$\frac{1}{f_1(u)} + \frac{1}{f_2(v)} = \frac{1}{f_3(w)}$$

which is the desired form.

It should be noted that $\dfrac{R}{S} = \dfrac{m_u}{m_v}$. Therefore, to construct an alignment chart for

the form

$$\frac{1}{f_1(u)} + \frac{1}{f_2(v)} = \frac{1}{f_3(w)}$$

1. Graduate the outer axes in accordance with the scale equations:

$$X_u = m_u f_1(u) \qquad \text{and} \qquad X_v = m_v f_2(v)$$

2. Locate the middle axis for w by employing the relation $\dfrac{R}{S} = \dfrac{m_u}{m_v}$.

3. Graduate the B-axis with a temporary w-scale, using the equation

$$S = m_v f_3(w)$$

and project the graduations of this scale onto the C-axis by parallels to the A-axis.

4. Or, as an alternative to step (3), graduate the A-axis with a temporary w-scale, using the equation

$$R = m_u f_3(w)$$

and project the graduations of this scale onto the C-axis by parallels to the B-axis.

In Figure 61, for example, the alternative method is preferable to that of step (3) because the horizontal parallels cut the C-axis at larger angles, thereby increasing the accuracy.

Direct Graduation of w-Scale

A method of graduating the w-scale directly can be developed by trigonometry in the following manner:

$$X_w^2 = R^2 + S^2 - 2RS \cos(180° - \theta)$$
$$= R^2 + S^2 + 2RS \cos \theta$$

Let $\qquad\qquad\qquad\qquad X_w = m_w f_3(w)$

Substituting this and $\qquad R = m_u f_3(w), \qquad S = m_v f_3(w)$

and dividing out the common term $[f_3(w)]^2$, we get

$$m_w^2 = m_u^2 + m_v^2 + 2m_u m_v \cos \theta.$$

* This is the intercept form of the equation of line $u_1 v_1$ with respect to the oblique axes OA and OB.

The *w*-scale can now be graduated directly from the relation,

$$X_w = m_w f_3(w)$$

where
$$m_w = (m_u{}^2 + m_v{}^2 + 2m_u m_v \cos \theta)^{\frac{1}{2}}$$

The *w*-scale can be located by the relation $\dfrac{R}{S} = \dfrac{m_u}{m_v}$.

Example

$$\frac{1}{u} + \frac{1}{v} = \frac{1}{f} \text{ (lens formula) (Figure 62)}$$

where *u* = object distance (0 to 100), *v* = image distance (0 to 80), *f* = focal distance (0 to 50).

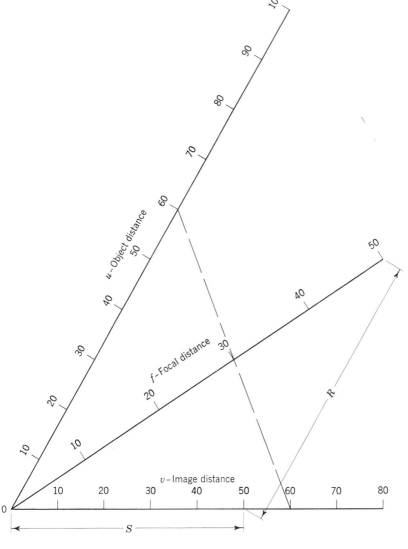

Figure 62. Alignment chart for the relation $\dfrac{1}{u} + \dfrac{1}{v} = \dfrac{1}{f}$.

The scale equations are:

$$X_u = m_u u; \qquad m_u = \tfrac{6}{100}; \qquad X_u = 0.06u$$

where the length of the u-scale is 6 in.

$$X_v = m_v v; \qquad m_v = \tfrac{4}{80}; \qquad X_v = 0.05v$$

where the length of the v-scale is 4 in.

Let $\qquad\qquad\qquad \theta = 60°$

$$m_f = (m_v^2 + m_u^2 + 2m_u m_v \cos\theta)^{\frac{1}{2}}$$
$$= (0.06^2 + 0.05^2 + 2 \times 0.06 \times 0.05 \times 0.5)^{\frac{1}{2}}$$
$$= (0.0036 + 0.0025 + 0.003)^{\frac{1}{2}}$$
$$= 0.0955$$
$$X_f = 0.0955f$$
$$\frac{R}{S} = \frac{0.06}{0.05} = \frac{6}{5} \quad \left(\text{recall that } \frac{R}{S} = \frac{m_u}{m_v}\right)$$

Only one point, such as point 50, need be located on the f-scale from the scale equation $X_f = 0.0955f$. The other points may be projected geometrically. The same is true of the u- and v-scales.

Special Case 1

If $m_v = m_u$ and $\theta = 120°$,

$$X_w = m_w f_3(w) = m_u f_3(w); \qquad \frac{R}{S} = \frac{m_u}{m_v} = 1$$

It can be shown easily by geometry that whenever $R/S = 1$ the w-scale bisects the angle θ; i.e., $\beta = \theta/2$ (see Figure 63).

$$m_w = [m_u^2 + m_u^2 + 2m_u^2(-\tfrac{1}{2})]^{\frac{1}{2}}$$
$$= m_u$$

Hence the three scales would have the same modulus.

Example

$$\frac{1}{r_1} + \frac{1}{r_2} = \frac{1}{r} \text{(Figure 63)}$$

Let r_1 and r_2 vary from 0 to 10 ohms, and r from 0 to 5 ohms. If the scale lengths for r_1 and r_2 are $2\frac{1}{2}$ in., then

$$m_{r_1} = \frac{2.5}{10} = 0.25; \qquad m_{r_2} = m_{r_1} = 0.25$$

Therefore, the scale equations are:

$$X_{r_1} = 0.25r_1; \qquad X_{r_2} = 0.25r_2$$

Since the angle between the scales is $120°$, $m_r = m_{r_1} = 0.25$. Thus the scale equation for the r-scale is $X_r = 0.25r$. Again, since $m_{r_2} = m_{r_1}$, the r-scale bisects the angle between the r_1- and r_2-scales. The completed chart is shown in Figure 63.

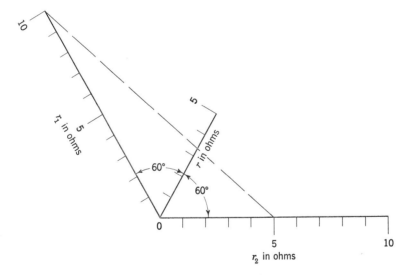

Figure 63. Alignment chart for the equation $\dfrac{1}{r_1} + \dfrac{1}{r_2} = \dfrac{1}{r}$.

Special Case 2

If $\theta = 90°$, we have

$$m_w = (m_u^2 + m_v^2 + 2m_u m_v \cos 90°)^{\frac{1}{2}}$$
$$m_w = (m_u^2 + m_v^2)^{\frac{1}{2}}$$
$$\frac{R}{S} = \frac{m_u}{m_v} = \tan \beta$$
$$\beta = \tan^{-1}\left(\frac{m_u}{m_v}\right)$$

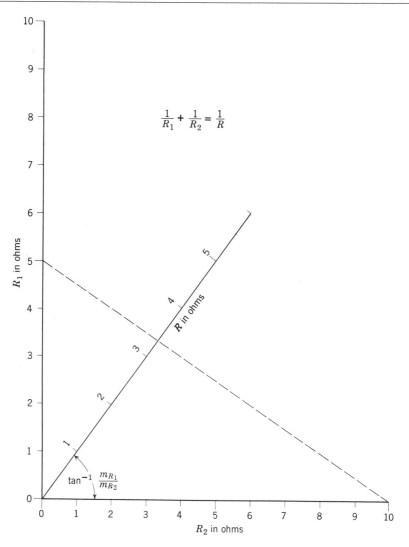

Figure 64. Alignment chart for the equation $\dfrac{1}{R_1} + \dfrac{1}{R_2} = \dfrac{1}{R}$. Two scales at right angles.

Example

Let R_1 and R_2 vary from 0 to 10 ohms, and R from 0 to 5 ohms. Suppose that the R_1-scale is 4 in. long; that the R_2-scale is 3 in. long; and that the angle between the scales is 90°. Now

$$m_{R_1} = \tfrac{4}{10} = 0.4; \qquad X_{R_1} = 0.4R_1$$

Furthermore,
$$m_{R_2} = \tfrac{3}{10} = 0.3; \qquad X_{R_2} = 0.3R_2$$

From the above, it follows that

$$m_R = (0.4^2 + 0.3^2)^{1/2} = 0.5$$

Therefore
$$X_R = 0.5R$$

The R-scale is located by the ratio $m_{R_1}/m_{R_2} = 0.4/0.3$. The completed nomogram is shown in Figure 64.

EXERCISES

6.1 $\dfrac{1}{u^2} + \dfrac{1}{v} = \dfrac{1}{w^3}$

where u varies from 0 to 10 and v varies from 0 to 5.

6.2 $\dfrac{1}{u} + \dfrac{2}{v^2} = \dfrac{1}{w}$

where u varies from 0 to 15 and v varies from 0 to 10.

6.3 $\dfrac{1}{R_1} + \dfrac{1}{R_2} = \dfrac{1}{R}$

where R_1 varies from 5 to 20 ohms and R_2 varies from 10 to 30 ohms.

6.4 $\dfrac{1}{u} + \dfrac{1}{v} = \dfrac{1}{f}$ (lens formula)

where u = object distance (50 to 100);
      v = image distance (25 to 75).

6.5 $\bar{S} = \dfrac{2S_1 S_2}{S_1 + S_2}$

where S_1 = one half of given distance traveled by plane at (0 to 400 mph);
      S_2 = remaining half traveled at (0 to 400 mph);
      $\bar{S}$ = average speed traveled (0 to 400 mph).

6.6 $D_e = \dfrac{4wd}{w + 2d}$ [equivalent diameter of a rectangular channel, or partly filled duct (used

in the determination of Reynolds number)]

where d = depth of liquid (1 to 10 ft);
      w = width of channel (1 to 12 ft).

CHAPTER

7

Alignment Charts—Parallel Scales for Four or More Variables of the Form

$$f_1(u) + f_2(v) + f_3(w) \cdots = f_4(q)$$

Example 1

Let us consider the relation:

$$u + 2v + 3w = 4t$$

Let
$$u + 2v = Q \tag{1}$$

then
$$Q + 3w = 4t \tag{2}$$

These two equations are of the form discussed in Chapter 3.

Suppose [equation (1)] that $m_u = 1$; $m_u = \frac{1}{2}$; then

$$X_u = u; \qquad X_v = \frac{1}{2}(2v) = v$$

Now
$$\frac{m_u}{m_v} = \frac{1}{\frac{1}{2}} = \frac{2}{1}; \qquad m_Q = \frac{1 \times \frac{1}{2}}{1 + \frac{1}{2}} = \frac{1}{3}$$

If [equation (2)] $m_w = \frac{1}{3}$; $X_w = \frac{1}{3}(3w) = w;$ then

$$\frac{m_Q}{m_w} = \frac{\frac{1}{3}}{\frac{1}{3}} = \frac{1}{1}; \qquad m_t = \frac{\frac{1}{3} \times \frac{1}{3}}{\frac{1}{3} + \frac{1}{3}} = \frac{\frac{1}{9}}{\frac{2}{3}} = \frac{1}{6}$$

Therefore
$$X_t = \frac{1}{6}(4t) = \frac{2}{3}t$$

From the above calculations, we may now proceed to construct the chart (Figure 65).

Now consider *equation (1)*, $u + 2v = Q$. Scales u and v are placed a convenient distance apart. Scale u is graduated from its scale equation $X_u = u;$ and scale v is graduated from its scale equation $X_v = \frac{1}{2}(2v) = v$. The Q-scale is located in accordance with the ratio $m_u/m_v = 1/\frac{1}{2} = 2/1$. This scale is *not* graduated.

Now consider *equation (2)*, $Q + 3w = 4t$. Scale w is placed a convenient distance from the Q-scale. Graduations on the w-scale are located in accordance with its scale equation $X_w = \frac{1}{3}(3w) = w$. The t-scale is located from the ratio $m_Q/m_w = \frac{1}{3}/\frac{1}{3} = 1/1$. The t-scale is then graduated from the scale equation $X_t = \frac{1}{6}(4t) = \frac{2}{3}t$.

It should be carefully noted that in most of the practical applications of this form, it is necessary to locate a point on the fourth scale (by a computation from the given equation) before graduating that scale. Once a value, t_1, is located on the t-scale, the scale equation is actually $X_t = \frac{2}{3}(t - t_1)$. The chart is shown in Figure 65.

$$u + 2v + 3w = 4t$$

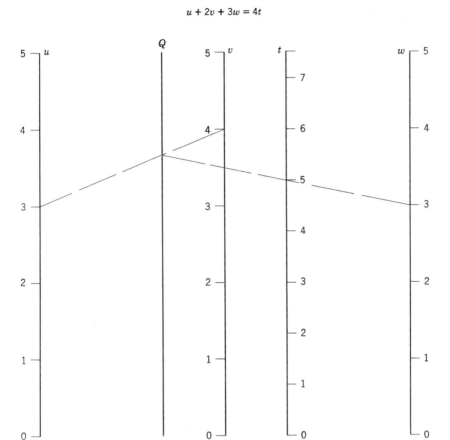

Figure 65. Alignment chart for the equation $u + 2v + 3w = 4t$.

Example 2

$$R = 19.64Cd^2\sqrt{h}$$

where R = rate of flow through an orifice, in gallons per minute; C = orifice coefficient (0.6 to 1.6); d = orifice diameter (0.1 to 1.0 in.); and h = head (10 to 100 ft).

Case a:

Our first step is to write the given equation in type form:

$$\log R - \log 19.64 = \log C + 2 \log d + \tfrac{1}{2} \log h$$

Let
$$\log C + 2 \log d = T \tag{1}$$

and
$$\log R - \log 19.64 = T + \tfrac{1}{2} \log h \tag{2}$$

Equations (1) and (2) are now of the form $f_1(u) + f_2(v) = f_3(w)$. The nomogram would look like Figure 66.

With this arrangement of scales, it will be observed that the operation of the chart would require, first, a line (isopleth) joining points on the C- and d-scales. The intersection of this line with the T-scale (dummy or turning axis) would then be joined with a point on the h-scale. The intersection of the latter line with the R-scale would give the result.

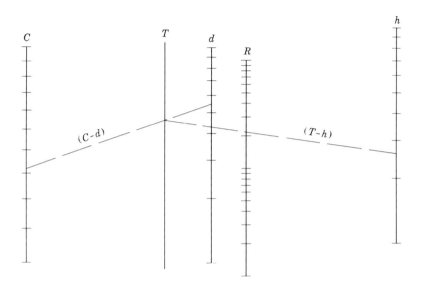

Figure 66. Arrangement of scales for the equation $R = 19.64 \, Cd^2\sqrt{h}$. *Case a.*

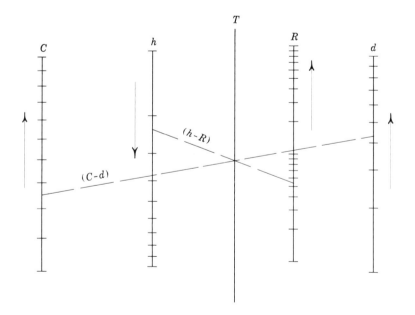

Figure 67. Arrangement of scales for the equation $R = 19.64 \, Cd^2\sqrt{h}$. *Case b.*

Case b:

Now let us try a different analysis of the problem. Suppose we write the equations:

$$\log C + 2 \log d = T$$

and
$$\log R - \log 19.64 - \tfrac{1}{2} \log h = T$$

Now the arrangement of scales would look like Figure 67. *Note:* Graduations on the *h*-scale will be directed downwardly, since a minus sign precedes $\tfrac{1}{2} \log h$.

Case c:

A third analysis of the given equation shows that we could write:

$$\log R - \log 19.64 = T + \tfrac{1}{2} \log h$$

and
$$T - \log C = 2 \log d$$

The arrangement of scales in this case would look like Figure 68. Note that this arrangement is much better than the first two, since there is greater clarity in operation and reading.

Having completed the preliminary studies, let us now make the necessary computations for the final design of the chart which is shown in Figure 68. Consider the equation $T - \log C = 2 \log d$.

For scale C

$$m_C = \frac{X_C}{(\log C_n - \log C_0)} = \frac{4 \text{ in. } \pm}{\log 1.6 - \log 0.6} = 9.4 \text{ (use 10.0)}$$

or
$$X_C = 10(\log C - \log 0.6), \text{ scale equation for } C$$

For scale d

$$m_d = \frac{4 \text{ in. } \pm}{2 \log 1.0 - 2 \log 0.1} = 2$$

$$X_d = 2(2 \log d - 2 \log 0.1), \text{ scale equation for } d$$

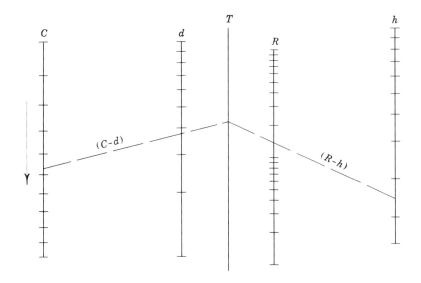

Figure 68. Arrangement of scales for the equation $R = 19.64 \, Cd^2 \sqrt{h}$. Case c.

Now
$$m_d = \frac{m_C \cdot m_T}{m_C + m_T} \quad \text{or} \quad 2 = \frac{10 m_T}{10 + m_T}$$

$$m_T = 2.5; \quad \frac{m_C}{m_T} = \frac{10}{2.5} = \frac{4}{1}$$

The sketch layout for $T - \log C = 2 \log d$ is shown in Figure 69. Now let us consider the equation

$$\log R - \log 19.64 = T + \tfrac{1}{2} \log h$$

For scale h

$$m_h = \frac{7.5 \text{ in.}}{\tfrac{1}{2} \log 100 - \tfrac{1}{2} \log 10} = 15$$

or
$$X_h = 15(\tfrac{1}{2} \log h - \tfrac{1}{2} \log 10) = 7.5(\log h - \log 10)$$

$$\frac{m_T}{m_h} = \frac{2.5}{15} = \frac{1}{6}$$

The modulus for the R-scale is

$$m_R = \frac{m_T \cdot m_h}{m_T + m_h} = \frac{2.5 \times 15}{2.5 + 15} = 2.14$$

and
$$X_R = 2.14(\log R - \log R_1)$$

where R_1 is a point on the R-scale. This point is computed from the original equation.

The sketch layout for $\log R - \log 19.64 = T + \tfrac{1}{2} \log h$ is shown in Figure 70. The completed chart is shown in Figure 71.

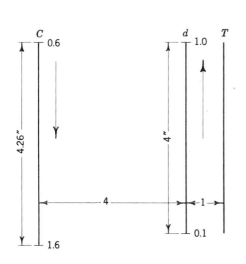

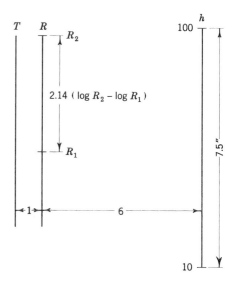

Figure 69. Arrangement of scales for the equation $T - \log C = 2 \log d$.

Figure 70. Arrangement of scales for the equation $\log R - \log 19.64 = T + \tfrac{1}{2} \log h$.

The designer is cautioned to check the positioning of the R-scale in each case, before the adoption of the final form. In some cases, it will be found that the most desirable form, case c in the above example, may yield one scale whose graduations are not properly oriented with respect to the other scales, i.e., one scale may be practically out of reach in spite of the fact that the "length" of the graduated scale is satisfactory.

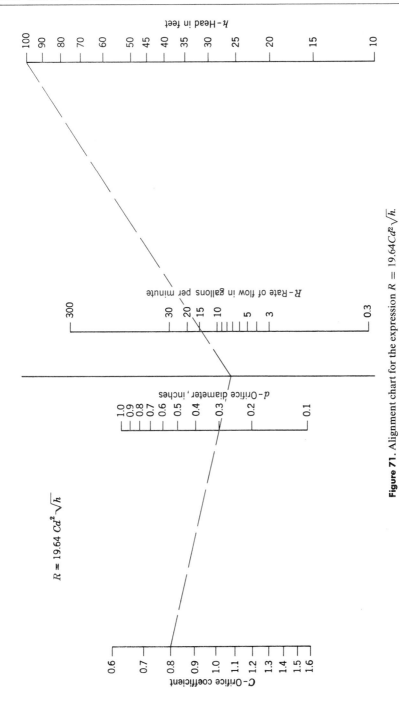

Figure 71. Alignment chart for the expression $R = 19.64 C d^2 \sqrt{h}$.

Example 3

Let us consider the equation

$$f_1(u) - f_2(v) = f_3(w) - f_4(q) \tag{1}$$

Suppose we let

$$f_1(u) - f_2(v) = Q \tag{2}$$

and

$$f_3(w) - f_4(q) = Q \tag{3}$$

Each of these equations is of the general form $f_1(u) + f_2(v) = f_3(w)$.

A nomogram for equation (1) would, then, look like Figure 72.

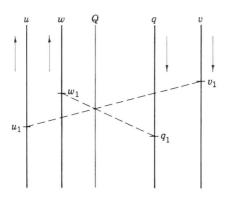

Figure 72.

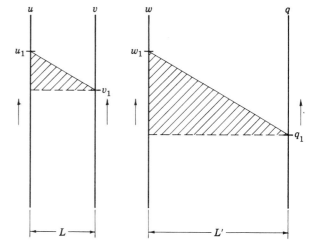

Figure 73. Alternative solution #1 for $f_1(u) - f_2(v) = f_3(w) - f_4(q)$.

Alternative Solution #1

Suppose we consider Figure 73, which shows parallel scales u and v, distance L apart; and parallel scales w and q, distance L' apart. (Note that no turning axis such as Q in Figure 72 is used.)

The nomogram will be so designed that a line which joins u_1 and v_1 and one that joins w_1 and q_1 will be parallel to each other. We assume, of course, that values u_1, v_1, w_1, and q_1 satisfy the given equation.

Our problem, then, is to determine:

(a) the ratio L/L', and

(b) the relationship among the moduli.

The scale equations in general are:

$$X_u = m_u f_1(u); \qquad X_w = m_w f_3(w)$$
$$X_v = m_v f_2(v); \qquad X_q = m_q f_4(q)$$

Based on the similar triangles shown shaded,

$$\frac{m_u f_1(u_1) - m_v f_2(v_1)}{m_w f_3(w_1) - m_q f_4(q_1)} = \frac{L}{L'}$$

When $m_u = m_v$ and $m_w = m_q$

$$\frac{m_u[f_1(u_1) - f_2(v_1)]}{m_w[f_3(w_1) - f_4(q_1)]} = \frac{L}{L'}$$

Since $f_1(u) - f_2(v) = f_3(w) - f_4(q)$, $\dfrac{m_u}{m_w} = \dfrac{L}{L'}$.

Therefore, to design a nomogram for an equation of the form $f_1(u) - f_2(v) = f_3(w) - f_4(q)$ using parallel scales and *no turning axis*, proceed as follows:

1. Graduate the scales in accordance with the scale equations:

$$X_u = m_u f_1(u)$$
$$X_v = m_u f_2(v)$$
$$X_w = m_w f_3(w)$$
$$X_q = m_w f_4(q)$$

2. Place the parallel scales u and v a convenient distance apart, i.e., distance L.

3. Place the parallel scales w and q a distance apart equal to L', where $\dfrac{L}{L'} = \dfrac{m_u}{m_w}$.

4. Graduate three of the scales from the scale equations, then locate a point on the fourth scale from a calculation based upon the given equation before employing the corresponding scale equation.

Alternative Solution #2

Instead of using parallels to read values which satisfy the equation, perpendiculars can be used. This is made possible by arranging the pairs of scales (u and v) and (w and q) at right angles to each other as shown in Figure 74.

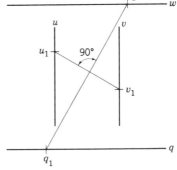

Figure 74. Alternative solution #2 for $f_1(u) - f_2(v) = f_3(w) - f_4(q)$.

Example 4

Now let us consider the equation $u^2 - v^2 = w - q$. We will assume the values of the moduli. Let $m_u = 1$ and $m_w = 2$. Now

$$X_u = u^2$$
$$X_v = v^2 \text{ (remember } m_u = m_v)$$
$$X_w = 2w$$
$$X_q = 2q \text{ (recall that } m_w = m_q)$$

The distance between the u- and v-scales will be taken as $1\frac{1}{2}$ in.

Since $\dfrac{m_u}{m_w} = \dfrac{L}{L'} = \dfrac{1}{2}$, hence $L' = 2L = 3$ in.

The completed nomogram is shown in Figure 75. The alternative solution is shown in Figure 76.

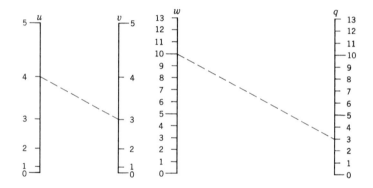

Figure 75. $u^2 - v^2 = w - q$. Example: When $u = 4$, $v = 3$, and $w = 10$, then $q = 3$.

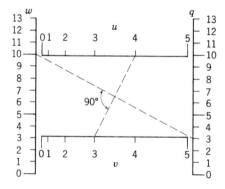

Figure 76. Alternative solution #2 for $u^2 - v^2 = w - q$.

Example 5

If the equation is $u + v = w + q$, then

$$\left. \begin{array}{l} X_u = m_u u \\ X_v = -m_u v \end{array} \right\} \text{ scales plotted in opposite directions}$$

$$X_w = m_w w$$

$$X_q = -m_w q$$

The nomogram is shown in Figure 77, and the alternative solution #2 in Figure 78.

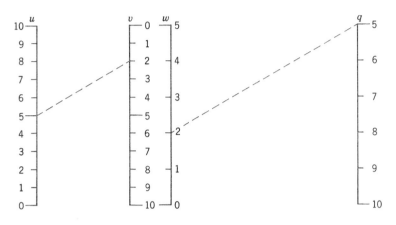

Figure 77. $u + v = w + q$.

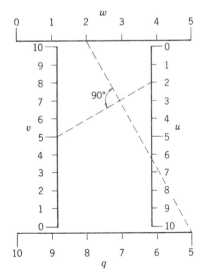

Figure 78. Alternative solution #2
for $u + v = w + q$.

EXERCISES

7.1 $D = 68.5 \sqrt[3]{\dfrac{P}{NS}}$

where D = shaft diameter (1 to 6 in.);
$\quad\quad\ P$ = horsepower (10 to 1500);
$\quad\quad\ N$ = speed (100 to 1000 rpm);
$\quad\quad\ S$ = design stress (2000 to 8000 psi).

7.2 $S = \dfrac{32}{\pi}\ \dfrac{M}{A^2 B}$ (maximum bending stress in an elliptical bar)

where S = bending stress in pounds per square inch;
$\quad\quad\ M$ = bending moment about x-x axis in pound-inches (0 to 15,000);
$\quad\quad\ A$ = length of ellipse perpendicular to x-x axis (1 to 5 in.);
$\quad\quad\ B$ = length of ellipse parallel to x-x axis (1 to 6 in.).

7.3 $P_r = \dfrac{C_P \mu}{k}$ (Prandtl's modulus)

where P_r = Prandtl's modulus (dimensionless);
$\quad\quad\ \mu$ = viscosity in pounds per hour-foot (0.01 to 0.3);
$\quad\quad\ C_P$ = specific heat in Btu per pound-degree Fahrenheit (0.1 to 1.5);
$\quad\quad\ k$ = thermal conductivity in Btu per hour-foot-degree Fahrenheit (0.0025 to 0.02).

7.4 $\dfrac{P_1}{P_2} = \left(\dfrac{V_2}{V_1}\right)^{1.41}$ (adiabatic expansion of air)

where P_1 = initial pressure (5 to 350 psi);
$\quad\quad\ P_2$ = final pressure (3 to 300 psi);
$\quad\quad\ V_1$ = initial volume (1 to 100 cf);
$\quad\quad\ V_2$ = final volume (1 to 120 cf).

7.5 $T = I N_S N_P \left(\dfrac{2\pi}{60}\right)^2$ (gyroscopic couple)

where T = gyroscopic couple in inch-pounds;
$\quad\quad\ I$ = mass moment of inertia of the mass about its axis in pound-second³-inches (1 to 10);
$\quad\quad\ N_S$ = angular velocity of the mass about its axis (10 to 1000 rpm);
$\quad\quad\ N_P$ = angular velocity of the axis of the mass or angular velocity of precession (10 to 100 rpm).

7.6 $Q = \dfrac{(D + 2)LH}{27}$ (earthwork quantities for pipe trenching)

where D = diameter of pipe (6 to 72 in.);
$\quad\quad\ L$ = length of trench (15 to 400 ft);
$\quad\quad\ H$ = depth of trench (2 to 18 ft);
$\quad\quad\ Q$ = earth quantity in cubic yards.

7.7 $Q = \dfrac{(A_1 + A_2)L}{54}$ (roadway earth quantities)

where A_1 = one end area (50 to 1500 sq ft);
$\quad\quad\ A_2$ = adjacent end area (50 to 1500 sq ft);
$\quad\quad\ L$ = distance between end areas (10 to 100 ft);
$\quad\quad\ Q$ = earth quantity in cubic yards.

Proportional Charts for the Form

$$\frac{f_1(u)}{f_2(v)} = \frac{f_3(w)}{f_4(q)}$$

This equation can be solved in a manner similar to the examples of Chapter 7. This simply means transforming the above equation to the form

$$\log f_1(u) - \log f_2(v) = \log f_3(w) - \log f_4(q)$$

In many cases, however, where the functions are linear, the proportional-type alignment chart has a distinct advantage in that the scales are uniform, thus permitting more accurate readings and also simplifying the construction of the scales.

Consider the figure shown in Figure 79. Scales A and B are parallel to each other, and graduated in accordance with the scale equations:

$$X_u = m_u f_1(u) \qquad \text{and} \qquad X_v = m_v f_2(v), \text{ respectively.}$$

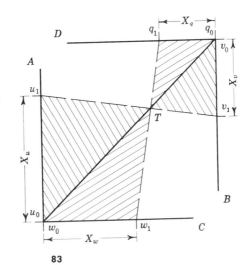

Figure 79. Arrangement of scales for the type form $\dfrac{f_1(u)}{f_2(v)} = \dfrac{f_3(w)}{f_4(q)}$.

In a similar manner, scales C and D are parallel to each other, and are graduated in accordance with the scale equations:

$$X_w = m_w f_3(w) \quad \text{and} \quad X_q = m_q f_4(q).$$

The angle between scales A and C may be of any convenient magnitude.

Triangles $u_1 u_0 T$ and $v_1 v_0 T$ are similar, hence

$$\frac{X_u}{X_v} = \frac{u_0 T}{v_0 T}$$

Likewise, triangles $w_0 T w_1$ and $q_0 T q_1$ are similar, hence

$$\frac{X_w}{X_q} = \frac{w_0 T}{q_0 T}$$

But lengths $u_0 T = w_0 T$; and $v_0 T = q_0 T$. Therefore

$$\frac{X_u}{X_v} = \frac{X_w}{X_q} \quad \text{or} \quad \frac{m_u f_1(u)}{m_v f_2(v)} = \frac{m_w f_3(w)}{m_q f_4(q)}$$

Since

$$\frac{f_1(u)}{f_2(v)} = \frac{f_3(w)}{f_4(q)}$$

it follows that

$$\frac{m_u}{m_v} = \frac{m_w}{m_q}$$

This means that three moduli may be determined from the given data, but *the fourth modulus will be dependent upon the first three.*

Note: u_0, v_0, w_0, and q_0 are the zero values of the respective functions.

Example 1 (Figure 80)

$$t = \frac{Pd}{2f} \text{(thickness of a pipe to withstand internal pressures)}$$

where P = pressure (25 to 100 psi), f = allowable stress (3000 to 15,000 psi), d = diameter of pipe (10 to 60 in.), and t = thickness of pipe ($\frac{1}{8}$ to $\frac{1}{2}$ in.). The given equation may be put in type form by writing $\frac{t}{d} = \frac{P}{2f}$.

Now

$$m_t = \frac{5 \text{ in.}}{\frac{1}{2}} = 10 \text{ in.}$$

and

$$X_t = 10t \text{ (scale equation for } t)$$

$$m_d = \frac{5 \text{ in. } \pm}{60} = 0.0833 \text{ (use 0.1)}$$

and

$$X_d = 0.1d \text{ (scale equation for } d)$$

$$m_f = \frac{5 \text{ in } \pm}{30,000} = 0.000166 \text{ (use 0.0002)}$$

and

$$X_f = 0.0002(2f) = 0.0004f$$

The modulus for P is now computed from $m_t/m_d = m_p/m_f$; or $10/0.1 = m_p/0.0002$; $m_P = 0.02$ and $X_P = 0.02P$. (See Figure 80 for completed chart.)

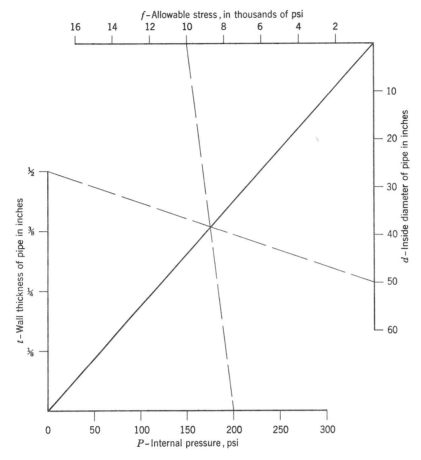

Figure 80. Proportional-type chart for the relation $t = \dfrac{Pd}{2f}$.

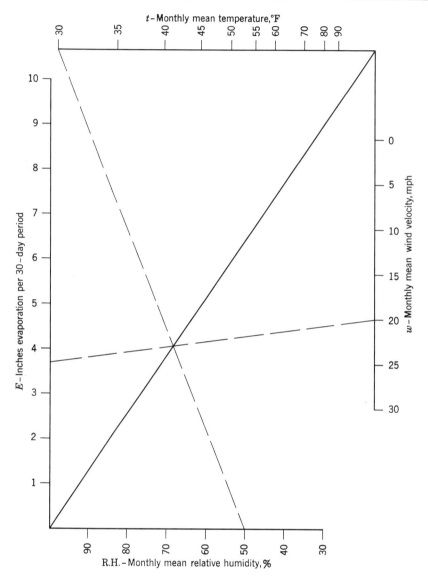

Figure 81. Meyer's evaporation formula $E = 15(V - v)\left(1 + \dfrac{w}{10}\right)$.

Example 2

$$E = 15(V - v)\left(1 + \frac{w}{10}\right) \text{ (Meyer's evaporation formula) (Figure 81)}$$

where E = evaporation in inches per month (0 to 10); V = saturated vapor pressure corresponding to monthly mean temperature, t, in degrees Fahrenheit, which varies from 30° to 90°; v = actual vapor pressure; w = monthly mean wind velocity in miles per hour (0 to 30).

Since $$v = V \times \text{R.H.}$$

where R.H. = monthly mean relative humidity (30% to 90%), then

$$E = 15V(1 - \text{R.H.})(1 + w/10)$$

Now,

$$\frac{E}{10 + w} = \frac{1.5(1 - \text{R.H.})}{\dfrac{1}{f(t)}}$$

where V is a function of t.

$$m_E = \frac{6.25}{10} = \frac{5}{8}; \qquad X_E = \frac{5}{8}E$$

The range of $f(t)$ is 0.164 to 1.408.

$$m_t = \frac{4\frac{1}{2}}{\dfrac{1}{0.164}} = 0.738 \text{ (use 0.75)}; \qquad X_t = 0.75\,\frac{1}{f(t)}$$

$$m_w = \frac{5}{10 + 30} = \frac{1}{8}; \qquad X_w = \frac{1}{8}(10 + w)$$

$$\frac{\frac{5}{8}}{\frac{1}{8}} = \frac{m_{\text{R.H.}}}{0.75}$$

Therefore $m_{\text{R.H.}} = \frac{15}{4};$ $X_{\text{R.H.}} = \frac{15}{4} \times 1.5(1 - \text{R.H.}) = \frac{90}{16}(1 - \text{R.H.})$

$$= \frac{45}{8}(1 - \text{R.H.})$$

Alternative Arrangements of Scales

The angle between scales A and C (or D and B), Figure 79, need not be 90°. In fact, scale C could coincide with scale A, which means that scale D would coincide with scale B. A study of Figure 82 will reveal that the above statement is true.

Figure 82. Alternative arrangement of scales for the equation $\dfrac{f_1(u)}{f_2(v)} = \dfrac{f_3(w)}{f_4(q)}$.

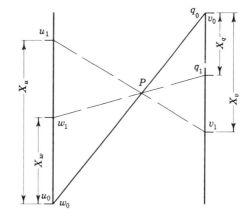

$$\frac{X_u}{X_v} = \frac{u_0 P}{P v_0}; \qquad \frac{X_w}{X_q} = \frac{w_0 P}{P q_0}$$

and since $u_0 \equiv w_0$ and $v_0 \equiv q_0$,

$$\frac{X_u}{X_v} = \frac{X_w}{X_q}$$

Hence, when

$$X_u = m_u f_1(u)$$
$$X_v = m_v f_2(v)$$
$$X_w = m_w f_3(w)$$
$$X_q = m_q f_4(q)$$

and

$$\frac{m_u}{m_v} = \frac{m_w}{m_q}$$

then

$$\frac{f_1(u)}{f_2(v)} = \frac{f_3(w)}{f_4(q)}$$

Variations of the above charts are shown in Figures 83, 84, and 85.

Drawing parallels, as in Figures 83 and 84, and perpendiculars, as in Figure 85, can be facilitated by the use of transparent overlays or by properly oriented triangles. These methods will be described in subsequent examples.

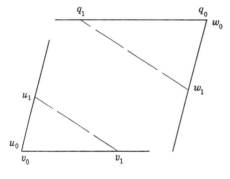

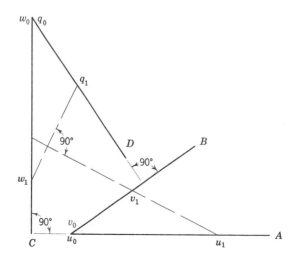

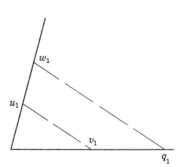

Figure 83. Alternative arrangement of scales for the equation $\dfrac{f_1(u)}{f_2(v)} = \dfrac{f_3(w)}{f_4(q)}$.

Figure 84. Alternative arrangement of scales for the equation $\dfrac{f_1(u)}{f_2(v)} = \dfrac{f_3(w)}{f_4(q)}$.

Figure 85. Alternative arrangement of scales for the equation $\dfrac{f_1(u)}{f_2(v)} = \dfrac{f_3(w)}{f_4(q)}$.

Example 3

Let us consider the equation:

$$\frac{u}{v} = \frac{w}{q^2}$$

Suppose the ranges of the variables are:

$$u \text{ (0 to 10);} \qquad v \text{ (0 to 5);} \qquad w \text{ (0 to 20);} \qquad q \text{ (0 to 3)}$$

The moduli and scale equations are easily determined.

$$m_u = \frac{10}{10} = 1 \qquad m_w = \frac{10}{20} = 0.5 \qquad m_v = \frac{10}{5} = 2$$

$$X_u = 1 \times u = u \qquad X_w = 0.5w \qquad X_v = 2v$$

Now we recall that $\qquad \dfrac{m_u}{m_v} = \dfrac{m_w}{m_q}$

Therefore $\qquad m_q = \dfrac{m_v m_w}{m_u} = \dfrac{2 \times 0.5}{1} = 1 \qquad$ and $\qquad X_q = q^2$

A nomogram similar to Figure 84 can be constructed, as shown in Figure 86. In order to avoid the confusion that might arise due to the graduations of the u- and w-scales on one line, and the graduations of the v- and q-scales on the other line, we can redesign the nomogram to eliminate this feature. This is shown in Figure 87.

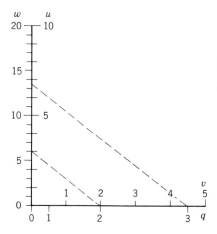

Figure 86. $\dfrac{u}{v} = \dfrac{w}{q^2}$. Example: When $u = 3$, $v = 2$, and $q = 3$, then $w = 13.5$.

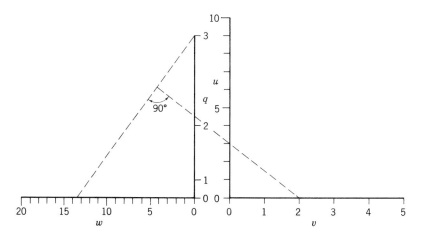

Figure 87. Alternative solution of $\dfrac{u}{v} = \dfrac{w}{q^2}$ to avoid double graduations shown in Figure 86.

EXERCISES

Hydraulics

8.1 $N_S = \dfrac{NQ}{H^{3/4}}$

where N_S = specific speed of a centrifugal pump;
      Q = flow rate (1000 to 10,000 gpm);
      N = speed (100 to 4000 rpm);
      H = head (20 to 200 ft).

8.2 $t = \dfrac{Pd}{2f}$ (required thickness of a pipe to withstand an internal pressure)

where t = thickness in inches (0 to $\frac{1}{4}$);
  P = internal pressure in pounds per square inch (0 to 100);
  f = allowable stress in pounds per square inch (0 to 15,000);
  d = diameter of pipe in inches (0 to 60).

8.3 $V = C\sqrt{RS}$ (Chezy formula for velocity in an open channel in feet per second)

where R = hydraulic radius (0 to 25 ft);
  S = slope of channel (0 to 0.01);
  C = (60 to 140).

8.4 $Q = C_d a\sqrt{2gh}$ [discharge from an orifice or nozzle in cubic feet per second (0 to 20)]

where C_d = coefficient of discharge (0.5 to 1.0);
  a = area of the orifice (0 to 1.0 sq ft);
  h = head of water on the orifice (0 to 20 ft);
  g = 32.2 ft. per sec².

8.5 $R = \dfrac{\rho v l}{\mu}$ [Reynolds number as used for fluid motion (0 to 1,000,000)]

where v = velocity in feet per second (0 to 10);
  l = characteristic dimension (0 to 2 ft);
  ρ = 62.4/32.2 (for water);
  μ = coefficient of viscosity, and for water is a function of temperature given by the following table:

$T(°F)$	μ
32	374×10^{-7}
50	273×10^{-7}
68	211×10^{-7}
86	167×10^{-7}
104	137×10^{-7}
122	115×10^{-7}
140	97.8×10^{-7}
158	84.6×10^{-7}
176	74.4×10^{-7}
194	66.1×10^{-7}
212	59.2×10^{-7}

8.6 $v = \dfrac{1.486}{n} R^{\frac{2}{3}} S^{\frac{1}{2}}$ [velocity in an open channel (0 to 30 ft/sec) (Manning's formula)]

where n = coefficient of roughness (0.009 to 0.035);
  R = hydraulic radius (0 to 20 ft);
  S = slope of channel (0 to 0.01).

8.7 $\dfrac{N_s}{N} = \dfrac{\sqrt{hp}}{H^{5/4}}$ (formula for a reaction turbine)

where N_s = specific speed (10 to 100);
  N = speed in revolutions per minute (100 to 2000);
  hp = horsepower (to 1000);
  H = head of water (10 to 200 ft).

Strength of Materials

8.8 $P = 0.196 \dfrac{d^3}{r} f$ (load supported by a helical compression spring)

where d = diameter of wire corresponding to B & S gage numbers (0000 to 10);
r = mean radius of spring (0.5 to 2 in.);
f = shearing stress of material (10,000 to 60,000 psi).

8.9 $\phi = \dfrac{360}{2\pi} \cdot \dfrac{TL}{\dfrac{\pi d^4}{32} \cdot 12 \cdot 10^6}$ (angle of twist of a cylindrical shaft)

where ϕ = angle of twist in degrees;
d = diameter of shaft (0.5 to 2.5 in.);
T = applied torque (50,000 to 500,000 in.-lb);
L = shaft length (2 to 20 in.).

8.10 $f = \dfrac{6M}{bH^2}$ (stress in the outer fiber of a section of a rectangular beam)

where M = bending moment on the section in inch-pounds (10,000 to 300,000);
b = breadth of section in inches (2 to 16);
h = depth of section in inches (3 to 20);
f = fiber stress in pounds per square inch (750 to 1300).

8.11 $f = \dfrac{Mc}{I}$ (fiber stress in a beam of any cross section)

where f = fiber stress in pounds per square inch (3000 to 15,000);
M = bending moment on section in inch-pounds (25,000 to 300,000);
c = distance from neutral axis where stress is to be found (0 to 10 in.);
I = moment of inertia of section (100 to 10,000 in.[4]).

8.12 $d = 68.5 \sqrt[3]{\dfrac{H}{n(T_{max})}}$ (required diameter of a shaft in torsion)

where H = horsepower to be transmitted—varies from (0 to 500 hp);
n = speed of rotation in revolutions per minute (0 to 4000);
T_{max} = working stress in shear, pounds per square inch (5000 to 15,000);
d = diameter (0 to 3 in.).

8.13   Euler's column formula: $\dfrac{P}{A} = \dfrac{C\pi^2 E}{\left(\dfrac{L}{\rho}\right)^2}$

where P/A = critical average stress in pounds per square inch, varies from (500 to 20,000);
C = fixity coefficient (1 to 4);
E = modulus of elasticity (1 to 30 million psi);
L/ρ = radius of gyration (70 to 200).

Civil

8.14 $v = \dfrac{V}{\frac{7}{8}bd}$ (unit shear in reinforced concrete beam)

where v = unit shear (0 to 800 psi);
d = effective depth of beam (10 to 50 in.);
b = width of beam (4 to 40 in.);
V = total shear on section (1 to 80 kips).

8.15 $S = \dfrac{l^2}{2R_cL_c}$ (the "spiral angle" or total inclination of curve to tangent at any point on a spiral easement curve, range 0° to 30°)

where l = distance in feet from T.S. (point of spiral), range 0 to 600;
R_c = radius of circle in feet (300 to 6000);
L_c = total length of spiral in feet (0 to 600).

8.16 $X = \dfrac{l^3}{6R_cL_c}$ (offset from the tangent in a spiral easement curve, range 0 to 75)

where l, R_c, and L_c are as defined in Problem 8.15.

8.17 Since $D = \dfrac{5729.65}{R_c}$, double-graduate the R_c scale in Problem 8.15 or 8.16 to read D, range 1° to 20°.

8.18 $f_c = \dfrac{2M}{A_F(d - 0.5t)}$ (unit compression in T-beams)

where M = bending moment (1 to 100 ft-kips);
A_F = flange area (25 to 500 sq in.);
$(d - 0.5t)$ = effective depth, d, minus one-half of flange thickness (5 to 50 in.);
f_c = maximum unit compression (20 to 2000 in.-kips).

8.19 $e = \dfrac{gv^2}{32.2R}$ (elevation of track in feet)

where g = gauge of track;
v = velocity in feet per second (0 to 60);
R = radius of curve in feet (300 to 6000).

8.20 $fs = \dfrac{M}{A_sjd}$ (unit fiber stress in steel)

where M = total external bending moment at a cross section (10,000 to 1,500,000 in.-lb);
A_s = area of cross section of steel (0.2 to 6 sq in.);
j = ratio of arm of resisting couple to effective depth = $\frac{7}{8}$ (for this problem);
d = distance from compression face to plane of centroid of tensile steel, known as the effective depth (5 to 40 in.).

8.21 $C_s = \dfrac{W^2L^3}{24P^2}$ [correction to a steel tape due to sag (0 to 0.5)]

where W = weight of tape in pounds per foot (0 to 0.04);
L = length of tape between supports (0 to 100 ft);
P = applied tension in pounds (0 to 10).

8.22 $W = \dfrac{DH^2F}{B}$ (minimum weight of square chimney required to withstand force of wind)

where D = average width of side (1 to 15 ft);
H = height of chimney (10 to 100 ft);
F = force of wind (50);
B = breadth of base (2 to 20 ft).

Mechanical

8.23 $C = \dfrac{w(hs - he)}{42.42 \text{ hp}}$ (refrigeration coefficient of performance)

where w = refrigerant flow rate (20 to 200 lb/min);
  $(hs - he)$ = difference between enthalpy at entrance and discharge of evaporator (100 to 1000 Btu/lb);
        hp = compressor horsepower (10 to 100).

8.24 $hp = \dfrac{2\pi LNW}{33,000}$ [horsepower as measured by a prony brake (hp, 0 to 75)]

where L = length of brake arm in feet (0.5 to 1.5);
        N = shaft speed in revolutions per minute (0 to 4000);
        W = load on scales (0 to 200 lb).

8.25 $M = 0.3155 A_t \sqrt{\dfrac{P_1}{V_1}}$ [discharge from a steam nozzle in a turbine in pounds per second

      (0 to 6)]

where A_t = exit area of nozzle in square inches (0 to 5);
        P_1 = pressure of steam (15 to 300 psi);
        V_1 = specific volume in cubic feet per pound (0 to 26).

8.26 $q = hA(T_1 - T_2)$ (convection equation)

where q = heat flow rate in Btu per hour;
          A = area of surface on which heat-transfer coefficient is based (5 to 100 sq ft);
  $(T_1 - T_2)$ = difference between higher and lower temperatures (20 to 500°F);
          h = surface conductance in Btu per (hour) (square foot) (degree Fahrenheit); for air a flat surface h = 2, 3, and 10 at mean velocities of 5 fps, 10 fps, and 50 fps, respectively.

8.27 $h_i = 155(1 + 0.011T)\dfrac{v^{0.8}}{d^{0.2}}$ (simplified equation for water in tubes)

where h_i = inside surface coefficient;
        d = inside diameter ($\frac{1}{4}$ to 3 in.);
        T = mean temperature of the water (40 to 200°F);
        v = velocity through tube (2 to 10 fps).

8.28 $F = tN \cdot \text{rpm}$ (milling operation)

where F = feed per minute (0.006 to 0.022 in.);
        t = feed per tooth per revolution (0.005 to 0.020 in.);
        N = number of teeth in cutter (6 to 30).

8.29 $T = \dfrac{W}{N \cdot f}$ (shaper operation)

where T = time in minutes (1 to 240);
        W = width of the piece (2 to 18 in.);
        f = feed in inches per stroke (0.005 to 0.030 in.);
        N = number of strokes per minute (10 to 100 strokes).

8.30 $\dfrac{T_1}{T_2} = e^{f\theta}$ (Belt friction formula—differential band brake)

where T_1 = maximum pull (0 to 1000 lb);
        T_2 = minimum pull (0 to 1000 lb);
        f = coefficient of friction (0 to 0.4);
        θ = angle of contact (π to 2π radians).

Electrical

8.31 $P = 3EI \cos \theta$ (power in a balanced Y system and in a balanced Δ system)

where P = power in watts;
$\quad\quad E$ = line voltage (0 to 220 volts);
$\quad\quad I$ = line current (0 to 30 amp);
$\quad \cos \theta$ = power factor (0.75 to 1.00).

8.32 $A = \dfrac{21.6Id}{E}$ (required wire size for allowable voltage drop in d-c circuit)

where A = area of wire in circular mils (express in B & S wire size);
$\quad\quad I$ = current (0 to 50 amp);
$\quad\quad d$ = distance from source to installation (100 to 1000 ft);
$\quad\quad E$ = maximum allowable line voltage drop (1.0 to 10 volts).

8.33 $H = \dfrac{2\pi Ir^2}{d^3}$ (field intensity at any point P as shown by the figure)

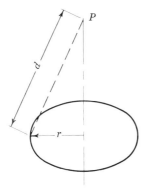

where I = current in wire in ab-amperes (0 to 500);
$\quad\quad r$ = in centimeters (1 to 10);
$\quad\quad d$ = in centimeters (1 to 20);
$\quad\quad H$ = in lines per square centimeter (0 to 50).

8.34 $R = \dfrac{\rho}{10^6} \dfrac{l}{D^2}$ [resistance of a wire in ohms (0 to 25)]

where l = length of wire in feet (0 to 100);
$\quad\quad \rho$ = specific resistance (0 to 1000);
$\quad\quad D$ = diameter of the wire (0 to 0.1 in.).

8.35 $\dfrac{J}{V} = n_h B_{\max}^{1.6}$ (ergs) (hysteresis loss per cubic centimeter per cycle in iron)

where n_h = constant varying from 0.001 to 0.004 for different types of iron;
$\quad\quad J$ = hysteresis loss in ergs (or convert to watts since 1 erg = 10^{-7} watt) (0 to 50 watts);
$\quad\quad V$ = volume of iron in cubic centimeters (0 to 1000);
$\quad B_{\max}$ = maximum flux density (0 to 20,000).

8.36 $\dfrac{R_2}{R_1} = \dfrac{234.5 + t_2}{234.5 + t_1}$ (change in resistance of copper wire with temperature)

where t_1 = initial temperature (0 to 150°C);
$\quad R_1$ = corresponding resistance (0 to 15 ohms);
$\quad t_2$ = final temperature (0 to 150°C);
$\quad R_2$ = corresponding resistance (0 to 15 ohms).

8.37 $I = \dfrac{580P}{EF_P}$ (current in amperes for a three-phase, three-wire, a-c circuit)

where P = load (0 to 15 kw);
$\quad E$ = circuit voltage (100 to 500 volts);
$\quad F_P$ = power factor (0.50 to 1.00).

Aeronautical

8.38 $F_{pr} = \dfrac{550n(\text{hp})}{V}$ [propeller thrust in pounds (100 to 1000)]

where n = propeller efficiency in per cent varying from (65 to 90%);
$\quad$ hp = engine horsepower (25 to 600);
$\quad V$ = velocity of airplane in feet per second (50 to 400).

8.39 $L = 0.00256\, C_L A V^2$ [lift of an airfoil in pounds (1000 to 20,000)]

where C_L = lift coefficient of airfoil section (0 to 2.0);
$\quad A$ = area of airfoil in square feet (100 to 1000);
$\quad V$ = velocity in miles per hour (50 to 300).

8.40 $R = \dfrac{(Kb)^2}{A}$ [aspect ratio of a wing, varies (4 to 8)]

where K = Monk's span factor for biplanes, for monoplanes $K = 1.0$, varies from 1 to 1.5;
$\quad b$ = span of longest wing in feet (20 to 80);
$\quad A$ = total wing area in square feet (0 to 1500).

8.41 $V = 77.3 \left(n\dfrac{d}{P} \right)^{1/3}$ [airspeed at level in feet per second (50 to 400)]

where n = propeller efficiency (65 to 90%);
$\quad d = W/A_D$, where W is the weight of the airplane and A_D is the equivalent drag area in square feet; d varies from (150 to 1000);
$\quad P = W/\text{hp}$, where hp is the horsepower of the engine, P varies from (1 to 15).

8.42 $\dfrac{db}{dt} = \dfrac{88TV}{W}$ (rate of climb)

where T = excess jet thrust (5000 to 25,000 lb);
$\quad V$ = speed of plane (100 to 600 mph);
$\quad W$ = gross weight of plane (10,000 to 100,000 lb).

Chemical

8.43 $W = VNM$ (titration equation where V milliliters of N normal reagent are required to titrate W grams of a substance, the milliequivalent of which is M)

where V = milliliters (10 to 25);
$\quad N$ = normal reagent (0.1 to 0.5);
$\quad M$ = milliequivalent (0.02 to 0.20);
$\quad W$ = grams of substance (0 to 2.5).

8.44 $Q = 0.010386\dfrac{a}{k}i$ [Faraday's law of electrolysis; $Q = \dfrac{m}{t}$ is the quantity deposited per

second due to electrolysis and varies (0 to 10)]

where a = the atomic weight (select a number of elements used in electrolysis);
   k = the valence of the element (1 to 4);
   i = electric current in amperes (1 to 10).

8.45 $W = \dfrac{144mP}{1544(t + 460)}$ [weight of a gas (0 to 6 lb/cu ft)]

where P = pressure in pounds per square inch absolute (10 to 1000);
   m = molecular weight (2 to 200);
   t = temperature (0° to 600°F).

8.46 $X_A = \dfrac{\dfrac{W_A}{M_A}}{\dfrac{W_A}{M_A} + \dfrac{(1 - W_A)}{M_B}}$ (conversion of weight fraction to mole fraction)

where X_A = mole fraction of A (0.01 to 1);
       W_A = weight fraction of A (0.01 to 1);
   M_A and M_B = molecular weights of A and B (1 to 100).

General

8.47 $I = PRT$ (simple interest law)

where I = interest ($0 to $400);
   P = principal ($1 to $1000);
   R = rate of interest per year period (4% to 8%);
   T = time or period in years (0 to 5 years) (subdivide time scale into months).

8.48 $Pu = \dfrac{C_q}{q\left(1 - \dfrac{m}{100}\right)}$ (retail price per unit)

where C_q = total cost for quotation quantity ($10 to $100);
   q = quotation quantity (dozen, gross, etc.) (1 to 10);
   m = markup (10% to 80%).

8.49 $C = \dfrac{WV^2}{gR}$ (centrifugal force on a body due to a rotation)

where W = weight in pounds of the body (1 to 150);
   V = velocity in feet per second (1 to 50);
   R = the radius of the path in feet (0.1 to 10);
   g = 32.2 ft. per sec²;
   C = centrifugal force in pounds (0 to 1500).

8.50 $(\Delta L) = L\alpha(t_2 - t_1)$ (increase in length of a bar due to temperature changes)

where $(t_2 - t_1)$ = change in temperature in degrees centigrade (0° to 100°);
   L = length of bar (0 to 100 ft);
   α = coefficient of expansion as given by the following table:

Aluminum	= 0.0000244	Hardened steel	= 0.000010
Lead	= 0.000029	Copper	= 0.0000171
Wrought iron and mild steel	= 0.000011	Brass	= 0.0000198
Crown glass	= 0.000009	Tin	= 0.000027

8.51 $A = \frac{1}{2}bc \sin \alpha =$ area of a triangle shown in the figure

where $\alpha = (20°$ to $160°)$; $b = (0$ to $10)$; $c = (0$ to $10)$; $A = (0$ to $50)$.

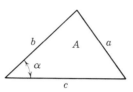

8.52 $A = ab \sin \theta$ (area of parallelogram)

where $a =$ length of one side (2 to 30 in.);
   $b =$ length of adjacent side (2 to 20 in.);
   $\theta =$ angle between sides a and b (10° to 90°).

Alignment Charts
for the Form

$$f_1(u) + f_2(v) = \frac{f_3(w)}{f_4(q)}$$

An equation of the above form can be solved by a combination of two types already discussed (Figure 88).

Let $\qquad\qquad f_1(u) + f_2(v) = T \qquad$ (1) $\qquad$ (3 parallel scales)

and $\qquad\qquad T = \dfrac{f_3(w)}{f_4(q)} \qquad$ (2) $\qquad\qquad$ (Z chart)

or $\qquad\qquad f_3(w) = Tf_4(q)$

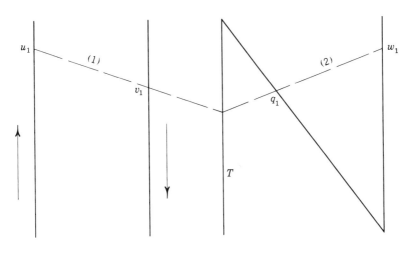

Figure 88.

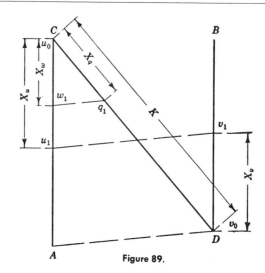

Figure 89.

Now let us consider another method for solving the above equation (Figure 89). Suppose that the parallel scales, A and B, are graduated in accordance with the scale equations:

$$X_u = m_u f_1(u) \qquad \text{and} \qquad X_v = m_v f_2(v)$$

and that scale A also carries graduations for the $f_3(w)$, the scale equation of which is $X_w = m_w f_3(w)$. Let us further suppose that the diagonal is graduated in accordance with the scale equation $X_q = m_q f_4(q)$.

A study of Figure 89 reveals the following relation:

$$\frac{X_u + X_v}{K} = \frac{X_w}{X_q}$$

since triangles CAD and Cw_1q_1 are similar.

Or

$$\frac{m_u f_1(u) + m_v f_2(v)}{K} = \frac{m_w f_3(w)}{m_q f_4(q)}$$

When

$$f_1(u) + f_2(v) = \frac{f_3(w)}{f_4(q)}$$

then

$$m_v = m_u \qquad \text{and} \qquad \frac{m_u}{K} = \frac{m_w}{m_q}$$

or

$$m_q = \frac{K m_w}{m_u}$$

Hence, to construct an alignment chart of the above form:

1. Graduate the left side of scale A from its scale equation $X_u = m_u f_1(u)$.
2. Graduate scale B from $X_v = m_v f_2(v)$.
3. Graduate the right side of scale A from its scale equation $X_w = m_w f_3(w)$.
4. Graduate the diagonal scale from $X_q = m_q f_4(q)$, where $m_q = K m_w / m_u$.

Caution: Do not overlook the fact that point C is the zero value of functions u, w, and q; that point D is the zero value of function v.

Example 1

$$V = \frac{\pi h}{9}\left(\frac{5}{4}D^2 + d^2\right) \text{ (volume of a buoy) (Figure 90)}$$

where h = height of buoy (0 to 10 ft); D = diameter of midsection (0 to 10 ft); d = diameter of base (0 to 10 ft); and V = volume of buoy.

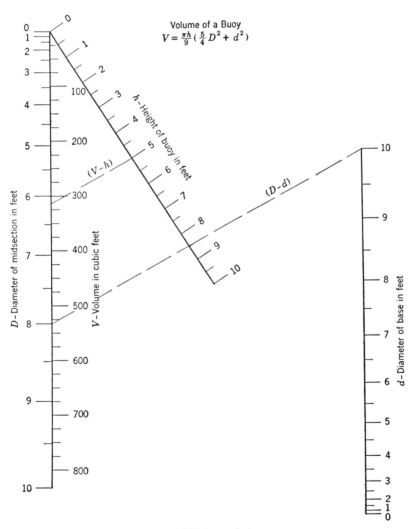

Figure 90. Volume of a buoy.

Now $\frac{5}{4}D^2 + d^2 = \frac{9V}{\pi h}$ is of the form

$$f_1(u) + f_2(v) = \frac{f_3(w)}{f_4(q)}$$

$X_D = m_D \frac{5}{4}D^2 = 0.06\frac{5}{4}D^2 = 0.075D^2$ (scale length 7.5 in.)

$X_d = m_d d^2 = 0.06 d^2$ (scale length 6 in.)

$X_V = m_V 9V = 0.001 \times 9V = 0.009V$ (scale length approx. 7 in.)

$$\frac{m_V}{m_h} = \frac{m_D}{K}$$

or $\quad m_h = \frac{Km_V}{m_D} = \frac{0.001 \times K}{0.06} = \frac{0.1}{6}\frac{30}{\pi}$

$$= \frac{0.5}{\pi}, \text{ when } K = \frac{30}{\pi}$$

$$X_h = m_h \pi h = \frac{0.5}{\pi}\pi h = 0.5h$$

Example: *Given:* $D = 8$; $d = 10$; $h = 5$. Solution: Join points 8 and 10 on the D- and d-scales, respectively. Through point 5 on the h-scale draw a parallel line. This line cuts the V-scale in point $V = 315$. By computation, $V = 314.29$.

Note: It should be recognized that the actual drawing of the parallel can be eliminated by scribing a family of parallels (so spread as to give the desired accuracy in reading) on a *transparent sheet*. The prepared sheet can then be placed over the chart so that one of the parallels passes through 8 and 10 and another parallel* passes through point 5.

An alternative method can be used. An ordinary drafting triangle, with a line scratched in and inked close to and parallel to one of the edges, can be slid along a guide (which could be another triangle). The inked-line triangle can be placed to contain the 8 and 10, and then slid along the guide until the inked line passes through point 5.

If the equation is of the form $f_1(u) - f_2(v) = f_3(w)/f_4(q)$, positive values of u and v will be laid off in the same direction. This is shown in Figure 91.

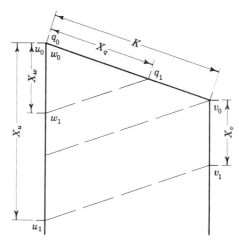

Figure 91.

*In some cases it will be necessary to interpolate between two parallels.

$$\frac{X_u - X_v}{K} = \frac{X_w}{X_q}$$

Again, if

$$X_u = m_u f_1(u)$$
$$X_v = m_u f_2(v)$$
$$X_w = m_w f_3(w)$$
$$X_q = m_q f_4(q)$$

and

$$\frac{m_u}{K} = \frac{m_w}{m_q}$$

then

$$f_1(u) - f_2(v) = \frac{f_3(w)}{f_4(q)}$$

Example 2

$$u^2 - v^2 = \frac{w}{4q} \text{ (Figure 92)}$$

with ranges $\qquad u\ (0\text{ to }5); \qquad v\ (0\text{ to }5); \qquad q\ (0\text{ to }6)$

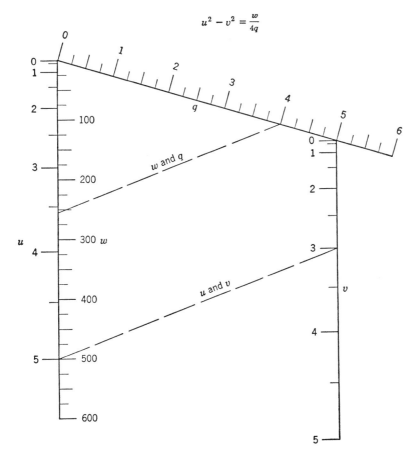

Figure 92. Alignment chart for the equation $u^2 - v^2 = \dfrac{w}{4q}$.

$$X_u = m_u u^2 = 0.20u^2 \text{ (for scale length of 5 in.)}$$
$$X_v = m_u u^2 = 0.20v^2 \text{ (for scale length of 5 in.)}$$
$$X_w = m_w w = 0.01w \text{ (for scale length of 6 in.)}$$

$$\frac{m_w}{m_q} = \frac{m_u}{K}$$

$$m_q = \frac{m_w}{m_u}K = \frac{0.01}{0.20}K = 0.05K = 0.05 \times 5 = 0.25, \text{ where } K = 5 \text{ in.}$$

$$X_q = m_q 4q = 0.25 \times 4q = q$$

Example: *Given:* $u = 5$; $v = 3$; $q = 4$. *Required: w. Solution.* Join points 5 and 3 on the u- and v-scales, respectively. Through point 4 on the q-scale draw a line parallel to line 1 and read $w = 255$. By computation, $w = 256$.

Elimination of Double Scales

If it is desired to construct a nomogram for an equation of the type form $f_1(u) + f_2(v) = f_3(w)/f_4(q)$ so that no double scales will be necessary, another arrangement can be made which will overcome this situation.

Let us consider Figure 93. Scales u and w are at right angles. Similarly, scale q and the diagonal AB, which joins the zero values of functions u and v, are at right angles. Scales u and v are parallel.

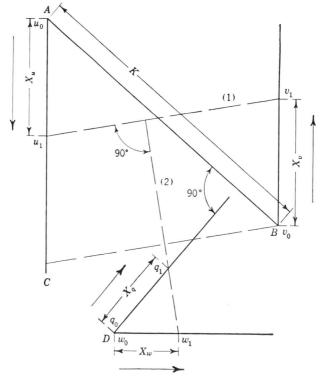

Figure 93.

The geometric relations can easily be determined by studying a typical case. Suppose line 1 joins any two points u_1 and v_1. Then let us draw line 2 through point w_1 and perpendicular to line 1. The intersection of line 2 with the q-scale will give us point q_1, the desired solution. Why is this true?

In Figure 93 it will be seen that line BC is parallel to line 1. Again, triangles ABC and Dq_1w_1 are similar. Therefore

$$\frac{X_u + X_v}{K} = \frac{X_w}{X_q}$$

The remainder of the development is the same as shown previously.

There is an advantage in this design over the one which uses parallels, in that (1) there is a separate scale for each function and (2) the readings can be made by placing a transparent sheet, having but two lines at right angles, over the nomogram. Proper orientation of the lines can be made very quickly.

An alternative method makes use of two triangles properly oriented. If a triangle and a guide (another triangle) are available, the "transparent" sheet could be one of the triangles with a single straight line, scratched in and inked, close to and parallel to one of the perpendicular edges. This triangle could be slid along the guide to effect the solution to a given problem. For example, in Figure 93 an edge of the guide could be so placed as to pass through the given values u_1 and v_1; the other triangle could be slid along the edge so that the inked line on the triangle passes through w_1. The required value of q_1 would lie on the inked line at its intersection with the q-scale.

Example

Let us consider the equation:

$$M = (T_1 - T_2)r$$

where M = torque exerted on a brake (0 to 10,000 in.-lb); r = radius of brake drum (0 to 12 in.); and T_1 and T_2 = tensile forces (0 to 1000 lb).

In type form the equation is:

$$T_1 - T_2 = \frac{M}{r}$$

We will assume the length of the T_1- and T_2-scales to be 10 units.

Therefore $$m_{T_1} = m_{T_2} = \frac{10}{1000} = 0.01$$

The scale equations are:

$$X_{T_1} = 0.01T_1 \quad \text{and} \quad X_{T_2} = 0.01T_2$$

In a similar manner, if the r-scale is 12 units long,

$$m_r = \tfrac{12}{12} = 1 \quad \text{and} \quad X_r = r$$

Now $$\frac{m_T}{K} = \frac{m_M}{m_r} \quad \text{or} \quad \frac{0.01}{K} = \frac{m_M}{1}$$

When $K = 10$, then $m_M = 0.001$, and

$$X_M = 0.001M$$

The completed nomogram is shown in Figure 94.

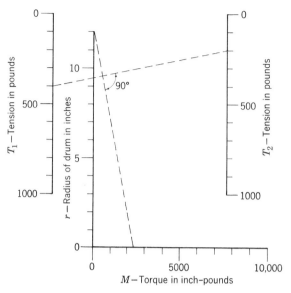

Figure 94. $M = (T_1 - T_2)r$. Example: When $T_1 = 400$, $T_2 = 200$, and $r = 12$, then $M = 2400$.

EXERCISES

9.1   Weight of a hollow steel tube: $W = \dfrac{l\pi(d^2 - d_1^2)}{4} \cdot \rho$

where W = weight (0 to 100 lb);
    l = length in inches (0 to 100);
    d = outside diameter (0 to 2 in.);
    d_1 = inside diameter (0 to 1.9 in.);
    ρ = density = 489.6/1728 psi.

9.2 $R = (P - d)t\,55{,}000$ (strength of a riveted steel plate between rivet holes)

where P is the pitch of the rivets and d the diameter.

$$P = (0 \text{ to } 5 \text{ in.})$$
$$d = (0 \text{ to } 1 \text{ in.})$$
$$R = (0 \text{ to } 100{,}000 \text{ lb})$$
$$t = (0 \text{ to } 1 \text{ in.})$$

9.3 $A = \dfrac{d(b_1 + b_2)}{2}$ (area of a trapezoid—see figure)

where b_1 = (0 to 100); b_2 = (0 to 80); d = (0 to 50); A = limits corresponding.

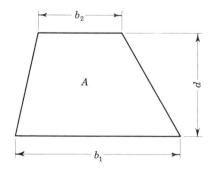

9.4 $\quad KV = p_1 + p_2$

where V is the volume of earthwork per station;

$p_1 + p_2$ are average planimeter readings in square inches from the cross-section drawings;

K is a constant depending on the length of section and the scale: $V = (0 \text{ to } 1000)$ in cubic yards, p_1 or p_2 (0 to 10), and $K = $ corresponding limits.

9.5 $\quad F = \dfrac{k}{t^a}$ (wall thickness sensitivity)

where F is the tensile strength of a metal or alloy, t is the thickness, k and a are constants depending on the kind of material.

$$F = (10 \text{ to } 50 \text{ kg/sq mm})$$
$$k = \text{constant } (10 \text{ to } 50 \text{ kg/sq mm})$$
$$t = (10 \text{ to } 90 \text{ mm})$$
$$a = (0.2 \text{ to } 0.7)$$

9.6 $\quad t = \dfrac{h_D + 0.5d}{f \cdot \text{rpm}}$ (estimated drilling time in minutes)

where $\quad h_D = $ hole depth (1 to 6 in.);

$\quad d = $ hole diameter ($\frac{1}{4}$ to 1 in.);

$\quad f = $ feed in inches per revolution (0.005 to 0.040 in.);

$\quad \text{rpm} = $ revolutions per minute (50 to 600 rpm).

9.7 $\quad T = \dfrac{L + D/2}{F}$ (time for rough facing cuts)

where $T = $ time in minutes;

$\quad L = $ length of workpiece (6 to 24 in.);

$\quad D = $ diameter of cutter (6 to 12 in.);

$\quad F = $ feed per minute (0.006 to 0.022 in.).

9.8 $\quad I_x = I_G + \dfrac{W}{32.2} \cdot \left(\dfrac{d}{12}\right)^2$ (transfer of mass moment of inertia)

where $I_x = $ mass moment of inertia of given mass about axis parallel to c.g. axis in pound-foot-seconds^2

$\quad I_G = $ mass moment of inertia about axis through the c.g. in pound-foot-seconds^2 (0 to 1.7);

$\quad W = $ weight of mass (0 to 500 lb);

$\quad d = $ distance between axes (0 to 10 in.).

10

Alignment Charts for the Forms

$$f_1(u) + f_2(v) \cdot f_3(w) = f_4(w) \text{ and}$$

$$f_2(u) = \frac{f_3(v)f_6(w) - f_5(w)f_4(v)}{f_3(v) - f_5(w)}$$

Suppose the parallel scales, A and B (Figure 95), are graduated in accordance with the scale equations:

$$X_u = m_u f_1(u); \qquad X_v = m_v f_2(v)$$

It is further supposed that a straight line joining points u_1 and v_1 cuts the curved scale, C, in point w_1, which satisfies the equation.

Points on the scale C are located by coordinates, X_w and Y_w. Let us develop expressions for X_w and Y_w.

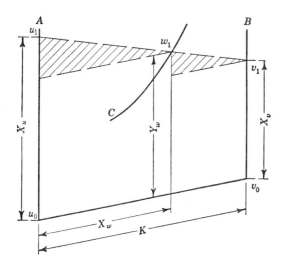

Figure 95. Type form, $f_1(u) + f_2(v) \cdot f_3(w) = f_4(w)$.

From the similar triangles (shaded),

$$\frac{X_u - Y_w}{Y_w - X_v} = \frac{X_w}{K - X_w}$$

from which

$$X_u(K - X_w) + X_v X_w = KY_w$$

or

$$X_u + X_v\left(\frac{X_w}{K - X_w}\right) = \left(\frac{KY_w}{K - X_w}\right)$$

Now

$$m_u f_1(u) + m_v f_2(v)\left(\frac{X_w}{K - X_w}\right) = \left(\frac{KY_w}{K - X_w}\right)$$

This is true since $X_u = m_u f_1(u)$ and $X_v = m_v f_2(v)$. Careful study of the above equation will show that $X_w/(K - X_w)$ must equal $Cf_3(w)$ and that the right-hand member, $KY_w/(K - X_w)$, must equal $C_1 f_4(w)$. In order to obtain the equation $f_1(u) + f_2(v) \cdot f_3(w) = f_4(w)$, it will be seen that $C = m_u/m_v$ and $C_1 = m_u$. This means that

$$\frac{X_w}{K - X_w} = \frac{m_u}{m_v} f_3(w) \quad \text{and} \quad \frac{KY_w}{K - X_w} = m_u f_4(w)$$

From

$$\frac{X_w}{K - X_w} = \frac{m_u}{m_v} f_3(w)$$

$$X_w = \frac{K m_u f_3(w)}{m_u f_3(w) + m_v}$$

and from

$$\frac{KY_w}{K - X_w} = m_u f_4(w)$$

$$Y_w = \frac{K m_u f_4(w) - X_w m_u f_4(w)}{K}$$

or

$$Y_w = m_u f_4(w) - \frac{m_u f_3(w) m_u f_4(w)}{m_u f_3(w) + m_v}$$

$$Y_w = \frac{m_u m_v f_4(w)}{m_u f_3(w) + m_v}$$

Hence, to construct an alignment chart of the above form,

1. Graduate the A and B scales from their scale equations:

$$X_u = m_u f_1(u); \qquad X_v = m_v f_2(v)$$

2. Locate the curved scale by its coordinates:

$$X_w = \frac{K m_u f_3(w)}{m_u f_3(w) + m_v}$$

$$Y_w = \frac{m_u m_v f_4(w)}{m_u f_3(w) + m_v}$$

Caution. The axis from which distances Y_w are laid off is the line which joins the zero value of the function $f_1(u)$ with the zero value of the function $f_2(v)$.

Interesting Note: If $f_3(w) = 1$

$$X_w = \left(\frac{m_u}{m_u + m_v}\right) K$$

$$Y_w = \frac{m_u m_v}{m_u + m_v} f_4(w)$$

which are in agreement with the results for the first type form (p. 30).

Example 1

$$w^2 + pw + q = 0 \text{ (quadratic formula)}$$

Transposing $$q + pw = -w^2$$

which is of the form

$$f_1(u) + f_2(v) \cdot f_3(w) = f_4(w)$$

$$X_q = m_q q = 0.6q \qquad X_p = m_p p = 0.6p$$

where m_q and m_p were arbitrarily chosen as 0.6.

$$X_w = \frac{K m_u f_3(w)}{m_u f_3(w) + m_v}$$

When $$K = 5 \text{ in.}$$

$$X_w = \frac{5 \times 0.6 \times w}{0.6w + 0.6} = \frac{5w}{w + 1}$$

$$Y_w = \frac{m_u m_v f_4(w)}{m_u f_3(w) + m_v}$$

$$= \frac{0.6 \times 0.6(-w^2)}{0.6w + 0.6} = \frac{-0.6w^2}{w + 1}$$

See Figure 96 for the graphical solution.

Example 2

Let

$$w^2 - 5w + 6 = 0$$

Now $$p = -5 \quad \text{and} \quad q = 6$$

The straight line which joins $p = -5$ and $q = 6$ intersects the curve at $w = 2$ and $w = 3$ which satisfy the given equation.

Example 3

Let $$w^2 + w - 6 = 0$$

The line which joins $p = 1$ and $q = -6$ intersects the curve at $w = 2$ which is one value of w that satisfies the equation.

To obtain the other value of w let us first take the negative function of the equation. Let $w = -w_1$; then $w_1^2 - w_1 - 6 = 0$. Now $p = -1$ and $q = -6$. The line which joins these values intersects the curve at $w_1 = 3$. Therefore, $w = -3$, the other value of w that satisfies the equation.

Example 4

Let $$w^2 - 20w + 75 = 0$$

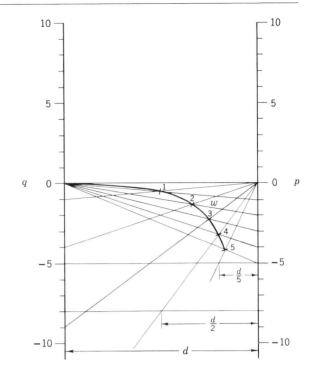

Figure 96. $w^2 + pw + q = 0$.

In this case $p = 20$ and $q = 75$, values which exceed the limits shown in the nomogram, Figure 96.

In order to use this nomogram,

let
$$w = kw_1.$$

Now
$$k^2w_1^2 - 20kw_1 + 75 = 0$$

or
$$w_1^2 - \frac{20}{k}w_1 + \frac{75}{k^2} = 0$$

When $k = 5$
$$w_1^2 - 4w_1 + 3 = 0$$

The straight line which joins $p = -4$ and $q = 3$ intersects the curve at $w_1 = 1$ and $w_1 = 3$. Therefore, $w = 5$ and $w = 15$ are the values which satisfy the given equation.

Practical Short-Cut Method

Example 1

Let us again consider the equation:

$$w^2 + pw + q = 0; \qquad p(-10 \text{ to } +10)$$
$$q(-10 \text{ to } +10)$$

When $w = 1, 2, 3, \cdots, n$,

$$q + p \; = -1$$
$$q + 2p = -4$$
$$q + 3p = -9$$
$$q + np = -n^2$$

First, in each of the above equations, let $q = 0$ and draw lines joining $q = 0$ with $p = -1$, $-2, -3, \cdots$.

Second, let $p = 0$ and draw a set of lines joining $p = 0$ with $q = -1, -4, -9, \cdots$. Now locate the intersection of corresponding rays, i.e. line $q = 0, p = -1$ and line $p = 0, q = -1$; line $q = 0, p = -2$ and line $p = 0, q = -4$, etc. These intersections are $w = 1, 2, 3, \cdots$. The curve which passes through these points is the w curve. See Figure 96.

Example 2

Consider the equation,

$$S = 0.0982 \frac{D^4 - d^4}{D} \text{ (section modulus for tubes and bars)}$$

where D and $d = (0$ to 10 in.$)$ and $S = (0$ to 100 in.^{3} $)$.

The equation may be converted to the form $0.0982d^4 + DS = 0.0982D^4$, which is in the type form $f_1(u) + f_2(v) \cdot f_3(w) = f_4(w)$.

The chart will consist of two parallel scales for d and S, respectively, and a curved scale for D. A preliminary sketch of the chart would look something like Figure 97.

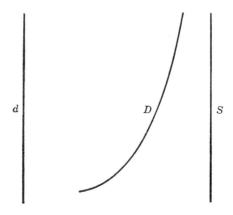

Figure 97.

The following procedure is suggested:

1. Draw the d and S scales a convenient distance apart.

2. Mark the lower point on the d-scale 0 and the upper point 10.

3. Likewise, mark the lower and upper points on the S-scale 0 and 100, respectively. Since the function of S is linear, this scale will be uniform and can be readily graduated.

4. The d-scale can be graduated by first laying out a d^4-scale and then projecting this scale to the d-scale.

5. If $S = 0$, then $d^4 = D^4$. Draw lines through $S = 0$ and points on the d-scale. Somewhere on these lines will be found the corresponding values of D.

6. Now let $d = 0$; then $DS = 0.0982D^4$. From this equation, we can determine values of S for given values of D.

D	5	6	7	8	9	10
S	12.3	21.2	33.7	50.3	71.6	98.2

Now draw lines through $d = 0$ and the values of S shown in the table above.

7. Obtain the points of intersection of those lines having a common value of D. The curve joining these points constitutes the D-scale. (See Figure 98.)

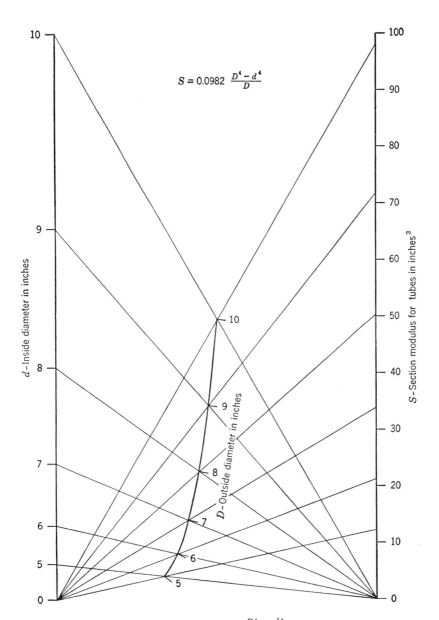

Figure 98. Alignment chart for the equation $S = 0.0982 \dfrac{D^4 - d^4}{D}$, constructed by the short-cut method.

Alignment Charts for the Form

$$f_2(u) = \frac{f_3(v)f_6(w) - f_5(w)f_4(v)}{f_3(v) - f_5(w)}$$

Let us consider Figure 99, which shows one straight line scale, $f_2(u)$, and curved scales for the variables v and w. The straight line which joins u_1 with v_1 intersects the w curve in w_1, which satisfies the given equation.

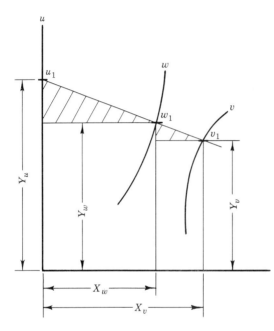

Figure 99. Type form,
$$f_2(u) = \frac{f_3(v)f_6(w) - f_5(w)f_4(v)}{f_3(v) - f_5(w)}.$$

The parametric equations of each scale may be written in the following form:

$$X_u = m_u f_1(u) = 0 \qquad X_v = m_v f_3(v) \qquad X_w = m_w f_5(w)$$

$$Y_u = m_u' f_2(u) \qquad Y_v = m_v' f_4(v) \qquad Y_w = m_w' f_6(w)$$

Now from the similar triangles (shown shaded),

$$\frac{Y_u - Y_w}{Y_w - Y_v} = \frac{X_w}{X_v - X_w}$$

or
$$Y_u = \frac{X_v Y_w - X_w Y_v}{X_v - X_w}$$

Substituting the values given in the parametric equations

$$m_u' f_2(u) = \frac{m_v f_3(v) m_w' f_6(w) - m_w f_5(w) m_v' f_4(v)}{m_v f_3(v) - m_w f_5(w)}$$

When $m_u' = m_v' = m_w'$, and $m_u = m_v = m_w$, then

$$f_2(u) = \frac{f_3(v)f_6(w) - f_5(w)f_4(v)}{f_3(v) - f_5(w)}$$

Example

Consider the equation, $\qquad\qquad L = \dfrac{a^2 + b^2}{a + b}$

This equation can be put in the type form by multiplying each term of the right-hand side of the equation by $\left(-\dfrac{1}{ab}\right)$.

Now $\qquad\qquad\qquad\qquad L = \dfrac{a\left(-\dfrac{1}{b}\right) - b\left(\dfrac{1}{a}\right)}{-\dfrac{1}{b} - \dfrac{1}{a}}$

Suppose that the moduli equal 1; then the parametric equations are:

$$X_L = 0 \qquad X_a = \frac{1}{a} \qquad X_b = -\frac{1}{b}$$

$$Y_L = L \qquad Y_a = a \qquad Y_b = b$$

The completed nomogram is shown in Figure 100.

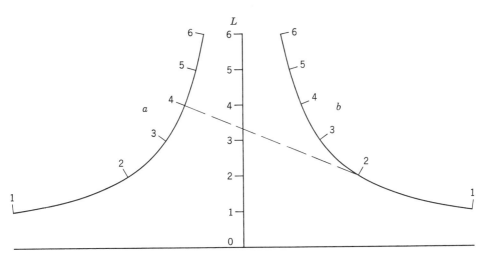

Figure 100. $L = \dfrac{a^2 + b^2}{a + b}$. Example: When $a = 4$ and $b = 2$, then $L = 3\frac{1}{3}$.

Nomogram—Three Curves

The development of a type form for a nomogram consisting of three curved scales should offer the reader no resistance. The development is fundamentally the same as the one above.

EXERCISES

10.1 $S = V_0 t - \frac{1}{2}gt^2$ (distance traveled by a body projected upward with a velocity, v_0, after a time, t)

where S = distance in feet (calculate limits);
v_0 = velocity in feet per second (0 to 100);
t = time in seconds (0 to 5);
g = 32.2. ft/sec².

10.2 $\left(\dfrac{I}{y}\right) = 0.0982 \left(\dfrac{D^4 - d^4}{D}\right)$ (section modulus of a hollow tube whose inside and outside diameters are D and d, respectively)

where D varies (0 to 10 in.) and d varies (0 to 9 in.)

10.3 $V = 0.649 \dfrac{T}{p} - \dfrac{22.58}{p^{\frac{1}{4}}}$ (specific volume in cubic feet of superheated steam under a pressure of p pounds per square inch and with a temperature, T, in degrees Fahrenheit)

where T varies (220 to 600) and p = (30 to 200).

10.4 $Q = 3.33(B - 0.2H)H^{\frac{3}{2}}$ (Francis' formula for the quantity of water flowing over a contracted weir)

where B = width of the weir in feet (0 to 5);
H = head over the crest (0 to 5 ft);
Q = calculated limits.

10.5 $V = \frac{1}{2}\pi r^2 h + \frac{1}{6}\pi h^3$ (volume of a spherical segment with one base)

where h = altitude of the segment;
r = radius of the sphere.
r varies (0 to 10 in.) and h varies (0 to 10 in.).

10.6 $\left(\dfrac{V}{V_0}\right)^2 = \dfrac{1}{x + f^2(1 - x)}$ (flow of wet steam)

where V/V_0 = ratio of actual velocity of discharge through nozzle to velocity (assumption being that steam and water drops have the same velocity);
x = quality of steam (0.80 to 1.0);
f = friction factor (0.05 to 0.20).

10.7 $\dfrac{\overline{I}}{W} = \left(\dfrac{T}{2\pi}\right)^2 r + \dfrac{r^2}{386}$ (determination of mass-moment of inertia,)

where $\overline{I}/W$ = ratio of mass moment of inertia about the center of gravity to the weight of the the part in inch-pound-seconds² per pound;
T = time required for one oscillation (0.1 to 2.0 sec);
r = distance from center of oscillation to the center of gravity (0.5 to 12 in.).

10.8 $V = 0.5236(3A^2 + D^2)D$ (volume of segment of sphere)

where D = height of segment (1 to 10 ft);
A = radius of base (2 to 10 ft);
V = volume in cubic feet.

10.9   Log mtd $= \dfrac{\Delta T_1 \Delta T_2}{\log_e \dfrac{\Delta T_1}{\Delta T_2}}$ (log mean temperature difference)

where ΔT_1 = temperature difference at inlet (5° to 100°F);
$\quad\quad \Delta T_2$ = temperature difference at outlet (0° to 100°F);
$\quad$ log mtd varies from 5° to 40°F.

10.10 $V = 5.34 \dfrac{h_1^{3/2} - h_2^{3/2}}{h_1 - h_2}$ (rectangular orifice—low head)

where h_1 = head to lower edge of orifice (0.5 to 4.5 ft);
$\quad\quad h_2$ = head to upper edge of orifice (0.4 to 4.3 ft);
$\quad\quad V$ = velocity in feet per second (4.5 to 12).

10.11 $(1 + L)h_2 - L \cdot h(1 + p) - \tfrac{1}{3}(1 - L)(1 + 2p) = 0$ (retaining walls $ABCD$ and $AEGD$
$\quad\quad$ withstand the same pressure—see figure)

where $h = \dfrac{BF}{BC}$ (0.75 to 1.00);

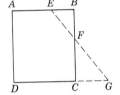

$\quad\quad L = \dfrac{AE}{AB}$ (0.5 to 1.0);

$\quad\quad p = \dfrac{\text{density of earth}}{\text{density of masonry}}.$

Hint: Solution will consist of three curved scales.

11

Miscellaneous Forms

$$1. \quad \frac{f_1(u) + f_2(v)}{f_1(u) - f_2(v)} = \frac{f_3(w)}{f_4(q)}$$

This form can be solved by a combination of the simple type forms already considered. For example, we could let

$$f_1(u) + f_2(v) = T \tag{1}$$

and

$$f_1(u) - f_2(v) = Q \tag{2}$$

then

$$\frac{T}{Q} = \frac{f_3(w)}{f_4(q)} \tag{3}$$

Equation (1) could be represented by a nomogram such as Figure 101, and equation (2) by the nomogram shown in Figure 102. Equation (3) could be represented by a nomogram such as Figure 103.

A combination of the above nomograms would be Figure 104. This solution, Figure 104, is not very satisfactory since two separate scales are required for each of the variables u and v.

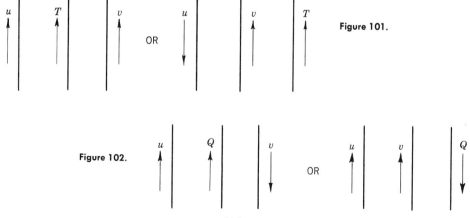

Figure 101.

Figure 102.

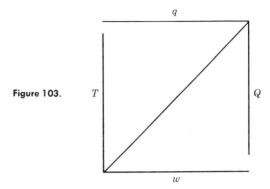

Figure 103.

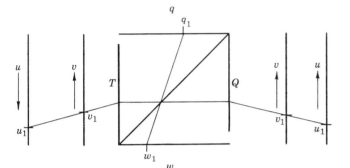

Figure 104.

A more effective solution is shown in either Figure 105 or Figure 106. The geometric relations are established in the following manner:

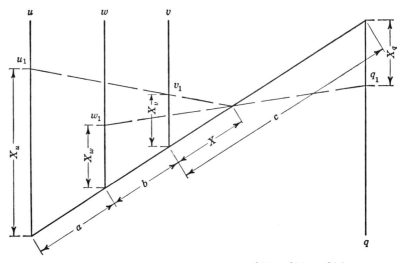

Figure 105. Chart for an equation of the form $\dfrac{f_1(u) + f_2(v)}{f_1(u) - f_2(v)} = \dfrac{f_3(w)}{f_4(q)}$.

Let
$$X_u = m_u f_1(u) \qquad X_w = m_w f_3(w)$$
$$X_v = m_v f_2(v) \qquad X_q = m_q f_4(q)$$

From similar triangles,
$$\frac{X_u}{X_v} = \frac{a + b + X}{X} \; ; \quad \frac{X_w}{X_q} = \frac{b + X}{c - X}$$

Eliminating X,
$$\frac{X_w}{X_q} = \frac{b + \dfrac{a + b}{\dfrac{X_u}{X_v} - 1}}{c - \dfrac{a + b}{\dfrac{X_u}{X_v} - 1}}$$

and simplifying,
$$\frac{X_w}{X_q} = \frac{bX_u + aX_v}{cX_u - (a + b + c)X_v}$$

then
$$\frac{m_w f_3(w)}{m_q f_4(q)} = \frac{bm_u f_1(u) + am_v f_2(v)}{cm_u f_1(u) - (a + b + c)m_v f_2(v)}$$

When
$$b = \frac{m_v}{m_u} \cdot a, \qquad a + b + c = c\frac{m_u}{m_v}$$

and
$$\frac{m_w}{m_q} = \frac{am_v}{cm_u}$$

it can be shown that
$$\frac{f_1(u) + f_2(v)}{f_1(u) - f_2(v)} = \frac{f_3(w)}{f_4(q)}$$

By algebraic manipulation of the three previous substitutions,

$$\frac{m_u + m_v}{m_u - m_v} = \frac{m_q}{m_w}$$

$$\frac{a}{b} = \frac{m_u}{m_v}$$

$$\frac{a + b + c}{c} = \frac{m_u}{m_v}$$

Intermediate steps are left to the reader.

2. The type form discussed above can be represented by an alignment chart of the design shown in Figure 106. The scales for $f_1(u)$ and $f_2(u)$ are at right angles; likewise, the scales for $f_3(w)$ and $f_4(q)$ are at right angles; and a 45° angle exists between the $f_1(u)$ and $f_3(w)$ scales. If values u_1, v_1, and w_1 are selected, the value of q_1 is obtained by drawing a line through w_1, parallel to the line joining u_1 with v_1.

Let us examine the geometry of the figure. Triangles u_1v_1B and u_1AO are similar (from the construction shown). Therefore,

$$\frac{u_1C + CB}{u_1O} = \frac{v_1B}{AO} \quad \text{or} \quad \frac{X_u + X_v}{X_u - X_v} = \frac{v_1B}{AO}$$

Also. triangles AOv_1 and w_1Cq_1 are similar. Hence,

$$\frac{Ov_1}{AO} = \frac{X_w}{X_q}$$

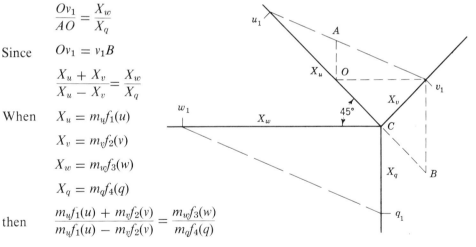

Since $Ov_1 = v_1B$

$$\frac{X_u + X_v}{X_u - X_v} = \frac{X_w}{X_q}$$

When $X_u = m_u f_1(u)$

$X_v = m_v f_2(v)$

$X_w = m_w f_3(w)$

$X_q = m_q f_4(q)$

then $$\frac{m_u f_1(u) + m_v f_2(v)}{m_u f_1(u) - m_v f_2(v)} = \frac{m_w f_3(w)}{m_q f_4(q)}$$

This means that $m_u = m_v$ and $m_w = m_q$ if

$$\frac{f_1(u) + f_2(v)}{f_1(u) - f_2(v)} = \frac{f_3(w)}{f_4(q)}$$

Figure 106. Alternative form of chart for the equation in Figure 105.

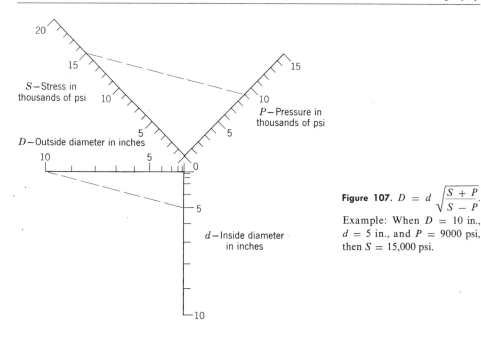

Figure 107. $D = d \sqrt{\dfrac{S + P}{S - P}}$.

Example: When $D = 10$ in., $d = 5$ in., and $P = 9000$ psi, then $S = 15,000$ psi.

Example

Let us consider the equation:

$$D = d \sqrt{\frac{S + P}{S - P}} \tag{1}$$

This equation can be written:

$$\frac{D^2}{d^2} = \frac{S + P}{S - P} \tag{2}$$

which is in the form

$$\frac{f_1(u) + f_2(v)}{f_1(u) - f_2(v)} = \frac{f_3(w)}{f_4(q)}$$

The graphical solution of equation (2) is shown in the nomogram, Figure 107.

3. $f_1(u) \cdot f_2(v) + f_3(w) \cdot f_4(q) = f_5(q)$

Let $$f_1(u) \cdot f_2(v) = T \tag{1}$$

and $$T + f_3(w) \cdot f_4(q) = f_5(q) \tag{2}$$

Thus a combination of a Z chart and one involving two straight lines and a curve can be formed to solve the above equation (Figure 108).

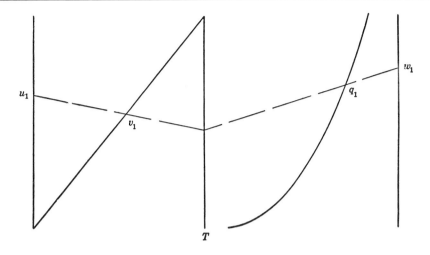

Figure 108. Alignment chart for an equation of the form $f_1(u) \cdot f_2(v) + f_3(w) \cdot f_4(q) = f_5(q)$.

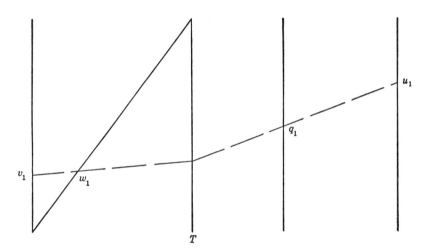

Figure 109. Alignment chart for an equation of the form $f_1(u) + f_2(v) \cdot f_3(w) = f_4(q)$.

4. $f_1(u) + f_2(v) \cdot f_3(w) = f_4(q)$ (Figure 109)

Let $$f_2(v) \cdot f_3(w) = T$$

and $$f_1(u) + T = f_4(q)$$

$$\textbf{5.}\ \ \frac{1}{f_1(u)} + \frac{f_4(w)}{f_2(v)} = \frac{1}{f_3(w)} \qquad \text{(Figure 110)}$$

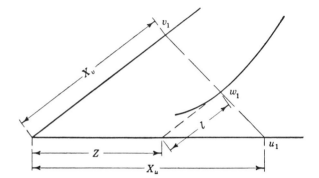

Figure 110. Alignment chart for an equation of the form

$$\frac{1}{f_1(u)} + \frac{f_4(w)}{f_2(v)} = \frac{1}{f_3(w)}.$$

The scale equations are:

$$X_u = m_u f_1(u) \qquad Z = m_u f_3(w)$$
$$X_v = m_v f_2(v) \qquad l = m_v f_3(w) f_4(w)$$

Points on the curve are located from

$$Z = m_u f_3(w) \qquad \text{and} \qquad l = m_v f_3(w) f_4(w)$$

in the following manner:

1. Graduate a *temporary* w-scale along the horizontal scale for $f_1(u)$.
2. Draw lines through points on the temporary w-scale, parallel to the v-scale.
3. On these lines lay off distances obtained from $l = m_v f_3(w) f_4(w)$, using the same value of w through which the parallels were drawn.

$$\textbf{6.}\ \ f_1(u) \cdot f_2(v) \cdot f_3(w) = f_4(q) \cdot f_5(r) \qquad \text{(Figure 111)}$$

Let
$$\frac{f_1(u)}{f_4(q)} = \frac{T}{f_2(v)} \qquad \text{(proportional chart) (1)}$$

and
$$\frac{f_5(r)}{T} = \frac{f_3(w)}{1} \qquad \text{(2)}$$

or
$$f_5(r) = Tf_3(w) \qquad \text{(Z chart)}$$

Note: An alternative form could be developed by expressing the given equation logarithmically, resulting in an alignment chart having parallel scales.

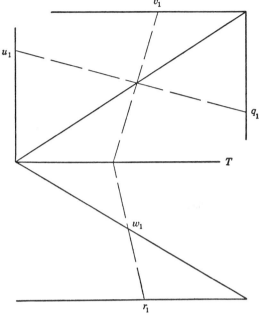

Figure 111. Combination proportional and Z chart for an equation of the form $f_1(u) \cdot f_2(v) \cdot f_3(w) = f_4(q) \cdot f_5(r)$.

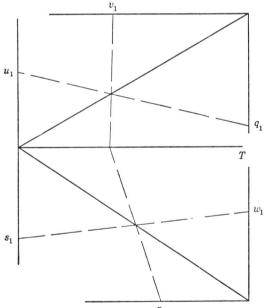

Figure 112. Combination proportional charts for an equation of the form $f_1(u) \cdot f_2(v) \cdot f_3(w) = f_4(q) \cdot f_5(r) \cdot f_6(s)$.

7. $f_1(u) \cdot f_2(v) \cdot f_3(w) = f_4(q) \cdot f_5(r) \cdot f_6(s)$ (Figure 112)

Let
$$\frac{f_1(u)}{f_4(q)} = \frac{T}{f_2(v)} \tag{1}$$

and
$$\frac{f_5(r)}{T} = \frac{f_3(w)}{f_6(s)} \tag{2}$$

EXERCISES

11.1 $y = \dfrac{\alpha x}{1 + (\alpha - 1)x}$ (vapor-liquid equilibrium for binary systems)

where x = the mole fraction (or weight fraction) of the more volatile component in the liquid (0 to 1.0);

y = the mole fraction (or weight fraction) of the corresponding vapor (0 to 1.0);

α = the relative volatility (2 to 20).

11.2 $N = 0.41QP - M$

where N = profit ($-\$1,000$ to $\$10,000$);

M = manufacturing cost ($\$1000$ to $\$20,000$);

P = selling price ($\$2$ to $\$15$);

Q = quantity sold (1000 to 15,000).

11.3

$$S_c = 0.798 \sqrt{\dfrac{\dfrac{P(D_1 - D_2)}{D_1 + D_2}}{\dfrac{1 - \gamma_1^2}{E_1} + \dfrac{1 - \gamma_2^2}{E_2}}}$$

[maximum contact stress between a cylinder and a circular groove (Hertz stress equation)]

where $\gamma_1 = \gamma_2 = 0.25$ for steel (Poisson's ratio);

E = modulus of elasticity = 30×10^6 psi ($E_1 = E_2 = E$ in this problem);

P = load per lineal inch (0 to 100 lb);

D_1 = diameter of groove (0 to 10 in.);

D_2 = diameter of cylinder (0 to 5 in.);

S_c = maximum contact stress in pounds per square inch.

11.4 $\Delta = \dfrac{8WD^3 n}{d^4 G}$

where Δ = deflection of a coil spring in inches;

W = load (200 to 2000 lb);

D = diameter of coil (0.5 to 5 in.);

n = number of active coils (3 to 15);

d = diameter of wire (0000 to 10 B & S gage);

G = shear modulus, 12×10^6 psi.

11.5 $\text{hp} = \dfrac{8.33 \times RHS}{33,000E}$

where R = rate of pumping (100 to 1000 gpm);

H = pumping head (15 to 30 ft);

S = specific gravity (1.0 to 3.0);

E = pump efficiency (50% to 80%).

11.6 $C_f = 0.002 + \dfrac{473\,VaND}{10^{10}PC}$ [coefficient of friction for a lubricated bearing (0.002 to 0.030)]

where Va = absolute viscosity (50 to 300 centipoises);

N = journal speed (100 to 1000 rpm);

P = pressure (100 to 1000 psi);

C = clearance (0.001 to 0.008 in.);

D = diameter of bearing (2 to 8 in.).

11.7 $\Delta_{\max} = \dfrac{Pl^3}{48EI}$

where Δ = deflection in inches of a simple beam with a concentrated load at the center;
  P = concentrated load (500 to 10,000 lb);
  l = length of beam (60 to 300 in.);
  E = modulus of elasticity (2×10^6 to 30×10^6 psi);
  I = moment of inertia (1000 to 20,000 in.^{4}).

11.8 $\Delta_{\max} = \dfrac{Wl_3}{KEI}$

where Δ = deflection in inches of simple beams loaded as follows: (*a*) uniformly ($K = 384/5$), (*b*) load increasing uniformly to one end ($K = 1000/13$), (*c*) load increasing uniformly to the center ($K = 60$);
  W = total load (10,000 to 300,000 lb);
E and I as above;
  l = (120 to 600 in.).

11.9 $f = \dfrac{9Wl}{bd^2}$

where f = fiber stress (500 to 2500 psi);
  l = length of wooden beam (5 to 30 ft);
  W = total load (1000 to 12,000 lb);
  b = width of beam (2 to 12 in.);
  d = depth of beam (4 to 16 in.).

11.10 $V = \dfrac{\pi h}{3}(r^2 + rR^2 + R^2)$ (volume of a frustum of a cone)

where h = altitude of frustum (5 to 25 ft);
  r = radius of upper base (0.5 to 2 ft);
  R = radius of lower base (1.0 to 5 ft);
  V = volume in cubic feet.

CHAPTER

12

Design of Net Charts

Problems involving four variables may also be solved by a net chart which makes it possible to read all four variables with one isopleth. The principles involved in the design of this type of chart are the same as those employed in the design of a chart of the form $f_1(u) + f_2(v) = f_3(w)$ or $f_1(u) = f_2(v)f_3(w)$.

Example 1

Suppose the given equation is:

$$q = uv + t.$$

We could solve the problem by designing two charts that have a common turning axis. For instance, suppose we let

$$R = uv \tag{1}$$

then

$$q = R + t \tag{2}$$

Equation (1) is of the Z-chart form $f_1(u) = f_2(v) \cdot f_3(w)$, and equation (2) is of the form $f_1(u) + f_2(v) = f_3(w)$. A combination of these two type forms will effect a solution to the given equation, Figure 113.

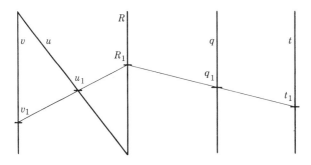

Figure 113. Alignment chart for the form $f_1(q) = f_2(u) \cdot f_3(v) + f_4(t)$.

Now let us consider the design of a net chart for the given equation. First we will rewrite the equation as

$$(q - t) = uv$$

Now let $t = 0, 1, 2, 3, \cdots, n$ (the range of t). For the values of t we get

$$q = uv \tag{3}$$
$$q - 1 = uv \tag{4}$$
$$q - 2 = uv \tag{5}$$
$$q - 3 = uv \tag{6}$$
$$\cdots\cdots$$
$$q - n = uv$$

Each of the above equations is of the form $f_1(u) = f_2(v) \cdot f_3(w)$. A nomogram for equation (3) is shown in Figure 114. A nomogram for equation (4) is shown in Figure 115. Similar nomo-

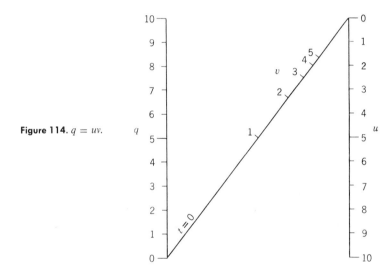

Figure 114. $q = uv$.

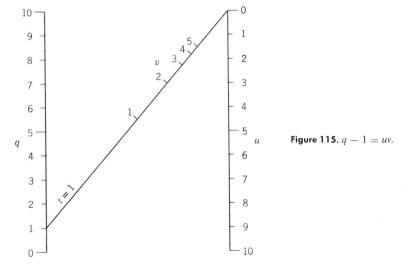

Figure 115. $q - 1 = uv$.

grams for equations (5), (6) $\cdots$ could be designed. It should be noted, however, that since the q- and u-scales are the same for each equation, a single net chart can be designed for all of the above equations and hence for the given expression: $q = uv + t$. See Figure 116.

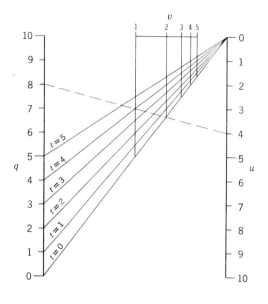

Figure 116. Net chart for $q = uv + t$. Example: When $u = 4$, $v = 1$, and $t = 4$, then $q = 8$.

Example 2

Suppose the given equation is $S = V_0 t + \frac{1}{2}at^2$, where $S =$ distance traversed in feet (0 to 15), $V_0 =$ initial velocity in feet per second (0 to 10), $a =$ acceleration in feet per second² (0 to 4), and $t =$ time interval in seconds (1 to 4).

Solution. Let $t = 1, 2, 3,$ and 4. With these values for t, the following equations result, namely:

$$S = V_0 + \frac{a}{2} \tag{1}$$
$$S = 2V_0 + 2a \tag{2}$$
$$S = 3V_0 + \tfrac{9}{2}a \tag{3}$$
$$S = 4V_0 + 8a \tag{4}$$

All the above equations are of the form $f_1(u) + f_2(v) = f_3(w)$.

Consider the first equation, $S = V_0 + a/2$. It may be written $V_0 - S = -a/2$ to conform with the type equation $f_1(u) + f_2(v) = f_3(w)$. Suppose that the desired length of the V_0- and S-scales is 10 units; then the scale equations are:

$$X_{v_0} = V_0 \quad \text{and} \quad X_s = \tfrac{2}{3}S$$

From the above moduli, the modulus for the a scale is $\dfrac{1 \times \tfrac{2}{3}}{1 + \tfrac{2}{3}} = \dfrac{2}{5}$; and its position is determined from the ratio $\dfrac{1}{\tfrac{2}{3}} = \dfrac{3}{2}$. The scale equation for a then becomes $X_a = \tfrac{2}{3}(a/2) = a/5$. The chart for the equation $V_0 - S = -a/2$ is shown in Figure 117.

Now, consider equation (2), $S = 2V_0 + 2a$. This equation can be rewritten in type form as $2V_0 - S = -2a$. If we are to use the same V_0- and S-scales as shown in Figure 117, the effective moduli for the scale equations, $X_{v_0} = m_v(2V_0)$ and $X_s = m_sS$, must be the same as those used in equation (1). This means that m_{v_0} must equal $\frac{1}{2}$ in order for the effective modulus to equal 1. Therefore, the scale equation for V_0 in equation (2) is $X_{v_0} = \frac{1}{2}(2V_0) = V_0$.

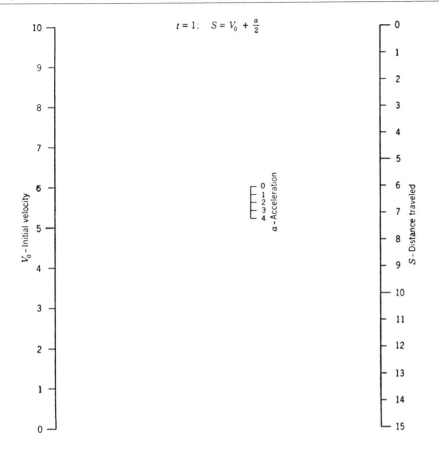

Figure 117. First step in designing a net chart for the equation $S = V_0 t + \frac{1}{2} a t^2$.

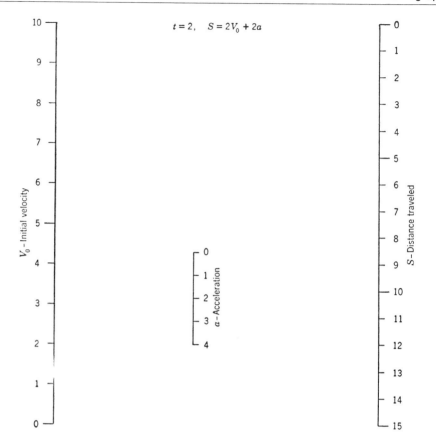

Figure 118. Second step in designing a net chart for the equation $S = V_0t + \frac{1}{2}at^2$.

Since the coefficient of S is the same in both equations (1) and (2), no change in modulus for the S-scale is necessary. Note, however, that the location of the a-scale is determined by the ratio $\dfrac{m_{v_0}}{m_s} = \dfrac{\frac{1}{2}}{\frac{2}{3}} = \dfrac{3}{4}$. The chart for equation (2) is shown in Figure 118.

If the two charts are superposed, the resulting chart, Figure 119, will be obtained.

It should be clear that similar calculations for equations (3) and (4) would be necessary to complete the net chart. It is not necessary to make separate charts for each of the four equations, since the V_0- and S-scales are the same in all cases. Calculations for positioning the a-scale are necessary and, in addition, the moduli for the a-scales must be computed in order to graduate these scales properly. Finally, curves drawn through like values of a will establish the net for the variable a. The net for the variable, t, consists of the vertical lines which first carried the values of a when t equaled 1, 2, 3, and 4. The completed chart is shown in Figure 119.

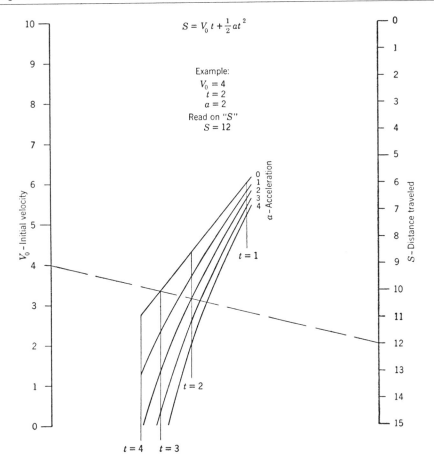

Figure 119. Net chart for the equation $S = V_0 t + \frac{1}{2} a t^2$.

EXERCISES

12.1 $A = P(1 + r)^n$ (amount at compound interest)

where P = principal sum ($1 to $1000);
r = interest rate per period (1% to 10%);
n = number of periods compounded (1 to 20).

12.2 $p = \dfrac{RT}{v - b} - \dfrac{a}{v^2}$ (Van der Waals' equation of state)

where p = pressure in atmospheres;
T = temperature (500° to 1000° R);
v = specific volume in feet³ per mole (5 to 25);
R = gas constant = 0.73 (atm-ft³/° R-mole);
a = constant depending on gas in atmosphere-feet³ per mole²;
b = constant depending on gas in feet³ per mole.

Gas	a	b
Air	344	0.585
CO_2	924	0.685
H_2	63	0.427
H_2O	1397	0.487
N_2	346	0.618
O_2	350	0.510

12.3 $C = \left(\dfrac{100 - r}{100}\right)^n Co$

where C = concentration after n washings in grams per liter (0.0001 to 100);
Co = concentration of original supernatant liquor in grams per liter (1 to 1000);
r = per cent of total volume decanted each washing (50% to 90%);
n = number of washings (1 to 10).

12.4 $P = \dfrac{A \cdot r}{(1 + r)^n - 1}$ (sinking fund payments)

where A = amount to be accumulated ($5000 to $100,000);
r = interest rate (3% to 8% annually);
n = number of annual payments (5 to 30);
P = annual payment.

12.5 $e_x = \dfrac{f_x}{E} - \dfrac{mf_y}{E}$ (unit elongation in the x direction)

where f_x = unit stress in the x direction (0 to 50,000 psi);
f_y = unit stress in the y direction (0 to 50,000 psi);
E = $10 \cdot 10^6$ to $30 \cdot 10^6$ psi;
e_x = unit elongation in x direction (0.0005 to 0.0050 in.).

13

Circular Nomograms

Circular nomograms may be designed for equations of the form $f_1(u) = f_2(v) \cdot f_3(w)$. The circular nomogram is quite advantageous in dealing with equations whose functions are trigonometric.

First let us consider the geometry of the circular nomogram, Figure 120. The upper half of the circle, radius R, will be graduated for values of v; the lower half for values of w; and the diameter for values of u.

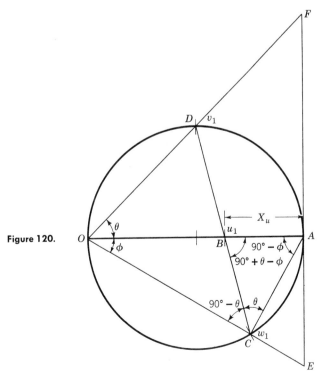

Figure 120.

In triangle ABC,

$$\frac{AB}{\sin\theta} = \frac{BC}{\cos\phi} \qquad (1)$$

In triangle OBC,

$$\frac{OB}{\cos\theta} = \frac{BC}{\sin\phi} \qquad (2)$$

Therefore

$$\frac{AB\cos\phi}{\sin\theta} = \frac{OB\sin\phi}{\cos\theta} \qquad (3)$$

and

$$\frac{AB}{OB} = \frac{\sin\theta\,\sin\phi}{\cos\theta\,\cos\phi} \qquad (4)$$

or

$$\frac{X_u}{2R - X_u} = \tan\theta\,\tan\phi \qquad (5)$$

Now, let

$$\frac{X_u}{2R - X_u} = m_u f_1(u) \qquad (6)$$

$$\tan\theta = m_v f_2(v) \qquad (7)$$

and

$$\tan\phi = m_w f_3(w) \qquad (8)$$

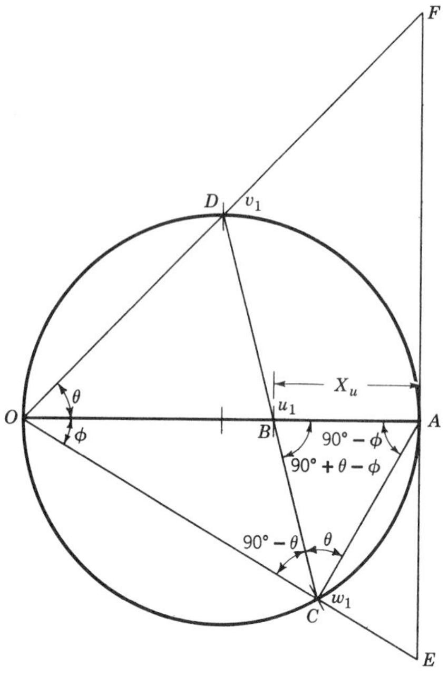

Figure 120.

Therefore $\qquad m_u f_1(u) = m_v f_2(v) \cdot m_w f_3(w) \qquad (9)$

When $\qquad\qquad m_u = m_v \cdot m_w,$

then $\qquad\qquad f_1(u) = f_2(v) \cdot f_3(w) \qquad (10)$

Example 1

Let us consider the equation:

$$u = vw \qquad v(0 \text{ to } 10)$$
$$w(0 \text{ to } 20)$$

Let R, the radius of the circle, equal 5 units.

Now $\qquad\qquad \dfrac{X_u}{10 - X_u} = m_u u$ [see equation (6) above]

Let us position the value $u = 100$ at the center of the circle

$$(u_{\max} = 10 \times 20 = 200)$$

Then $\qquad\qquad \dfrac{X_u}{10 - X_u} = \dfrac{5}{10 - 5} = 1$

and $\qquad 1 = m_u \times 100;$ therefore $m_u = \frac{1}{100}.$

Therefore $\qquad\qquad \dfrac{X_u}{10 - X_u} = \dfrac{1}{100}u$

or $\qquad\qquad\qquad X_u = \dfrac{10u}{100 + u}$

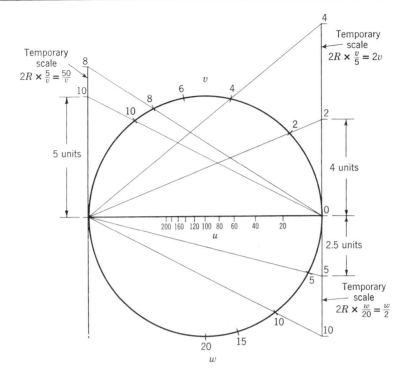

Figure 121. $u = vw$.

Values of u and X_u are shown below.

u	0	20	40	60	80	100	120	140	160	180	200
X_u	0	1.67	2.86	3.75	4.44	5.00	5.46	5.83	6.15	6.43	6.67

Since
$$m_u = m_v \cdot m_w$$
$$\tfrac{1}{100} = m_v \cdot m_w$$

Let $m_v = \tfrac{1}{5}$ and $m_w = \tfrac{1}{20}$ (other values might have been selected).

Therefore $\tan \theta = \tfrac{1}{5} v$

and $\tan \phi = \tfrac{1}{20} w$

Several values of v and $\tan \theta$ are shown below as follows:

v	0	2	4	6	8	10
$\tan \theta$	0	0.4	0.8	1.2	1.6	2.0

Several values of w and $\tan \phi$ are shown below:

w	0	5	10	15	20
$\tan \phi$	0	0.25	0.50	0.75	2.0

Values of θ and ϕ *need not be computed, since the tangents of these angles may be laid off directly.* Note in Figure 121 that once the values of the tangents of angles θ and ϕ are known, ratios such as AE/AO and AF/AO (see Figure 120) are easily established. The upper right-hand tangent carries a temporary scale $X_{v'} = 2R \times \dfrac{v}{5}$ or $X_{v'} = 2v$. When the values of v exceed 4 it is best to use the upper left-hand tangent which carries a temporary scale $X_v'' = 2R \times \dfrac{5}{v} = \dfrac{50}{v}$. The lower right-hand tangent carries a temporary scale $X_w' = 2R \times \dfrac{w}{20} = \dfrac{w}{2}$. If the values of w were to be increased beyond 20, then it would be best to employ the lower left-hand tangent which would carry a temporary scale $X_w'' = 2R \times \dfrac{20}{w} = \dfrac{200}{w}$.

Example 2

$$\text{Tan } \alpha = \sin \beta \tan \psi$$

Angle ψ, azimuthal angle ($0°$ to $90°$)

Angle β, beam angle ($10°$ to $90°$)

Angle α, dip angle ($0°$ to $90°$)

Since the ranges for angles α and ψ are the same, it may be desirable to have the α- and ψ-scales of the same length. Let us, then, rewrite the equation in the form,

$$\sin \beta = \tan \alpha \cot \psi$$

Again, we will assume R, the radius of the circle, equals 5 units.

Now

$$\frac{X_\beta}{10 - X_\beta} = m\beta \sin \beta$$

Let us position the value $\beta = 90°$ at the center of the circle.

Then

$$\frac{X_\beta}{10 - X_\beta} = \frac{5}{10 - 5} = 1$$

and $1 = m_\beta \times \sin 90°$ or $m_\beta = 1$.

Therefore

$$\frac{X_\beta}{10 - X_\beta} = 1 \times \sin \beta$$

or

$$X_\beta = \frac{10 \sin \beta}{1 + \sin \beta}$$

Values of β and X_β are shown below.

β	$10°$	$20°$	$30°$	$40°$	$50°$	$60°$	$70°$	$80°$	$90°$
X_β	1.48	2.54	3.33	3.90	4.33	4.64	4.84	4.96	5.00

Since $m_\beta = m_\alpha \cdot m_\psi = 1$, let $m_\alpha = m_\psi = 1$.

Now since $\quad \tan \theta = m_v f_2(v) \;\big\}$ [see page 136, equations (7) and (8)]
and $\qquad\quad \tan \phi = m_w f_3(w) \;\big\}$

it follows that

$$\tan \theta = \tan \alpha \quad \text{ or } \quad \theta = \alpha$$
and
$$\tan \phi = \cot \psi \quad \text{ or } \quad \phi = 90° - \psi$$

The above relations provide a simple means for graduating the α-angle and ψ-angle scales. See Figure 122.

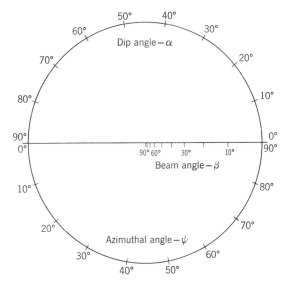

Figure 122. $\tan \alpha = \sin \beta \tan \psi$.

Had we decided to place $\beta = 45°$ at the center of the circle, then, $m_\beta = \sqrt{2}$. This value is computed from

$$\frac{X_\beta}{10 - X_\beta} = m_\beta \sin 45°$$

Now

$$X_\beta = \frac{10 \times \sqrt{2} \sin \beta}{1 + \sqrt{2} \sin \beta}$$

When $\beta = 90°$, $X_\beta = 5.86$. While this distance $X_\beta = 5.86$ lengthens the β scale, the increase is not very significant. *Let us then place $\beta = 30°$ at the center of the circle.*

Now

$$\frac{X_\beta}{10 - X_\beta} = m_\beta \sin 30° \quad \text{and} \quad m_\beta = 2$$

and

$$\frac{X_\beta}{10 - X_\beta} = 2 \sin \beta$$

Corresponding values of β and X_β are shown in the table below.

β	10	20	30	40	50	60	70	80	90
X_β	1.48	4.06	5.00	5.62	6.05	6.35	6.53	6.63	6.67

The relationship among the moduli is $m_\beta = m_\alpha \cdot m_\psi = 2$. Let $m_\alpha = m_\psi = \sqrt{2}$.

Therefore $\tan \theta = \sqrt{2} \tan \alpha$

and $\tan \phi = \sqrt{2} \cot \psi$

The completed circular nomogram is shown in Figure 123.

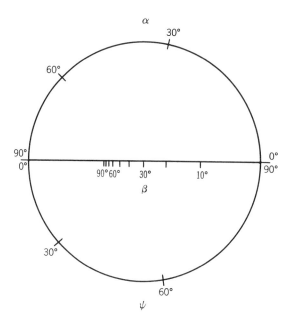

Figure 123. $\tan \alpha = \sin \beta \tan \psi$.

EXERCISES

13.1 $I_R = \dfrac{\sin I}{\sin R}$ (index of refraction)

where I = angle of incidence ($0°$ to $90°$);
        R = angle of refraction ($0°$ to $90°$);
        I_R = index of refraction.

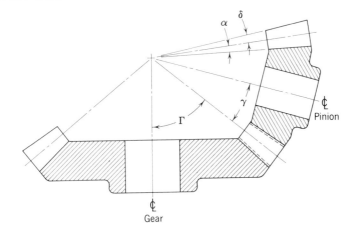

13.2 $\dfrac{Np}{Ng} = \dfrac{\sin \Gamma}{\sin \gamma}$ (bevel gear relations)

13.3 $\tan \alpha = \dfrac{2 \sin \gamma}{Np}$

13.4 $\tan \delta = \dfrac{2.376 \sin \gamma}{Np}$

where $\dfrac{Np}{Ng}$ = speed ratio, pinion to gear (1 : 1 to 8 : 1);

γ = center angle of pinion (10° to 80°);
Γ = center angle of gear (10° to 88°);
Np = number of teeth in pinion (12 to 40).
α and δ (2° to 15°).

13.5 $\tan \alpha = \sin \beta \tan \theta$

where α = dip angle (0 to 90°);
β = beam angle (0 to 90°);
θ = azimuthal angle (0 to 90°).

14

The Use of Determinants
in the Design
and Construction
of Alignment Charts

Most students find the geometric method discussed in the previous chapters a simple and direct approach to the design and construction of alignment charts. It is felt, however, that an introduction to the method which employs determinants is desirable so that students will be enabled to comprehend, more fully, treatments based on determinants exclusively.

Let us consider Figure 124. The area of the triangle may be obtained by the difference between the area of trapezoid 3 and the sum of the areas of trapezoids 1 and 2; or

$$\text{Area of triangle} = \tfrac{1}{2}[(y_2 + y_1)(x_2 - x_1) + (y_2 + y_3)(x_3 - x_2) - (y_1 + y_3)(x_3 - x_1)]$$

In determinant form this would be

$$A = \tfrac{1}{2} \begin{vmatrix} x_1 & y_1 & 1 \\ x_2 & y_2 & 1 \\ x_3 & y_3 & 1 \end{vmatrix}$$

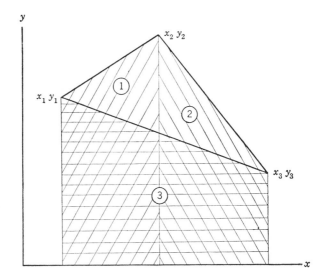

Figure 124.

If point $x_2 y_2$ is placed on the line joining $x_1 y_1$ with $x_3 y_3$, the points are said to be colinear, or the area of the triangle is zero. Hence

$$A = \tfrac{1}{2} \begin{vmatrix} x_1 & y_1 & 1 \\ x_2 & y_2 & 1 \\ x_3 & y_3 & 1 \end{vmatrix} = 0$$

or when

$$\begin{vmatrix} x_1 & y_1 & 1 \\ x_2 & y_2 & 1 \\ x_3 & y_3 & 1 \end{vmatrix} = 0$$

the points $x_1 y_1$, $x_2 y_2$, and $x_3 y_3$ are on the same line.

Example 1

Suppose we have the determinant

$$\begin{vmatrix} 0 & u & 1 \\ 1 & v & 1 \\ \dfrac{1}{2} & \dfrac{w}{2} & 1 \end{vmatrix} = 0$$

1. What does the determinant mean?
2. How can we construct an alignment chart from this determinant?

In order to answer the first question, we must learn how to expand, or evaluate, the determinant, which is done in the following manner:

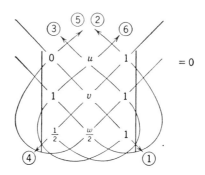

(a) Multiply 0, v, and 1. This is step 1 (see arrow).
(b) Multiply 1, w/2, and 1. This is step 2 (see arrow).
(c) Multiply $\frac{1}{2}$, 1, and u. This is step 3 (see arrow).
(d) Add the results of steps (a), (b), and (c). Thus far we have:

$$\left(0 + \frac{w}{2} + \frac{u}{2}\right)$$

Now start in the upper right-hand corner.
(e) Multiply 1, v, and $\frac{1}{2}$. This is step 4 (see arrow).
(f) Multiply 1, w/2, and 0. This is step 5 (see arrow).
(g) Multiply 1, 1, and u. This is step 6 (see arrow).
(h) Add the results of steps (e), (f), and (g). This is

$$\left(\frac{v}{2} + 0 + u\right)$$

Finally, subtract step (h) from (d), i.e.,

$$\frac{w}{2} + \frac{u}{2} - \frac{v}{2} - u = 0$$

or $$u + v - w = 0$$

Now with regard to the second question. If we consider 0, u as $x_1 y_1$; 1, v as $x_2 y_2$; and $\frac{1}{2}$, w/2 as $x_3 y_3$, we may plot points for u, v, and w by assigning definite values such as 0, 1, 2, 3 $\cdots$, n to each.

Since the x value is zero for all values of u, all points of u will lie on the Y-axis. Likewise, since $x_2 = 1$, all points of v will lie on a line parallel to the Y-axis and 1 unit to the right. Similarly, $x_3 = \frac{1}{2}$, and all points of w will lie on a line parallel to the Y-axis and $\frac{1}{2}$ unit to the right. It should be observed that since $y_3 = w/2$, the distance between consecutive values of w will be half the distance between consecutive values of u or v.

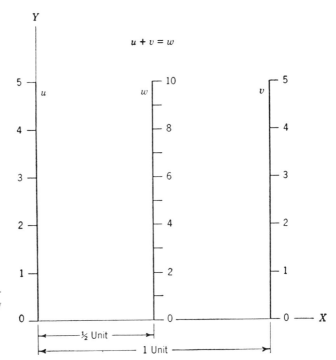

Figure 125. Chart for the equation $u + v = w$, constructed by the method of determinants.

A straight line which joins a point on the u-scale with one on the v-scale will cut the w-scale in a value which satisfies the equation $u + v = w$ (Figure 125). While the above material is easy to follow, one may wonder how the determinant

$$\begin{vmatrix} 0 & u & 1 \\ 1 & v & 1 \\ \dfrac{1}{2} & \dfrac{w}{2} & 1 \end{vmatrix} = 0$$

was developed in the first place. This could have been done by trial and error, observing that the right-hand column must consist of 1's, and that only one variable should appear in each row.

A better approach, one which is direct and mathematically correct, is this:

1. Write the equation $u + v - w = 0$.
2. Let $x = u$, and $y = v$.
3. Write the expressions

$$x - u = 0$$
$$y - v = 0$$
$$x + y - w = 0$$

It should be noted that we now have three equations in x and y. If they are consistent, the determinant made up from the coefficients of x and y and the constant term must vanish. (See Bôcher's text.*) This means that

* *Introduction to Higher Algebra,* Maxime Bôcher, The Macmillan Co., New York, 1924, Chapter 4.

$$\begin{vmatrix} 1 & 0 & -u \\ 0 & 1 & -v \\ 1 & 1 & -w \end{vmatrix} = 0$$

The value of this determinant is $u + v = w$. You will recall that the determinant must be in the form

$$\begin{vmatrix} x_1 & y_1 & 1 \\ x_2 & y_2 & 1 \\ x_3 & y_3 & 1 \end{vmatrix} = 0$$

before the chart can be constructed.

How can we manipulate the determinant in order to transform it to the form,

$$\begin{vmatrix} 0 & u & 1 \\ 1 & v & 1 \\ \dfrac{1}{2} & \dfrac{w}{2} & 1 \end{vmatrix} = 0$$

Let us start with

$$\begin{vmatrix} 1 & 0 & -u \\ 0 & 1 & -v \\ 1 & 1 & -w \end{vmatrix} = 0$$

Column 1 may be replaced by the sum of columns 1 and 2, yielding

$$\begin{vmatrix} 1 & 0 & u \\ 1 & 1 & v \\ 2 & 1 & w \end{vmatrix} = 0 \text{ (Note column 3 above was multiplied by } -1.)$$

Now the bottom row may be divided by 2, resulting in

$$\begin{vmatrix} 1 & 0 & u \\ 1 & 1 & v \\ 1 & \dfrac{1}{2} & \dfrac{w}{2} \end{vmatrix} = 0$$

By interchanging columns we get,

$$\begin{vmatrix} 0 & u & 1 \\ 1 & v & 1 \\ \dfrac{1}{2} & \dfrac{w}{2} & 1 \end{vmatrix} = 0$$

which is known as the "design determinant." All the steps shown above are permissible when the value of the determinant is zero.

Before we proceed with additional examples let us become acquainted with the operations on zero-valued third-order determinants.

1. Zero-Valued Third-Order Determinants

The following operations are valid for zero-valued third-order determinants:

(*a*) Corresponding rows and columns may be interchanged.

$$0 = \begin{vmatrix} x_1 & y_1 & z_1 \\ x_2 & y_2 & z_2 \\ x_3 & y_3 & z_3 \end{vmatrix} = \begin{vmatrix} x_1 & x_2 & x_3 \\ y_1 & y_2 & y_3 \\ z_1 & z_2 & z_3 \end{vmatrix} = 0$$

(*b*) Any two rows (or columns) may be interchanged.

$$0 = \begin{vmatrix} x_1 & y_1 & z_1 \\ x_2 & y_2 & z_2 \\ x_3 & y_3 & z_3 \end{vmatrix} = \begin{vmatrix} x_3 & y_3 & z_3 \\ x_2 & y_2 & z_2 \\ x_1 & y_1 & z_1 \end{vmatrix} = \begin{vmatrix} z_1 & y_1 & x_1 \\ z_2 & y_2 & x_2 \\ z_3 & y_3 & x_3 \end{vmatrix} = 0$$

(*c*) The elements of a row (or column) may be multiplied by a constant.

$$0 = \begin{vmatrix} x_1 & y_1 & z_1 \\ x_2 & y_2 & z_2 \\ x_3 & y_3 & z_3 \end{vmatrix} = \begin{vmatrix} ax_1 & y_1 & z_1 \\ ax_2 & y_2 & z_2 \\ ax_3 & y_3 & z_3 \end{vmatrix} = \begin{vmatrix} bx_1 & by_1 & bz_1 \\ x_2 & y_2 & z_2 \\ x_3 & y_3 & z_3 \end{vmatrix} = 0$$

(*d*) A row (or column) may be replaced by the sum of two rows (or columns).

$$0 = \begin{vmatrix} x_1 & y_1 & z_1 \\ x_2 & y_2 & z_2 \\ x_3 & y_3 & z_3 \end{vmatrix} = \begin{vmatrix} x_1 + y_1 & y_1 & z_1 \\ x_2 + y_2 & y_2 & z_2 \\ x_3 + y_3 & y_3 & z_3 \end{vmatrix} = \begin{vmatrix} x_1 + x_2 & y_1 + y_2 & z_1 + z_2 \\ x_2 & y_2 & z_2 \\ x_3 & y_3 & z_3 \end{vmatrix} = 0$$

(*e*) To a row (or column) may be added a constant multiple of another row (or column).

$$0 = \begin{vmatrix} x_1 & y_1 & z_1 \\ x_2 & y_2 & z_2 \\ x_3 & y_3 & z_3 \end{vmatrix} = \begin{vmatrix} x_1 + ay_1 & y_1 & z_1 \\ x_2 + ay_2 & y_2 & z_2 \\ x_3 + ay_3 & y_3 & z_3 \end{vmatrix} = \begin{vmatrix} x_1 + bx_2 & y_1 + by_2 & z_1 + bz_2 \\ x_2 & y_2 & z_2 \\ x_3 & y_3 & z_3 \end{vmatrix} = 0$$

2. Product of Two Third-Order Determinants

$$\begin{vmatrix} x_1 & y_1 & z_1 \\ x_2 & y_2 & z_2 \\ x_3 & y_3 & z_3 \end{vmatrix} \times \begin{vmatrix} a_1 & b_1 & c_1 \\ a_2 & b_2 & c_2 \\ a_3 & b_3 & c_3 \end{vmatrix} =$$

$$\begin{vmatrix} a_1 x_1 + b_1 y_1 + c_1 z_1 & a_2 x_1 + b_2 y_1 + c_2 z_1 & a_3 x_1 + b_3 y_1 + c_3 z_1 \\ a_1 x_2 + b_1 y_2 + c_1 z_2 & a_2 x_2 + b_2 y_2 + c_2 z_2 & a_3 x_2 + b_3 y_2 + c_3 z_2 \\ a_1 x_3 + b_1 y_3 + c_1 z_3 & a_2 x_3 + b_2 y_3 + c_2 z_3 & a_3 x_3 + b_3 y_3 + c_3 z_3 \end{vmatrix}$$

It should be observed that the first column of the product determinant is formed by summing the products of $a_1 \quad b_1 \quad c_1$ and the elements of each row of the given determinant, respectively. In a similar manner the second and third columns of the product determinant are formed.

An alternative method results in the following:

$$\begin{vmatrix} x_1 & y_1 & z_1 \\ x_2 & y_2 & z_2 \\ x_3 & y_3 & z_3 \end{vmatrix} \times \begin{vmatrix} a_1 & b_1 & c_1 \\ a_2 & b_2 & c_2 \\ a_3 & b_3 & c_3 \end{vmatrix} =$$

$$\begin{vmatrix} a_1x_1 + a_2y_1 + a_3z_1 & b_1x_1 + b_2y_1 + b_3z_1 & c_1x_1 + c_2y_1 + c_3z_1 \\ a_1x_2 + a_2y_2 + a_3z_2 & b_1x_2 + b_2y_2 + b_3z_2 & c_1x_2 + c_2y_2 + c_3z_2 \\ a_1x_3 + a_2y_3 + a_3z_3 & b_1x_3 + b_2y_3 + b_3z_3 & c_1x_3 + c_2y_3 + c_3z_3 \end{vmatrix}$$

In this solution, each row of the first column of the product determinant is formed by summing the products of a_1 a_2 a_3 and the elements of each row of the given determinant, respectively. In a similar manner the second and third columns of the product determinant are formed.

In either solution, constructional determinants can be formed by dividing each row by the corresponding element in the last column. The last column in each case will then consist of 1's.

$$\begin{vmatrix} \dfrac{a_1x_1 + a_2y_1 + a_3z_1}{c_1x_1 + c_2y_1 + c_3z_1} & \dfrac{b_1x_1 + b_2y_1 + b_3z_1}{c_1x_1 + c_2y_2 + c_3z_1} & 1 \\ \dfrac{a_1x_2 + a_2y_2 + a_3z_2}{c_1x_2 + c_2y_2 + c_3z_3} & \dfrac{b_1x_2 + b_2y_2 + b_3z_2}{c_1x_2 + c_2y_2 + c_3z_2} & 1 \\ \dfrac{a_1x_3 + a_2y_3 + a_3z_3}{c_1x_3 + c_2y_3 + c_3z_3} & \dfrac{b_1x_3 + b_2y_3 + b_3z_3}{c_1x_3 + c_2y_3 + c_3z_3} & 1 \end{vmatrix} = 0$$

when

$$\begin{vmatrix} x_1 & y_1 & z_1 \\ x_2 & y_2 & z_2 \\ x_3 & y_3 & z_3 \end{vmatrix} = 0 \quad \text{and} \quad \begin{vmatrix} a_1 & b_1 & c_1 \\ a_2 & b_2 & c_2 \\ a_3 & b_3 & c_3 \end{vmatrix} \neq 0$$

Example 2

Suppose we consider the equation $u + v = w$ again. Let us assume that u varies from 2 to 10 and that v varies from 5 to 15. You will recall that we had written the expressions,

$$x - u = 0$$
$$y - v = 0$$
$$x + y - w = 0$$

Now, however, let us introduce the scale moduli by writing

$$x - m_u u = 0$$
$$y - m_v v = 0$$

and

$$\frac{x}{m_u} + \frac{y}{m_v} - w = 0 \text{ (since } u + v - w = 0)$$

We can write the determinant,

$$
\begin{vmatrix}
1 & 0 & -m_u u \\
0 & 1 & -m_v v \\
\dfrac{1}{m_u} & \dfrac{1}{m_v} & -w
\end{vmatrix} = 0
$$

because the three equations above are consistent. This determinant may be reduced to the design determinant in the following manner:

$$
\begin{vmatrix}
1 & 0 & m_u u \\
0 & 1 & m_v v \\
\dfrac{1}{m_u} & \dfrac{1}{m_v} & w
\end{vmatrix}
=
\begin{vmatrix}
1 & 0 & m_u u \\
1 & 1 & m_v v \\
\dfrac{m_u + m_v}{m_u m_v} & \dfrac{1}{m_v} & w
\end{vmatrix}
=
\begin{vmatrix}
1 & 0 & m_u u \\
1 & 1 & m_v v \\
1 & \dfrac{m_u}{m_u + m_v} & \dfrac{m_u m_v}{m_u + m_v} w
\end{vmatrix}
=
$$

$$
\begin{vmatrix}
0 & m_u u & 1 \\
1 & m_v v & 1 \\
\dfrac{m_u}{m_u + m_v} & \dfrac{m_u m_v}{m_u + m_v} w & 1
\end{vmatrix} = 0 \quad \leftarrow \text{Design Determinant}
$$

If the lengths of the u- and v-scales are 6 in., then

$$
m_u = \frac{6}{10 - 2} = \frac{3}{4}
$$

and

$$
m_v = \frac{6}{15 - 5} = \frac{3}{5}
$$

The design determinant becomes:

$$
\begin{vmatrix}
0 & \tfrac{3}{4}(u - 2) & 1 \\
1 & \tfrac{3}{5}(v - 5) & 1 \\
\tfrac{5}{9} & \tfrac{1}{3}(w - 7) & 1
\end{vmatrix} = 0
$$

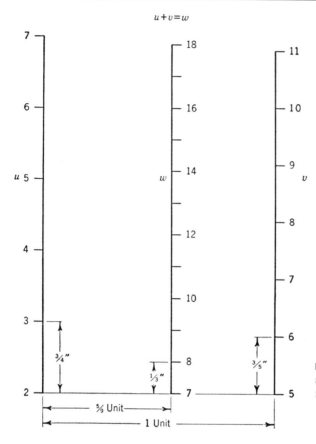

Figure 126. Chart for the equation $u + v = w$, constructed by the method of determinants.

The chart is constructed from this determinant (Figure 126). It should be noted that the u-, v-, and w-scales are graduated from points 2, 5, and 7, respectively.

Example 3

Consider an equation of the form:

$$f_1(u) = f_2(v) \cdot f_3(w); \qquad \text{i.e., } u = vw$$

Let $$x = m_u u \qquad \text{and} \qquad y = m_v v$$

Now we can set up three equations in x and y:

$$x - m_u u = 0 \tag{1}$$

$$y - m_v v = 0 \tag{2}$$

$$\frac{x}{m_u} - \frac{y}{m_v} w = 0 \qquad \text{[obtained by substituting values of } u \text{ and } v \text{ from} \tag{3}$$
equations (1) and (2) in the given equation]

If the above equations are consistent, then

$$\begin{vmatrix} 1 & 0 & -m_u u \\ 0 & 1 & -m_v v \\ \dfrac{1}{m_u} & \dfrac{-w}{m_v} & 0 \end{vmatrix} = 0$$

Multiplying columns 2 and 3 by -1 and then multiplying row 2 by -1, we obtain

$$\begin{vmatrix} 1 & 0 & m_u u \\ 0 & 1 & -m_v v \\ \dfrac{1}{m_u} & w & 0 \\ & m_v & \end{vmatrix} = 0$$

Now by replacing column 1 by the sum of the first two columns we get

$$\begin{vmatrix} 1 & 0 & m_u u \\ 1 & 1 & -m_v v \\ \dfrac{m_u w + m_v}{m_u m_v} & \dfrac{w}{m_v} & 0 \end{vmatrix} = 0$$

Dividing the bottom row by $\dfrac{m_u w + m_v}{m_u m_v}$, we obtain

$$\begin{vmatrix} 1 & 0 & m_u u \\ 1 & 1 & -m_v v \\ 1 & \dfrac{m_u w}{m_u w + m_v} & 0 \end{vmatrix} = 0$$

And finally by rearranging the columns, the constructional determinant is

$$\begin{vmatrix} 0 & m_u u & 1 \\ 1 & -m_v v & 1 \\ \dfrac{m_u w}{m_u w + m_v} & 0 & 1 \end{vmatrix} = 0$$

Now suppose that the range of u is 0 to 10, and of v, 0 to 5, and the length of the scale 10 units; then $m_u = 1$ and $m_v = 2$. The determinant becomes

$$\begin{vmatrix} 0 & u & 1 \\ 1 & -2v & 1 \\ \dfrac{w}{w + 2} & 0 & 1 \end{vmatrix} = 0$$

The nomogram is constructed from the above determinant, and is shown in Figure 127. A better arrangement is obtained by using oblique axes, as shown in Figure 128.

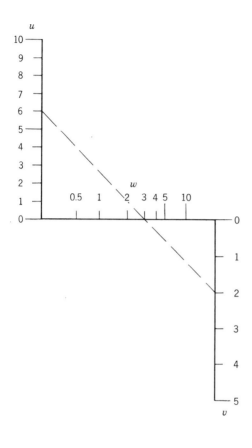

Figure 127. Chart for the equation $uv = w$, constructed by the method of determinants.

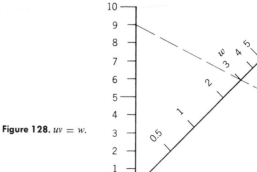

Figure 128. $uv = w$.

Example 4

Given: $u + vw = w^2$.
Required: The design determinant.
Solution: Let $x = u$ and $y = v$.

Now
$$x - u = 0 \tag{1}$$
$$y - v = 0 \tag{2}$$
$$x + yw - w^2 = 0 \tag{3}$$

If these equations are consistent, then

$$\begin{vmatrix} 1 & 0 & -u \\ 0 & 1 & -v \\ 1 & w & -w^2 \end{vmatrix} = 0$$

Replace column 1 by the sum of the first two columns.

$$\begin{vmatrix} 1 & 0 & u \\ 1 & 1 & v \\ w+1 & w & w^2 \end{vmatrix} = 0$$

Divide the bottom row by $w + 1$.

$$\begin{vmatrix} 1 & 0 & u \\ 1 & 1 & v \\ 1 & \dfrac{w}{w+1} & \dfrac{w^2}{w+1} \end{vmatrix} = 0$$

Rearrange the columns.

$$\begin{vmatrix} 0 & u & 1 \\ 1 & v & 1 \\ \dfrac{w}{w+1} & \dfrac{w^2}{w+1} & 1 \end{vmatrix} = 0$$

Construct the chart from the above determinant (Figure 129).

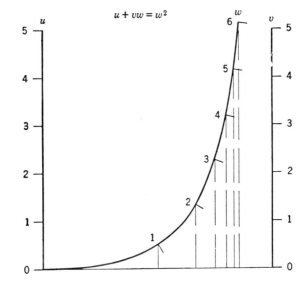

Figure 129. Chart for the equation $u + vw = w^2$, constructed by the method of determinants.

Points on the w-scale can be plotted from the following coordinates:

w	0	1	2	3	4	5
x-coordinate: $\dfrac{w}{w+1}$	0	$\frac{1}{2}$	$\frac{2}{3}$	$\frac{3}{4}$	$\frac{4}{5}$	$\frac{5}{6}$
y-coordinate: $\dfrac{w^2}{w+1}$	0	$\frac{1}{2}$	$\frac{4}{3}$	$\frac{9}{4}$	$\frac{16}{5}$	$\frac{25}{6}$

If scale moduli are used, then

$$x = m_u u \qquad \text{and} \qquad y = m_v v$$

and the three equations in x and y are:

$$x - m_u u = 0$$

$$y - m_v v = 0$$

$$\frac{x}{m_u} + \frac{yw}{m_v} - w^2 = 0$$

The first determinant is

$$\begin{vmatrix} 1 & 0 & -m_u u \\ 0 & 1 & -m_v v \\ \dfrac{1}{m_u} & \dfrac{w}{m_v} & -w^2 \end{vmatrix} = 0$$

By following the steps previously outlined we obtain the constructional determinant,

$$\begin{vmatrix} 0 & m_u u & 1 \\ 1 & m_v v & 1 \\ \dfrac{m_u w}{m_u w + m_v} & \dfrac{m_u m_v}{m_u w + m_v} w^2 & 1 \end{vmatrix} = 0$$

Suppose that the ranges of u and v for desired lengths of scales result in $m_u = 2$ and $m_v = 3$; then the final determinant is

$$\begin{vmatrix} 0 & 2u & 1 \\ 1 & 3v & 1 \\ \dfrac{2w}{2w+3} & \dfrac{6w^2}{2w+3} & 1 \end{vmatrix} = 0$$

The nomogram, Figure 130, is constructed from the above determinant.

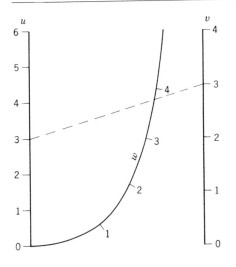

Figure 130. Chart for the equation $u + vw = w^2$, constructed by the method of determinants.

Example 5

Consider the equation:

$$a \sin \theta + b \cos \theta - 1 = 0$$

Let $$x = a \quad \text{and} \quad y = b$$

Now
$$x - a = 0 \tag{1}$$
$$y - b = 0 \tag{2}$$
$$x \sin \theta + y \cos \theta - 1 = 0 \tag{3}$$

If these equations are consistent, then

$$\begin{vmatrix} 1 & 0 & -a \\ 0 & 1 & -b \\ \sin \theta & \cos \theta & -1 \end{vmatrix} = 0 = \begin{vmatrix} 1 & 0 & a \\ 0 & 1 & b \\ \sin \theta & \cos \theta & 1 \end{vmatrix}$$

When we divide the first row by a and the second row by b, we obtain

$$\begin{vmatrix} \dfrac{1}{a} & 0 & 1 \\[2mm] 0 & \dfrac{1}{b} & 1 \\[2mm] \sin \theta & \cos \theta & 1 \end{vmatrix} = 0$$

which is the constructional determinant.

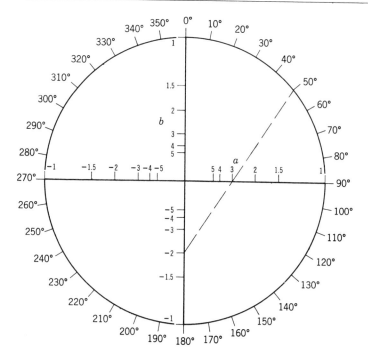

Figure 131. $a \sin \theta + b \cos \theta - 1 = 0$. Example: When $a = 3$ and $b = -2$, then $\theta = 50°$.

The nomogram shown in Figure 131 is constructed from the above determinant.

In the previous examples the initial determinant was set up directly from three consistent equations in x and y. For some equations it is not easy to proceed in this manner. (In fact, it may be quite cumbersome if not impossible.) The method that we will now employ is one of "matching" the terms of the given equation with the terms obtained from the expansion of the determinant

$$\begin{vmatrix} x_1 & y_1 & 1 \\ x_2 & y_2 & 1 \\ x_3 & y_3 & 1 \end{vmatrix} = 0$$

The value of this determinant is

$$x_1 y_2 + x_2 y_3 + x_3 y_1 - x_3 y_2 - x_1 y_3 - x_2 y_1 = 0$$

Matching Method

Example 1

Consider the equation:

$$d = \frac{a^2 + b^2}{a + b}$$

or

$$a^2 + b^2 - da - db = 0$$

or

$$aa + bb - da - db = 0$$

Let us make the following "matchings":

$$aa = x_1 y_2$$

$$bb = x_2 y_1 \text{ (where } x_2 = -b)$$

$$da = x_1 y_3 \text{ (where } y_3 = d, \text{ since } x_1 \text{ is already assigned to } a)$$

$$db = x_2 y_3$$

The remaining products $x_3 y_1$ and $-x_3 y_2$ must vanish.

Now the incomplete determinant is

$$\begin{vmatrix} a & b & ?_1 \\ -b & a & ?_2 \\ ?_4 & d & ?_3 \end{vmatrix} = 0$$

It now remains to determine the values of $?_1$, $?_2$, $?_3$, and $?_4$. If we expand the determinant we will obtain:

$$aa?_3 - bd?_1 + b?_2?_4 - a?_1?_4 - ad?_2 + bb?_3 = 0$$

Since our equation is $aa + bb - da - db = 0$, then,

$$?_3 = 1$$

$$?_1 = 1$$

$$?_2 = 1$$

$$?_4 = 0$$

Therefore the determinant is

$$\begin{vmatrix} a & b & 1 \\ -b & a & 1 \\ 0 & d & 1 \end{vmatrix} = 0$$

It should be noted, however, that the determinant is *not* quite in the constructional form since each of the first two rows contains both variables a and b.

Now, then, when we multiply the first column by $1/ab$ we do obtain the constructional determinant,

$$\begin{vmatrix} \dfrac{1}{b} & b & 1 \\ -\dfrac{1}{a} & a & 1 \\ 0 & d & 1 \end{vmatrix} = 0$$

The completed nomogram is shown in Figure 132.

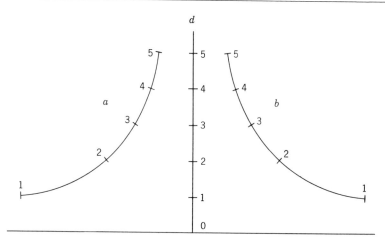

Figure 132. $d = \dfrac{a^2 + b^2}{a + b}$.

Example 2

Consider the equation:

$$\frac{1}{R} = \frac{1}{R_2} + \frac{1}{R_1}$$

This equation can be written in the form,

$$RR_1 + RR_2 - R_1R_2 = 0 \qquad \text{or} \qquad R_1R + RR_2 - R_1R_2 = 0$$

The latter equation simplifies the matching process.

We recall that the expansion of the basic determinant is:

$$x_1y_2 + x_2y_3 + x_3y_1 - x_3y_2 - x_1y_3 - x_2y_1 = 0$$

Let us make the following matchings:

$$x_1y_2 = R_1R \qquad x_3y_2 = 0$$
$$x_2y_3 = RR_2 \qquad x_1y_3 = R_1R_2$$
$$x_3y_1 = 0 \qquad x_2y_1 = 0$$

The initial determinant is:

$$\begin{vmatrix} R_1 & ?_1 & ?_2 \\ R & R & ?_3 \\ ?_5 & R_2 & ?_4 \end{vmatrix} = 0$$

In order to expand this determinant to the value $R_1R + RR_2 - R_1R_2 = 0$, the following relations must hold:

$$?_1 = 0$$
$$?_2 = 1$$
$$?_3 = 1$$
$$?_4 = 1$$
$$?_5 = 0$$

The determinant in final constructional form is:

$$\begin{vmatrix} R_1 & 0 & 1 \\ R & R & 1 \\ 0 & R_2 & 1 \end{vmatrix} = 0$$

The completed nomogram is shown in Figure 133. If oblique axes are used, the nomogram will appear as shown in Figure 134.

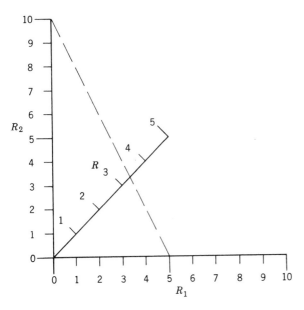

Figure 133. Nomogram for the equation $\dfrac{1}{R} = \dfrac{1}{R_1} + \dfrac{1}{R_2}$.

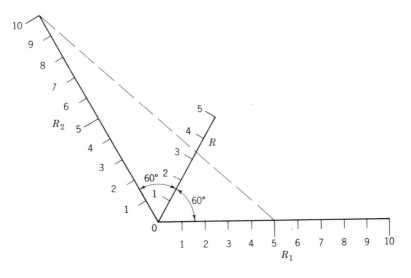

Figure 134. Nomogram for the equation $\dfrac{1}{R} = \dfrac{1}{R_1} + \dfrac{1}{R_2}$.

Example 3

Let us now examine the simple case:

$$f_1(u) + f_2(v) = f_3(w)$$

i.e. $\qquad u + v = w \qquad$ or $\qquad u + v - w = 0$

The six products of the basic determinant are:

$$x_1y_2 + x_2y_3 + x_3y_1 - x_3y_2 - x_1y_3 - x_2y_1 = 0$$

Now let us match these with the products of the equation

$$1{\cdot}u + 1{\cdot}v - 1{\cdot}w = 0$$

Then
$$x_1y_2 \;\; = 1{\cdot}u$$
$$x_2y_3 \;\; = 1{\cdot}v$$
$$x_2y_1 \;\; = 1{\cdot}w$$

The other three products must vanish. The initial determinant is:

$$\begin{vmatrix} 1 & w & ?_1 \\ 1 & u & ?_2 \\ ?_4 & v & ?_3 \end{vmatrix} = 0$$

We can easily establish the following:

$$?_1 \;\; = 1$$
$$?_2 \;\; = 0$$
$$?_3 \;\; = 1$$
$$?_4 \;\; = 0$$

The determinant now becomes
$$\begin{vmatrix} 1 & w & 1 \\ 1 & u & 0 \\ 0 & v & 1 \end{vmatrix} = 0$$

which can be reduced to
$$\begin{vmatrix} \dfrac{1}{2} & \dfrac{w}{2} & 1 \\ 1 & u & 1 \\ 0 & v & 1 \end{vmatrix} = 0$$

Example 4

Let us consider the equation:

$$u + vw - w^2 = 0$$

This equation can be written as:

$$1{\cdot}u + vw - 1{\cdot}w^2 = 0$$

Now we can match these products with those of the basic determinant:

$$x_1y_2 + x_2y_3 + x_3y_1 - x_3y_2 - x_1y_3 - x_2y_1 = 0$$

$$x_1y_2 \;\; = 1{\cdot}u$$
$$x_3y_1 \;\; = v{\cdot}w \qquad \text{(x_2y_3 was not used for vw in order to}$$
$$x_1y_3 \;\; = 1{\cdot}w^2 \qquad \text{avoid having two different variables}$$
$$\text{in the same row)}$$

The other products must vanish. The initial determinant is:

$$\begin{vmatrix} 1 & v & ?_1 \\ ?_4 & u & ?_2 \\ w & w^2 & ?_3 \end{vmatrix} = 0$$

Again we can readily establish the following:

$$?_1 = 0$$
$$?_2 = 1$$
$$?_3 = 1$$
$$?_4 = 0$$

The determinant now becomes $\begin{vmatrix} 1 & v & 0 \\ 0 & u & 1 \\ w & w^2 & 1 \end{vmatrix} = 0$

which can be reduced to $\begin{vmatrix} 1 & v & 1 \\ 0 & u & 1 \\ \dfrac{w}{w+1} & \dfrac{w^2}{w+1} & 1 \end{vmatrix} = 0$

General Remarks

1. An equation which can be reduced to the determinant

$$\begin{vmatrix} 0 & f_1(u) & 1 \\ f_2(v) & f_3(v) & 1 \\ f_4(w) & f_5(w) & 1 \end{vmatrix} = 0$$

will consist of a straight-line u-scale; and curved scales for v and w.

2. If the determinant is of the form

$$\begin{vmatrix} f_1(u) & f_2(u) & 1 \\ f_3(v) & f_4(v) & 1 \\ f_5(w) & f_6(w) & 1 \end{vmatrix} = 0$$

the alignment chart will consist of three curved scales.

The reduction of a three-variable equation to the constructional determinant form often requires ingenuity and resourcefulness on the part of the designer. The methods illustrated in the first and second sets of examples are very useful. In general, it is suggested that one should *first* try to set up three consistent equations from which an initial determinant can be written—as in the first set of examples. If this attack fails *then* one should use the "matching" method. In some cases neither method will work because *not all* three-variable equations can be reduced *to the constructional determinant form.*

In many cases the geometric method is quite adequate for the design of alignment nomograms. However, complicated expressions, especially those having more than one function of each variable, may be solved more easily when the equation can be reduced to the constructional determinant form.

EXERCISES

Use the determinant method for the design of nomograms for the following problems:

14.1 Problems 3.3, 3.5, and 3.6 (Hydraulics).

14.2 Problems 3.10, 3.19, 3.20, and 3.24 (Strength of Materials and Mechanical).

14.3 Problems 3.26, 3.31, 3.33, and 3.35 (Civil).

14.4 Problems 3.36, 3.39, and 3.41 (Electrical).

14.5 Problems 3.46, 3.48, and 3.52 (Aeronautical).

14.6 Problems 3.55, 3.56, and 3.61 (Chemical).

14.7 Problems 3.63, 3.65, and 3.66 (Statistics).

14.8 Problems 3.71, 3.77, and 3.79 (General).

14.9 Problems 5.1, 5.3, and 5.7.

14.10 Problems 6.1, 6.5, and 6.6.

14.11 Select problems from Chapters 7 and 8. These are four-variable problems. Write two third-order determinants in constructional form for each problem.

14.12 Problems 10.1 and 10.4.

14.13 Problems 10.9 and 10.10.

14.14 Problem 10.11.

14.15 Problems 13.1, 13.3, and 13.5.

14.16 $\sin \gamma = \sin \dfrac{(\alpha + \beta)}{\sin \alpha + \sin \beta}$

15

Projective Transformations

Nomograms of one form can be transformed to another form, which may be more advantageous than the original one, by perspective projection—a graphical method; or mathematically, an algebraic method.

Projective Transformation—Graphical Method

Example 1

Let us consider Figure 135, which shows an alignment nomogram, for the expression $u + v = w$, in the H-plane; point S, the center of projection; and the V-plane which is perpendicular to the H-plane.

We will project the given nomogram which lies in the H-plane upon the V-plane by locating the points in which rays drawn through point S and graduations of the given nomogram intersect the V-plane.

For example, the rays which join S with $w = 0$ and with $w = 10$, of the given nomogram, intersect the V-plane at points $0'$ and $10'$, respectively. The line which joins these points is the transformed scale, w'. Additional graduations may be located by finding the intersections of rays S-1, S-2, etc., with scale w'.

In a similar manner, scale u' and its graduations may be located. Scale v, obviously, will not change since it lies at the intersection of the H- and V-planes.

Now if we rotate the V-plane about its line of intersection with the H-plane in the direction indicated by the arrow until it coincides with the H-plane, we will obtain a flat-sheet representation as shown in Figure 136.

Careful study of this figure shows quite clearly that we can arbitrarily select the distance between the transformed scales v' and u' and then locate S_v consistent with the distance chosen. This permits us to fix the size of the transformed nomogram.

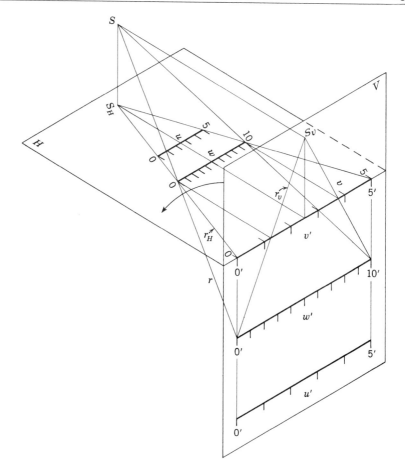

Figure 135. Projective transformation—graphical method. Example 1: $u + v = w$.

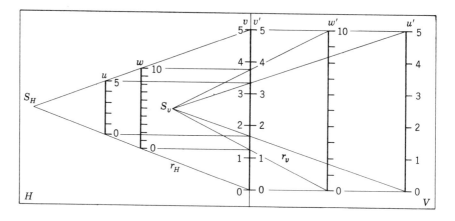

Figure 136. Flat-sheet representation of Figure 135.

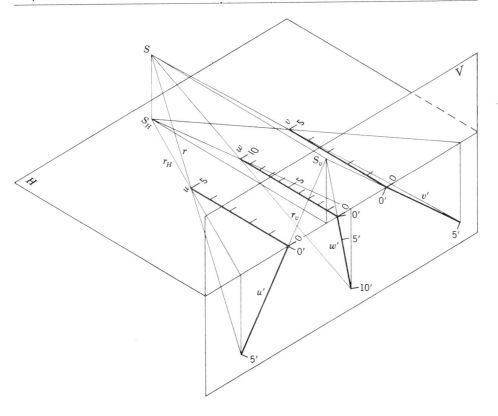

Figure 137. Projective transformation—graphical method. Example 2: $u + v = w$.

Example 2

Let us consider Figure 137, which shows an alignment nomogram, for the expression $u + v = w$, in the H-plane, but oriented so the scales are perpendicular to the V-plane. The method employed in the first example is applied to the current example. It should be noted that the orientation of the given nomogram results in a transformed nomogram whose scales are concurrent, whereas in the first example the transformed nomogram retained the parallelism of the scales. Figure 138 shows the flat-sheet representation of the projective transformation. Careful study of this figure shows that the nomogram with the concurrent scales could be regarded as the given nomogram and that the transformation was made to obtain the parallel-scales nomogram.

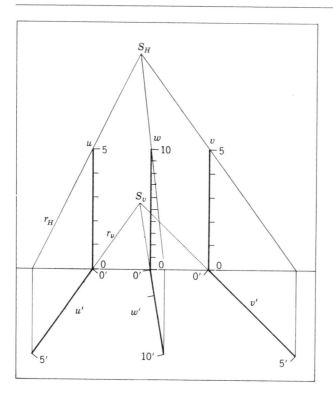

Figure 138. Flat-sheet representation of Figure 137.

Projective Transformation—Mathematical Method

Example 1

First, let us consider the simple equation $u + v = w$, which is expressed in constructional determinant form as

$$\begin{vmatrix} 0 & u & 1 \\ 1 & v & 1 \\ \dfrac{1}{2} & \dfrac{w}{2} & 1 \end{vmatrix} = 0$$

Second, suppose we multiply this determinant by another third-order determinant whose value is *not* zero. The elements of the latter may be selected arbitrarily. For example:

$$
\begin{vmatrix} 0 & u & 1 \\ 1 & v & 1 \\ \dfrac{1}{2} & \dfrac{w}{2} & 1 \end{vmatrix} \times \begin{vmatrix} 4 & 2 & 1 \\ 1 & 2 & 0 \\ 3 & 8 & 6 \end{vmatrix} = \begin{vmatrix} 2u + 1 & 2u & 8u + 6 \\ 2v + 5 & 2v + 1 & 8v + 9 \\ w + 3 & w + 0.5 & 4w + 7.5 \end{vmatrix} =
$$

$$
\begin{vmatrix} \dfrac{2u + 1}{8u + 6} & \dfrac{2u}{8u + 6} & 1 \\[2mm] \dfrac{2v + 5}{8v + 9} & \dfrac{2v + 1}{8v + 9} & 1 \\[2mm] \dfrac{w + 3}{4w + 7.5} & \dfrac{w + 0.5}{4w + 7.5} & 1 \end{vmatrix} = 0
$$

Now let us construct a nomogram from the above constructional determinant. This nomogram is shown in Figure 139. Only few values of each variable are included. For each multiplying determinant *(the operator)* whose value is not zero, a different transformed nomogram will result.

Our problem, then, is to find the values of the elements of the "operator" which will transform the shape of a given nomogram to a more suitable one. Usually this means a transformation of the "boundary quadrilateral" of the given nomogram to a rectangle of desired dimensions.

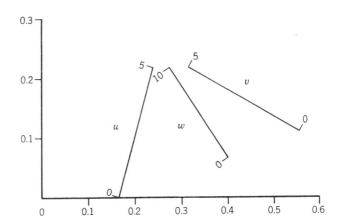

Figure 139. Nomogram for $u + v = w$ obtained from mathematical transformation.

Example 2

Suppose the given equation is $u + v = w$; that u varies from 0 to 10; v varies from 0 to 15; the u-scale is 10 units long; the v-scale is 15 units long and the distance between the scales is 15 units (can be different from units on u- and v-scales). One experiences no difficulty in designing a nomogram which complies with the above specification. The completed nomogram is shown in Figure 140.

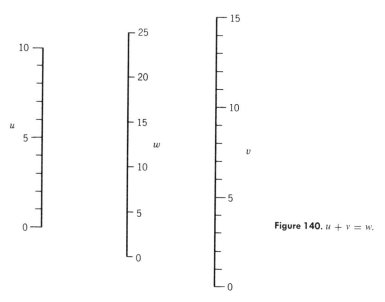

Figure 140. $u + v = w$.

Now let us plan to change the "boundary quadrilateral" (sides are the u-scale, line from $u = 10$ to $v = 15$; the v-scale and the line from $v = 0$ to $u = 0$) to a boundary rectangle 10 units wide and 10 units long. We know this can be done without making a mathematical transformation; however, we will proceed to do so simply as an example of the use of the method.

In order to determine the values of the elements of the "operator" which will provide a constructional determinant consistent with the specifications of the desired nomogram we know that

$$\begin{vmatrix} 0 & u & 1 \\ 1 & v & 1 \\ \dfrac{1}{2} & \dfrac{w}{2} & 1 \end{vmatrix} \times \begin{vmatrix} a_1 & b_1 & c_1 \\ a_2 & b_2 & c_2 \\ a_3 & b_3 & c_3 \end{vmatrix} = \begin{vmatrix} a_2 u + a_3 & b_2 u + b_3 & c_2 u + c_3 \\ a_1 + a_2 v + a_3 & b_1 + b_2 v + b_3 & c_1 + c_2 v + c_3 \\ \dfrac{a_1}{2} + \dfrac{a_2 w}{2} + a_3 & \dfrac{b_1}{2} + \dfrac{b_2 w}{2} + b_3 & \dfrac{c_1}{2} + \dfrac{c_2 w}{2} + c_3 \end{vmatrix} = 0$$

Since we must retain the first row (scale u is fixed) of the given determinant, it follows that

$$a_2 = 0, \qquad a_3 = 0$$
$$b_2 = 1, \qquad b_3 = 0$$
$$c_2 = 0, \qquad c_3 = 1$$

or

$$\begin{vmatrix} 0 & u & 1 \\ 1 & v & 1 \\ \dfrac{1}{2} & \dfrac{w}{2} & 1 \end{vmatrix} \times \begin{vmatrix} a_1 & b_1 & c_1 \\ 0 & 1 & 0 \\ 0 & 0 & 1 \end{vmatrix} = \begin{vmatrix} 0 & u & 1 \\ a_1 & b_1 + v & c_1 + 1 \\ \dfrac{a_1}{2} & \dfrac{b_1}{2} + \dfrac{w}{2} & \dfrac{c_1 + 1}{2} \end{vmatrix} = \begin{vmatrix} 0 & u & 1 \\ \dfrac{a_1}{c_1 + 1} & \dfrac{b_1 + v}{c_1 + 1} & 1 \\ \dfrac{a_1}{c_1 + 2} & \dfrac{b_1 + w}{c_1 + 2} & 1 \end{vmatrix} = 0$$

Now in accordance with the specification: u varies from 0 to 10; v varies from 0 to 15; therefore w varies from 0 to 25; the distance between the u- and v-scales is 10 units and the lengths of the scales are 10 units.

The abscissa value of the v-scale, then, is

$$\frac{a_1}{c_1 + 1} = 10 \qquad (1)$$

and

$$\frac{b_1 + 0}{c_1 + 1} = 0 \quad (\text{y-coordinate for } v = 0) \qquad (2)$$

therefore

$$b_1 = 0 \qquad (3)$$

now

$$\frac{b_1 + 15}{c_1 + 1} = 10 \quad (\text{y-coordinate for } v = 15)$$

therefore

$$c_1 = 0.5 \qquad (4)$$

From equations (1) and (4), $a_1 = 15$ $\qquad (5)$

The constructional determinant in its final form is

$$\begin{vmatrix} 0 & u & 1 \\ 10 & \dfrac{2v}{3} & 1 \\ 6 & \dfrac{2w}{5} & 1 \end{vmatrix} = 0$$

The nomogram is easily constructed from this determinant, Figure 141.

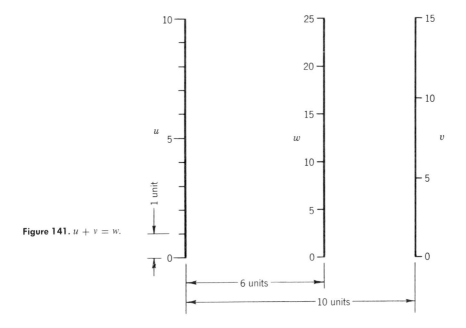

Figure 141. $u + v = w$.

Example 3

Let us again consider the equation $u + v = w$. Suppose the ranges of the variables are: u (5 to 10) and v (10 to 20); that the scale lengths are 10 units for the u-scale and 20 units for the v-scale; and the distance between the u- and v-scales is 10 units. See Figure 142. Now the basic determinant is

$$\begin{vmatrix} 0 & 2(u-5) & 1 \\ 1 & 2(v-10) & 1 \\ \tfrac{1}{2} & (w-15) & 1 \end{vmatrix} = 0$$

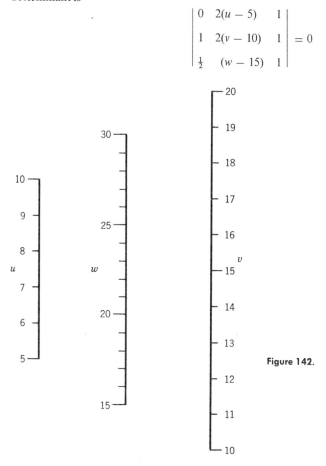

Figure 142.

Let us assume that the desired nomogram should comply with the following specification: distance between the u- and v-scales 10 units; length of each of the u- and v-scales 10 units.

It is necessary to evaluate the elements of the "operator" determinant which will satisfy the specification. Now

$$\begin{array}{ccc} 0 & 2(u-5) & 1 \\ 1 & 2(v-10) & 1 \\ \tfrac{1}{2} & (w-15) & 1 \end{array} \times \begin{array}{ccc} a_1 & b_1 & c_1 \\ a_2 & b_2 & c_2 \\ a_3 & b_3 & c_3 \end{array} =$$

$$\begin{vmatrix} 2a_2(u-5)+a_3 & 2b_2(u-5)+b_3 & 2c_2(u-5)+c_3 \\ a_1 + 2a_2(v-10)+a_3 & b_1 + 2b_2(v-10)+b_3 & c_1 + 2c_2(v-10)+c_3 \\ \dfrac{a_1}{2} + a_2(w-15)+a_3 & \dfrac{b_1}{2} + b_2(w-15)+b_3 & \dfrac{c_1}{2} + c_2(w-15)+c_3 \end{vmatrix} = 0$$

We must retain the first row since the u-scale is fixed. It follows, then, that

$$a_2 = 0, \qquad b_2 = 1, \qquad c_2 = 0,$$
$$a_3 = 0, \qquad b_3 = 0, \qquad c_3 = 1$$

This means that the last determinant will be:

$$\begin{vmatrix} 0 & 2(u-5) & 1 \\ a_1 & b_1 + 2(v-10) & c_1 + 1 \\ \dfrac{a_1}{2} & \dfrac{b_1}{2} + (w-15) & \dfrac{c_1}{2} + 1 \end{vmatrix} = \begin{vmatrix} 0 & 2(u-5) & 1 \\ \dfrac{a_1}{c_1+1} & \dfrac{b_1 + 2(v-10)}{c_1+1} & 1 \\ \dfrac{a_1}{c_1+2} & \dfrac{b_1 + 2(w-15)}{c_1+2} & 1 \end{vmatrix} = 0$$

The abscissa value of the v-scale, then, is

$$\frac{a_1}{c_1+1} = 10 \tag{1}$$

and

$$\frac{b_1 + 2(10-10)}{c_1+1} = 0 \qquad (v = 10 \text{ at } y = 0) \tag{2}$$

Therefore

$$b_1 = 0. \tag{3}$$

Now

$$\frac{b_1 + 2(20-10)}{c_1+1} = 10 \qquad (v = 20 \text{ at } y = 10)$$

Therefore

$$c_1 = 1. \tag{4}$$

Substituting equation (4) in (1), we obtain $a_1 = 20$ (5)

The constructional determinant in its final form is

$$\begin{vmatrix} 0 & 2(u-5) & 1 \\ 10 & (v-10) & 1 \\ \dfrac{20}{3} & \dfrac{2(w-15)}{3} & 1 \end{vmatrix} = 0$$

The resulting nomogram which complies with the specification is shown in Figure 143.

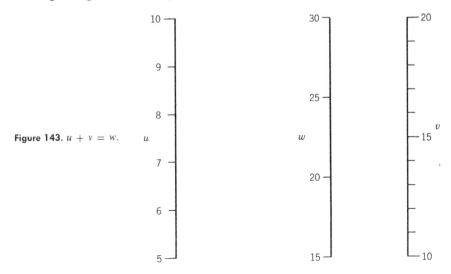

Figure 143. $u + v = w$.

Example 4

Let us consider the equation

$$d = \frac{a^2 + b^2}{a + b}$$

for which a nomogram was previously designed (see Figure 132). Now suppose we plan to transform the boundary trapezoid of this nomogram (shown in Figure 144) to a boundary rectangle (Figure 145) which is defined as follows:

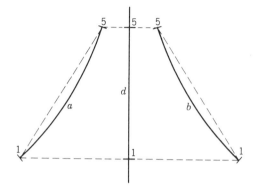

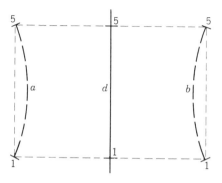

Figure 144.

Figure 145.

$$a = 1 \text{ at } x = 0, y = 0$$
$$a = 5 \text{ at } x = 0, y = 1$$
$$b = 1 \text{ at } x = 1, y = 0$$

and

$$b = 5 \text{ at } x = 1, y = 1$$

In order to make the desired transformation, it fill be necessary to evaluate the parameters of the "operator" determinant.

The product of the two determinants is

$$
\begin{vmatrix} o & d & 1 \\ -\dfrac{1}{a} & a & 1 \\ \dfrac{1}{b} & b & 1 \end{vmatrix}
\times
\begin{vmatrix} A_1 & B_1 & C_1 \\ A_2 & B_2 & C_2 \\ A_3 & B_3 & C_3 \end{vmatrix}
=
$$

$$
\begin{vmatrix}
\dfrac{B_1 d + C_1}{B_3 d + C_3} & \dfrac{B_2 d + C_2}{B_3 d + C_3} & 1 \\
\dfrac{-A_1 + B_1 a^2 + C_1 a}{-A_3 + B_3 a^2 + C_3 a} & \dfrac{-A_2 + B_2 a^2 + C_2 a}{-A_3 + B_3 a^2 + C_3 a} & 1 \\
\dfrac{A_1 + B_1 b^2 + C_1 b}{A_3 + B_3 b^2 + C_3 b} & \dfrac{A_2 + B_2 b^2 + C_2 b}{A_3 + B_3 b^2 + C_3 b} & 1
\end{vmatrix}
= 0
$$

Now let us consider $a = 1$ at $x = 0, y = 0$.

Substituting 1 for a in the second row of the last determinant, we obtain:

$$\frac{-A_1 + B_1 + C_1}{-A_3 + B_3 + C_3} = 0; \quad \frac{-A_2 + B_2 + C_2}{-A_3 + B_3 + C_3} = 0$$

For $a = 5$, at $x = 0$ and $y = 1$, we obtain:

$$\frac{-A_1 + 25B_1 + 5C_1}{-A_3 + 25B_3 + 5C_3} = 0; \quad \frac{-A_2 + 25B_2 + 5C_2}{-A_3 + 25B_3 + 5C_3} = 1$$

For $b = 1$, at $x = 1$ and $y = 0$, we obtain:

$$\frac{A_1 + B_1 + C_1}{A_3 + B_3 + C_3} = 1; \quad \frac{A_2 + B_2 + C_2}{A_3 + B_3 + C_3} = 0$$

And for $b = 5$, at $x = 1$ and $y = 1$, we obtain:

$$\frac{A_1 + 25B_1 + 5C_1}{A_3 + 25B_3 + 5C_3} = 1; \quad \frac{A_2 + 25B_2 + 5C_2}{A_3 + 25B_3 + 5C_3} = 1$$

From these equations we obtain the following:

$$-A_1 + B_1 + C_1 = 0 \tag{1}$$
$$-A_2 + B_2 + C_2 = 0 \tag{2}$$
$$-A_1 + 25B_1 + 5C_1 = 0 \tag{3}$$
$$-A_2 + 25B_2 + 5C_2 = -A_3 + 25B_3 + 5C_3 \tag{4}$$
$$A_1 + B_1 + C_1 = A_3 + B_3 + C_3 \tag{5}$$
$$A_2 + B_2 + C_2 = 0 \tag{6}$$
$$A_1 + 25B_1 + 5C_1 = A_3 + 25B_3 + 5C_3 \tag{7}$$
$$A_2 + 25B_2 + 5C_2 = A_3 + 25B_3 + 5C_3 \tag{8}$$

Now from equations (2) and (6), $\qquad A_2 = 0$

and from equations (4) and (8), $\qquad A_3 = 0$

From equations (1) and (3),

$$\frac{-A_1}{B_1} + \frac{C_1}{B_1} = -1 \quad \text{and} \quad \frac{-A_1}{B_1} + \frac{5C_1}{B_1} = -25$$

which yield $\qquad \dfrac{A_1}{B_1} = -5 \quad$ and $\qquad \dfrac{C_1}{B_1} = -6$

From (5) and (7),

$$\frac{B_3}{B_1} + \frac{C_3}{B_1} = -10 \quad \text{and} \quad \frac{25B_3}{B_1} + \frac{5C_3}{B_1} = -10$$

which yield $\qquad \dfrac{B_3}{B_1} = 2 \quad$ and $\qquad \dfrac{C_3}{B_1} = -12$

From (4) and (6),

$$\frac{25B_2}{B_1} + \frac{5C_1}{B_1} = -10 \quad \text{and} \quad \frac{B_2}{B_1} + \frac{C_2}{B_1} = 0$$

which yield $\qquad \dfrac{B_2}{B_1} = -\dfrac{1}{2} \quad$ and $\qquad \dfrac{C_2}{B_1} = \dfrac{1}{2}$

In summary:

$$\frac{A_1}{B_1} = -5 \qquad \frac{A_2}{B_1} = 0 \qquad \frac{A_3}{B_1} = 0$$

$$\frac{B_1}{B_1} = 1 \qquad \frac{B_2}{B_1} = -\frac{1}{2} \qquad \frac{B_3}{B_1} = 2$$

$$\frac{C_1}{B_1} = -6 \qquad \frac{C_2}{B_1} = \frac{1}{2} \qquad \frac{C_3}{B_1} = -12$$

When $B_1 = 2$, then

$$A_1 = -10 \qquad B_1 = 2 \qquad C_1 = -12$$
$$A_2 = 0 \qquad B_2 = -1 \qquad C_2 = 1$$
$$A_3 = 0 \qquad B_3 = 4 \qquad C_3 = 24$$

Substituting these values in the product determinant, we obtain

$$\begin{vmatrix} \dfrac{d-6}{2d-12} & \dfrac{-d+1}{4d-24} & 1 \\[2mm] \dfrac{10+2a^2-12a}{4a^2-24a} & \dfrac{-a^2+a}{4a^2-24a} & 1 \\[2mm] \dfrac{-10+2b^2-12b}{4b^2-24b} & \dfrac{-b^2+b}{4b^2-24b} & 1 \end{vmatrix} = \begin{vmatrix} \dfrac{1}{2} & \dfrac{1-d}{4(d-6)} & 1 \\[2mm] \dfrac{a^2-6a+5}{2a(a-6)} & \dfrac{1-a}{4(a-6)} & 1 \\[2mm] \dfrac{b^2-6b-5}{2b(b-6)} & \dfrac{1-b}{4(b-6)} & 1 \end{vmatrix} = 0$$

The last determinant is the design determinant. The transformed nomogram is shown in Figure 146.

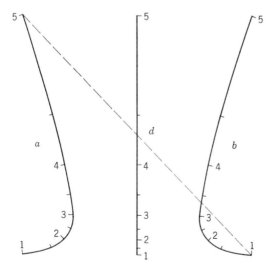

Figure 146. $d = \dfrac{a^2 + b^2}{a + b}$. Example: When $a = 5$ and $b = 1$ or $3\frac{1}{3}$, read $d = 4\frac{1}{3}$.

EXERCISES

15.1   Transform the nomogram for the expression $\dfrac{1}{d_1} + \dfrac{1}{d_2} = \dfrac{1}{d}$ from three concurrent scales to three parallel scales. d_1 varies from 10 to 30 ft; and d_2 varies from 15 to 50 ft.

15.2   Select problems from Chapter 10. Try Problem 10.11. Make a projective transformation which will result in a better "geometric shape" of the nomogram.

16

Relationship Between Concurrency and Alignment Nomograms with Applications to Experimental Data

Let us consider Figure 147, which is a concurrency nomogram (Cartesian coordinate chart) for the expressions $y = 0.5x + 3$ and $y = -0.5x + 3$. From our previous study (p. 10) of concurrency nomograms we recognize that any point such as E is the intersection of three lines: $x = 8, y = 7$, and $y = 0.5x + 3$.

Now in Figure 148, which is an alignment nomogram for $y = 0.5x + 3$, it will be shown that all the straight lines whose "line coordinates" satisfy the given equation pass through the fixed point P.

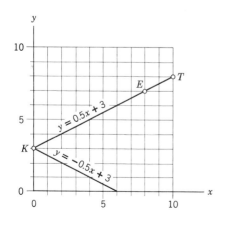

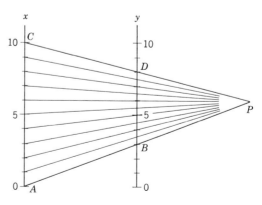

Figure 147. Concurrency nomogram for $y = \pm 0.5x + 3$.

Figure 148. Alignment nomogram for $y = 0.5x + 3$.

First let us establish line AB ($x = 0, y = 3$), where 3 is the intercept value of the given line $y = 0.5x + 3$, and then select any value of x, say 10. This is point C. Now let us lay off distance $BD = mx$ (m is the slope of the line) which in this case is $0.5 \times 10 = 5$.

The intersection of lines AB and CD is point P. If all of the straight lines whose line cooordinates satisfy the given equation pass through point P, then the location of point P must be independent of the choice of the value of x. This is clearly seen from the relations:

$$\frac{BP}{AP} = \frac{BD}{AC} = \frac{mx}{x} = m$$

Thus the ratio BP/AP locates point P independently of the value of x. The locations of points A and B are also independent of x.

When m is *negative*, then BP and AP are laid off in opposite directions which will, therefore, place point P between A and B. This is shown in Figure 149.

Figure 149. Alignment nomogram for $y = -0.5x + 3$. (Point P lies between the x- and y-scale for negative slope of line.)

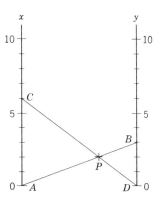

It should also be recognized that by graduating the x- and y-scales in opposite directions, point P will lie between the scales *when m is positive*. This is shown in Figure 150.

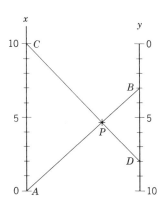

Figure 150. Alignment nomogram for $y = 0.5x + 3$. (Positive values of x and y graduated in opposite directions so that point P will be between the x- and y-scales.)

Now the relationship between the concurrency nomogram in Figure 147 and the corresponding alignment nomogram in Figure 147 is quite clear—"*for every line in Figure 147 there is a corresponding point in Figure 148.*" For example, line $y = 0.5x + 3$ in Figure 147 corresponds to point P of Figure 148. Points K and T in Figure 147 correspond to lines AB and CD respectively in Figure 148.

Example 1

Now let us consider the equation $u + v = w$. Figure 151a shows a concurrency nomogram for this equation. The corresponding alignment nomogram can easily be set up by employing the basic relationship—"for every line in the concurrency nomogram there is a corresponding point in the alignment nomogram." To construct the alignment nomogram we can proceed in the following manner:

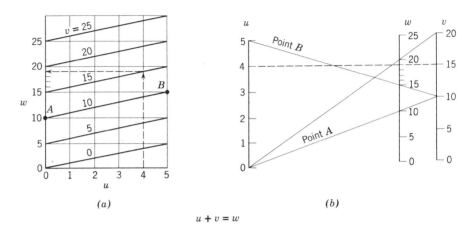

(a)   (b)

$$u + v = w$$

Figure 151. Application of the law of duality to transform a concurrency nomogram to an alignment nomogram.

1. Place the u- and w-scales a convenient distance apart (these are the line-coordinate axes).
2. For every line $u = 0$, $u = 1$, $\cdots$, $u = 5$ of Figure 151a there is a corresponding point $u = 0$, $u = 1$, $\cdots$, $u = 5$ of Figure 151b. These are the graduations on the u-axis. In a similar manner we obtain the graduations on the w-axis.
3. To locate the v-scale and its graduations, let us first consider the location of $v = 10$, for instance. Points A and B are any two points on the line $v = 10$ (Figure 151a). Point A is the intersection of three lines, $u = 0$, $w = 10$, and $v = 10$. Correspondingly each of these lines is a point in Figure 151b. Since the three lines of Figure 151a pass through point A, the corresponding three points must lie on a line, which corresponds to point A. To establish the latter it is only necessary to connect points $u = 0$ and $w = 10$ of Figure 151b. This line is marked "point A." *Point $v = 10$* must lie on this line since it corresponds to the line $v = 10$ of Figure 151a. Thus far we have determined the line on which $v = 10$ lies but not the exact location. To do this consider point B of Figure 151a. This point is the intersection of three lines: $u = 5$, $w = 15$, and $v = 10$. Each of these lines is a point in Figure 151b. These points lie on the line which is marked "point B." To establish the latter, points $u = 5$ and $w = 15$ are connected. *Point $v = 10$* must lie on this line. Hence the intersection of the two lines labeled "point A" and "point B" uniquely locates the point $v = 10$. In a similar manner additional values of v can be located to form the v-scale of the alignment nomogram.

It should be pointed out that the alignment nomogram could be constructed directly since the equation and the type form are known. The case cited was used merely to show an application of the basic relationship—*"for every line in the concurrency nomogram there is a corresponding point in the alignment nomogram"*—to an elementary problem. *The basic relationship is known as the Law of Duality or the duality principle.*

Example 2

Consider the equation $uv = w$. A concurrency nomogram for this expression is shown in Figure 152a. The corresponding alignment nomogram is shown in Figure 152b. It should be observed that in order to have the v-scale between the u- and w-scales it was necessary to graduate the latter scales in opposite directions since the slopes of the v-lines of Figure 152a are positive. (See Figure 150 for reference.)

Thus far we have dealt with concurrency nomograms made up of straight lines only. How shall we deal with concurrency nomograms that include a family of curves? In order to use the law of duality—"for every line of the concurrency nomogram there is a corresponding point in the alignment nomogram"—we should first consider rectification of curves.

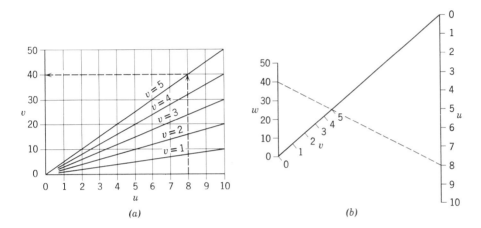

Figure 152. (a) Concurrency nomogram for $uv = w$. (b) Alignment chart for $uv = w$ (u and w plotted in opposite directions).

Rectification of Curves

Example 1. One Curve, Equation Known

The equation $y = x^2$ (parabola) is shown graphically as the concurrency nomogram in Figure 153a. An alignment nomogram could be constructed by employing the duality principle, provided we first establish tangents at various points of the curve and then locate the "corresponding points" of the tangents. The curve which passes through these points would correspond to the original curve $y = x^2$. Consistent values of x and y would then lie on lines tangent to the curve in the alignment nomogram (Figure 153b). Evidently little is gained by this transformation of the concurrency nomogram to the alignment nomogram. It would be much better to rectify the curve $y = x^2$ before constructing the alignment nomogram. We know (perhaps a little review of the material on pages 12–14 is in order at this time) that a functional scale (squared scale in this case) can be constructed for x^2. The curve $y = x^2$ when plotted in terms of the functional scale will appear as a straight line. See Figure 154.

Once the curve has been rectified it is a simple matter to apply the duality principle to the construction of the alignment nomogram. Whenever the function of the variable is known, as in this example, and a functional scale can be constructed so as to rectify the curve, then this should be done.

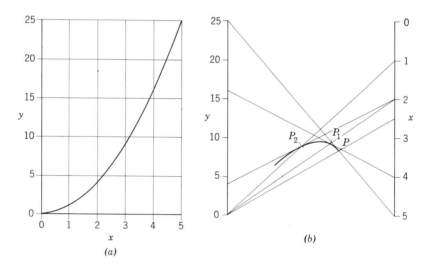

Figure 153. (a) $y = x^2$. (b) Alignment nomogram for $y = x^2$ when x- and y-scales are uniform.

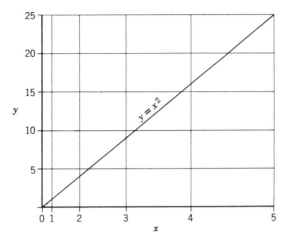

Figure 154. $y = x^2$ (when the x-scale is graduated as a squared scale).

Example 2. One Curve, Equation Not Known

Let us suppose, however, that the algebraic relation between the variables is *not* known. How shall we proceed to rectify the curve? The curve shown in Figure 155 can easily be rectified by drawing a straight line joining points $x = 0, y = 0$ and $x = 5, y = 50$. Now we can establish a new scale x', from the values on the x-scale in the following manner:

Through $x = 1$, for example, a vertical line is drawn to intersect the curve. Through this point a horizontal is drawn to intersect the diagonal straight line, and finally a vertical is drawn through the latter point to intersect the x'-scale at graduation 1. In a similar manner additional points are located on the new functional scale x'. Once the functional scale has been constructed it is a simple matter to design the alignment nomogram by drawing the

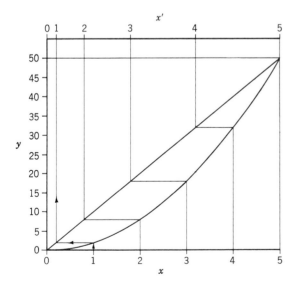

Figure 155. Graphical rectification of one curve.

parallel scales x' and y, any convenient distance apart, and by applying the duality principle to establish point P, which represents the original curve. Any line drawn through point P will intersect the parallel scales in consistent values. See Figure 156.

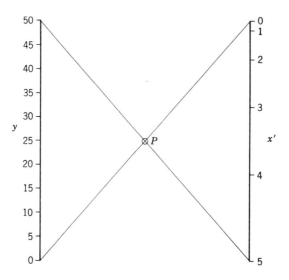

Figure 156. $y = x^2$, alignment nomogram of Figure 155.

Example 3. Two Curves

In the last two examples we were concerned with single curves. Now suppose two curves are given as shown in Figure 157. In this case it is quite possible to rectify the curves by employing *two functional scales* which are determined in the following manner.*

1. A steplike arrangement of lines such as $abc \cdots$ is drawn between the curves. This is shown in part (a) of Figure 157.

2. A corresponding steplike set $a'b'c' \cdots$ is drawn between the parallel lines shown in part (b). The parallels are placed at a convenient angle so that the functional scales, x' and y', are of suitable lengths.

3. Two transformation curves, parts (c) and (d), are now established. By extending the horizontals of the steps in part (a) to intersect the corresponding verticals of the steps in part (b), points are located to determine the transformation curve I shown in part (c). In a similar manner, the verticals of the steps in part (a) are extended to intersect the corresponding horizontals of the steps in part (b). The curve which passes through these points is the transformation curve II shown in part (d). The two transformation curves are now used to graduate the new functional scales x' and y'.

4. Graduations on the x'-scale are located by projecting vertically from the graduations of the x-scale to the transformation curve in part (d), and then horizontally to the x'-scale, the position of which is a matter of convenience, except that it must be perpendicular to the x-scale.

---

* The method is known as graphical anamorphosis and is credited to Col. A. LaFay. See pp. 298–299, Vol. 40, *Le Genie Civil*, 1902.

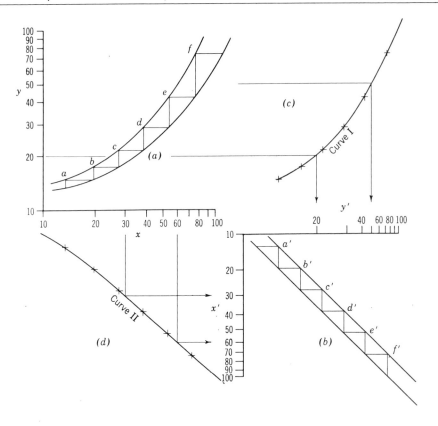

Figure 157. Rectification of two curves (graphical anamorphosis).

5. Graduations on the y'-scale are located by projecting horizontally from the graduations on the y-scale to the transformation curve in part (c), and then vertically to the y'-scale, the position of which is again a matter of convenience, except that it must be perpendicular to the y-scale.

Now that the functional scales x' and y' have been constructed it is a simple matter (duality principle) to design the corresponding alignment nomogram.

Example 4. Family of Curves

Let us consider the family of curves shown in Figure 158. Rectification of two adjacent curves can of course be obtained in the manner described above in Example 3. It does not necessarily follow that the other curves of the family will be rectified by the same functional scales x' and y'. Wertheimer* described a test for "bilineality" which, if satisfied by three curves having a common point, would assure rectification of the curves by two functional scales. Applications of this test to two sets of these curves is shown in Figure 158. Each set is said to have the "closure property" if the construction of the rectangular chain forms a closed loop. This must be true for all parts of the curves. Once this geometric test has been made satisfactorily for several locations, we can then employ the method of graphical anamorphosis shown in Figure 157 to obtain the functional scales which rectify the given curves. After the curves are rectified we can apply the law of duality to construct the alignment nomogram. Let us now apply the law of duality to a number of practical cases.

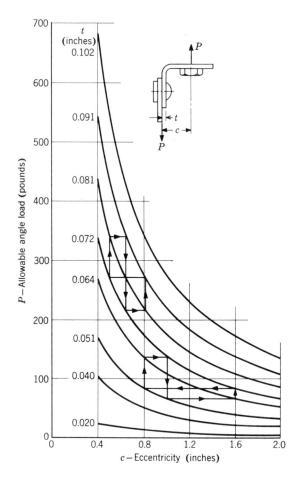

Figure 158. Test for bilineality.

---

*Wertheimer, A. See *Franklin Institute Journal,* March 1935.

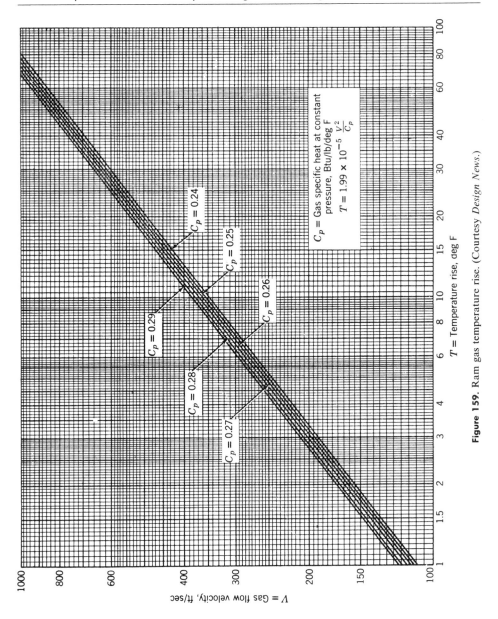

Figure 159. Ram gas temperature rise. (Courtesy *Design News*.)

The following labels appear on the nomogram:

C_p = Gas specific heat at constant pressure, Btu/lb/deg F

$$T = 1.99 \times 10^{-5} \frac{V^2}{C_p}$$

$C_p = 0.24$
$C_p = 0.25$
$C_p = 0.26$
$C_p = 0.27$
$C_p = 0.28$
$C_p = 0.29$

T = Temperature rise, deg F

V = Gas flow velocity, ft/sec

Applications of the Law of Duality

Example 1

Let us consider the concurrency nomogram shown in Figure 159. Values of T can be obtained for given values of V and C_p. However, one must be quite careful in selecting the correct diagonal line for the value C_p, because the diagonals are so close together. A more convenient solution to the problem is found in the alignment nomogram, Figure 160, which was constructed by an application of the law of duality. Of course, since the equation is given, the alignment nomogram could be designed directly. It should be noted that the scale for values of C_p eliminates the crowded condition shown in Figure 159.

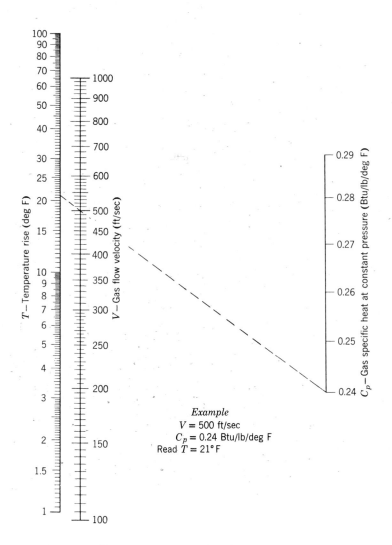

Figure 160. Ram gas temperature rise. (Courtesy *Design News.*)

Example 2

Figure 161 shows a concurrency nomogram for the determination of the number of time-study readings, N', that should be taken when values of N, EX, and R are known. The law of duality was used in the design of the alignment nomogram shown in Figure 162. In this case the equation for the relationship among the variables was not given.

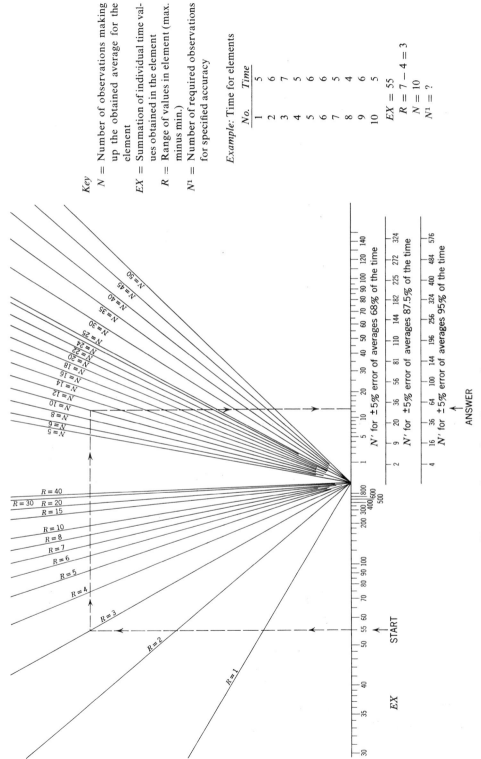

Key

N = Number of observations making up the obtained average for the element

EX = Summation of individual time values obtained in the element

R = Range of values in element (max. minus min.)

N^1 = Number of required observations for specified accuracy

Example: Time for elements

No.	Time
1	5
2	6
3	7
4	5
5	6
6	6
7	5
8	4
9	6
10	5

$EX = 55$
$R = 7 - 4 = 3$
$N = 10$
$N^1 = ?$

Figure 161. How many time-study readings to take.

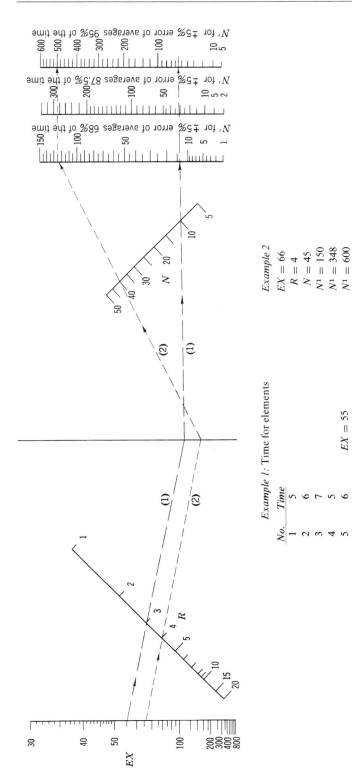

Example 1: Time for elements

No.	Time
1	5
2	6
3	7
4	5
5	6
6	6
7	5
8	4
9	6
10	5

$EX = 55$
$R = 7 - 4 = 3$
$N = 10$
$N^1 = 13$ (68% of the time)
$N^1 = 31$ (87.5% of the time)
$N^1 = 54$ (95% of the time)

Example 2
$EX = 66$
$R = 4$
$N = 45$
$N^1 = 150$
$N^1 = 348$
$N^1 = 600$

Figure 162. How many time-study readings to take. See Figure 161 for the explanation of the symbols.

Example 3

This problem deals with the determination of the maximum stress in an oval tube.* The concurrency nomogram shown in Figure 163 is a reproduction of Figure 5 of the reference cited. Figure 163 was transformed to the alignment nomogram shown in Figure 164; this diagram provides a simple means for reading values of S/P.

In the next examples both the method of graphical anamorphosis and the law of duality are employed to convert concurrency nomograms to alignment nomograms.

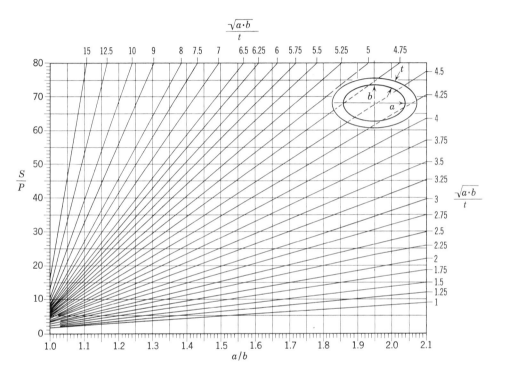

Figure 163.

* Weydert, J. C., "Stresses in Oval Tubes under Internal Pressure," *Proceedings of the Society for Experimental Stress Analysis,* Fig. 5, p. 44, Vol. XII, No. 1, 1954.

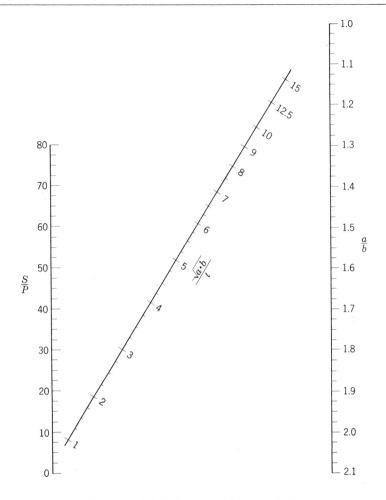

Figure 164. Elliptical pressure tube stress chart.

Example 4

The upper left portion of Figure 165 shows the concurrency nomogram identified as part of Stress Memo #89 of the Lockheed Aircraft Corporation. The bilineality test to check the feasibility of rectifying the curves is shown in Figure 158. Transformation of the family of curves (Figure 165) is effected by the method of graphical anamorphosis which was discussed previously (Figure 157). Once the new scales for the load, P, and eccentricity, c, are determined, the duality principle is applied to obtain the alignment nomogram shown in Figure 166.

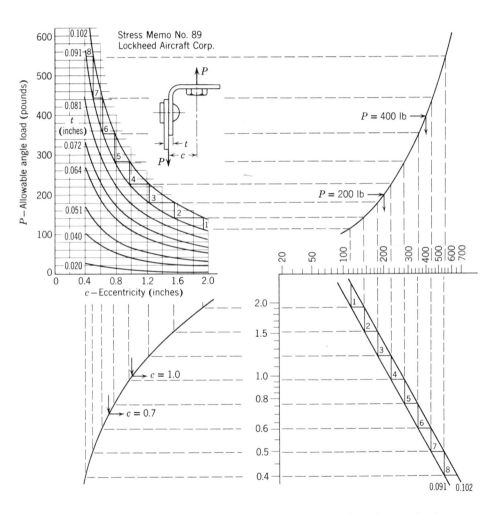

Figure 165. Transformation of curves into straight lines by means of two functional scales.

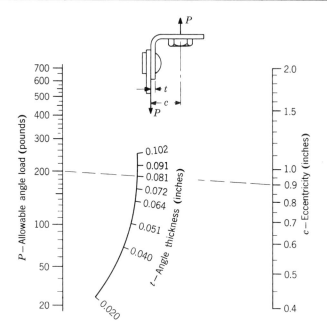

1. Attachment point spacing
   (a) Less than or equal to 1 in., P is lb/in. of angle.
   (b) Greater than 1 in., P is lb/attachment point.
2. For aluminum alloy angles other than 24S-T3 Alclad, multiply P by $F_{tu_x}/40{,}000$.
3. When two angles are placed back to back, multiply P by 2.5.
4. The ultimate allowable load, P, is defined as 1.5 times the load at 0.005-in. permanent set.

Figure 166. Nomogram for ultimate load for 24S-T3 Alclad sheet metal angles.

Example 5

This example deals with the determination of wall shear stress, t_0, on a tube of inside radius, R, during two-phase flow of water with weight flow rate per unit area, G.

The assumptions made were annular flow (vapor core and liquid annulus) and the $\frac{1}{7}$th power law for velocity distribution. Keenan and Keyes steam tables* were used for fluid properties.

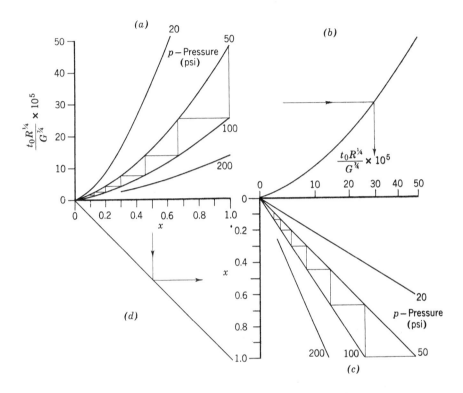

Figure 167.

The concurrency nomogram (Cartesian coordinate chart) in Figure 167, part (a), shows the relation among the variables, x, quality; p, pressure in pounds per square inch; and $\dfrac{t_0 R^{\frac{1}{4}}}{G^{\frac{1}{4}}} \times 10^5$.

The rectified curves are shown in part (c), with the functional scales obtained from the transformation curves shown in parts (b) and (d).

* Keenan, J. H., and Keyes, F. G., *Steam Tables,* American Society of Mechanical Engineers, New York, 1930.

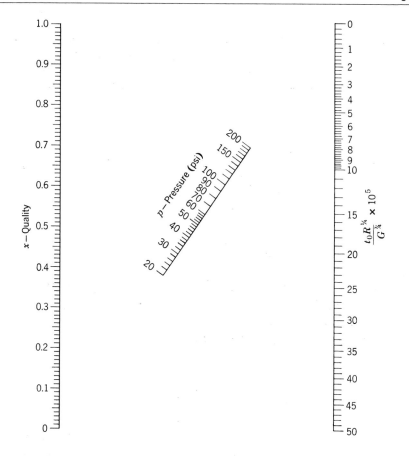

Figure 168.

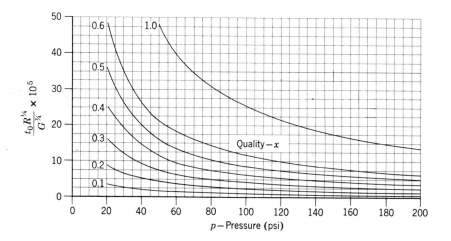

Figure 169.

The duality principle was then employed to construct the nomogram shown in Figure 168. In order to accurately subdivide the graduations on the diagonal scale, the variable, x, was plotted as the parameter (Figure 169), so that for a given value of x, corresponding values of p, pressure, and $\dfrac{t_0 R^{\frac{1}{4}}}{G^{\frac{1}{4}}} \times 10^5$ could be determined. In this manner graduations between $p = 20$ and 50, $p = 50$ and 100, etc., could be located quite accurately.

Example 6

This example is concerned with a concurrency nomogram dealing with the stress concentration factor, k, for a flat bar with a single notch in pure bending.* The concurrency nomo-

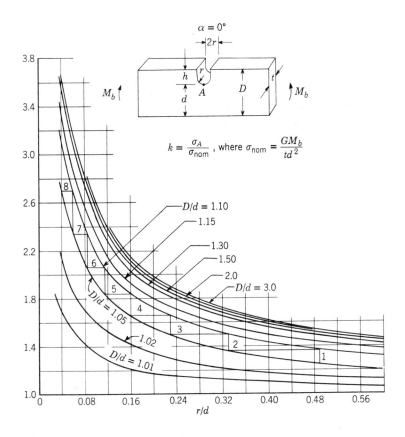

$$k = \frac{\sigma_A}{\sigma_{nom}}, \text{ where } \sigma_{nom} = \frac{GM_b}{td^2}$$

Figure 170.

---

* Leven, M. M., and Frocht, M. M., "Stress Concentration Factors for a Single Notch in a Flat Bar in Pure and Central Bending," *Proceedings of the Society for Experimental Stress Analysis,* Fig. 3, p. 181, Vol. XI, No. 2, 1954.

gram shown in Figure 170 is a reproduction of Figure 3 of the reference cited. The transformation to the alignment nomogram shown in Figure 171 was accomplished by the employment of the method previously discussed (Figures 157 and 165). *It should be pointed out, however, that the curves for $D/d = 1.01$ and 1.02 of Figure 170 were not fully rectified.* Curve $D/d = 1.02$ resulted in a very flat curve (Figure 172) so that the location of graduation 1.02 in Figure 171 is quite good. On the other hand, the curve $D/d = 1.01$ resulted in considerable curvature so that no single point in Figure 171 could correspond to $D/d = 1.01$. Tangents to the "rectified" curve were transformed to corresponding points (principle of duality) the locus of which is the "curve 1.01" shown in Figure 171. Lines tangent to this curve will intersect the parallel scales in corresponding values of k and r/d.

Evaluation of Data

If the curve for $D/d = 1.01$ shown in Figure 170 resulted from insufficient data and was merely "eyeballed" in, then, *assuming that there is a definite relationship among the variables,* one would expect rectification of curve $D/d = 1.01$. In such a case, there would be a corresponding point, rather than the curve shown in Figure 171. The extension of the curved scale, D/d, to the "curve" $D/d = 1.01$ would then locate the correct scale position of the value $D/d = 1.01$. *The nomographic method" provides an excellent tool for checking the validity of the experimental data.*

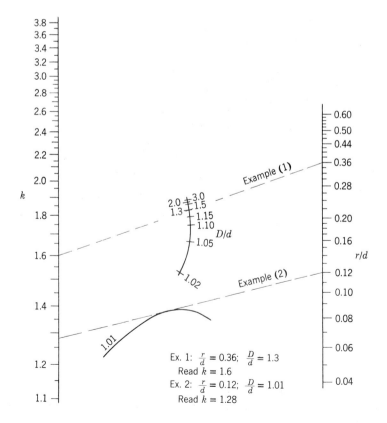

Figure 171. Stress concentration factor, k, for a flat bar with a single notch in pure bending.

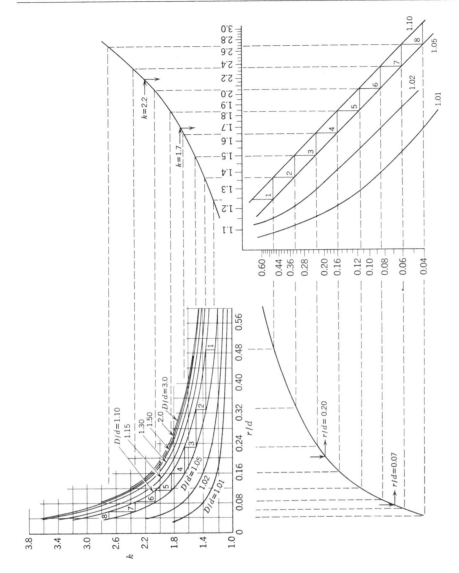

Figure 172. Transformation of curves into straight lines by means of two functional scales.

The alignment nomogram could then be used to plot, quite accurately, additional points for the curve $D/d = 1.01$ of Figure 170 if desirable. The ease of reading values of k for given values of D/d and r/d is quite evident in the alignment nomogram.

In each of the previous examples which included transformation curves, the rectified curves were taken as parallel lines.

A question that arises is: "What effect would there be on the functional scales if the rectified curves were convergent or divergent lines?"

Choice of Rectified Curves—Parallel Lines

Let us consider the family of curves shown in Figure 173. Let us assume that the family satisfies the bilineality test. The transformation curves I and II have been determined from the corresponding "steps" between curves C_2 and C_3 and the corresponding parallel rectified curves C_2' and C_3'. Functional scales X' and Y' have been established from the transformation curves. Note the nature of the functional scales. Segments of these scales between increasing values of X' and Y' *decrease.*

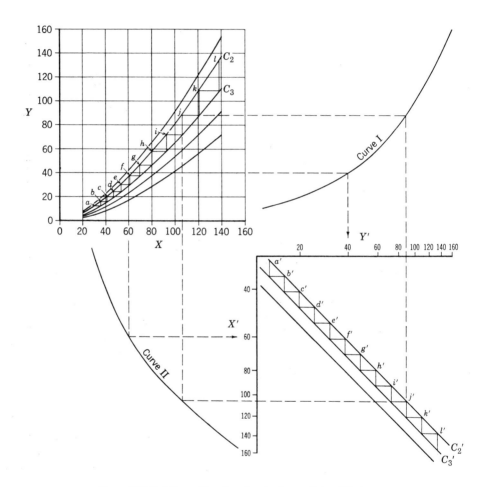

Figure 173. Relation of functional scales to parallel rectified curves.

Converging Lines

Now in Figure 174 the rectified curves were set up as converging lines. Note the change in the shapes of the transformation curves and the change in the functional scales X' and Y'. Both of these scales are much more uniform than those shown in Figure 173. There is now less congestion at the higher values of X' and Y'.

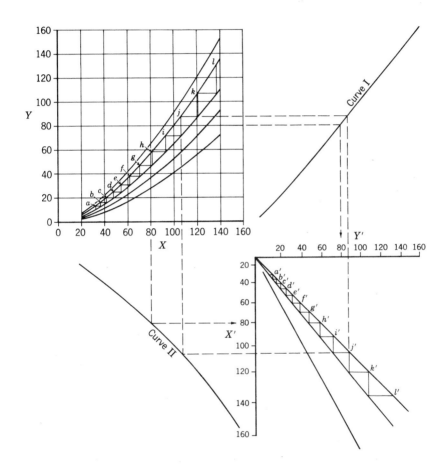

Figure 174. Relation of functional scales to converging rectified curves.

Diverging Lines

There is considerable change in the shapes of the transformation curves and in the functional scales X' and Y' when the rectified curves are set up as diverging lines, Figure 175. Here, too, there is considerable congestion at the higher values of X' and Y'

Further studies with families of curves plotted with logarithmic scales and with linear scales revealed the following:

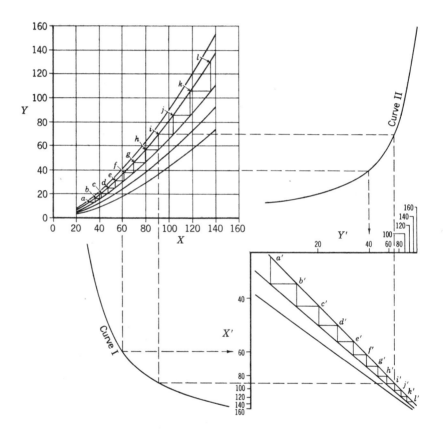

Figure 175. Relation of functional scales to diverging rectified curves.

1. A family of *converging curves plotted on a logarithmic coordinate system* can be transformed as straight lines having a linear (or nearly so) coordinate system if the *rectified curves are set up as parallels.*

2. A family of *diverging curves plotted on a linear coordinate system* can be transformed as straight lines having a logarithmic coordinate system if the rectified curves are *set up as parallels.*

These and some other combinations are summarized in Tables I and II.

Table I

Coordinate System	Desired Functional Scales		
	Case 1	Case 2	Case 3
Linear Logarithmic Reciprocal	Linear Logarithmic Reciprocal	Logarithmic Linear	Reciprocal Linear

Table II

Original Curves	Rectified Curves		
	Diverging	Parallel	Converging
Diverging	Case 1	Case 2	Case 3
Parallel	Case 2	Case 1	Case 2
Converging	Case 3	Case 2	Case 1

Example of the Use of Tables I and II

Suppose the original curves are converging and the rectified curves are diverging; then from Table II, Case 3 applies. If the original curves have been plotted on a coordinate sheet with reciprocal scales, then from Table I, we note under the column marked Case 3 that the desired functional scales would be approximately linear.

In all of the foregoing examples it is assumed that the family of curves has satisfied the bilineality test. Once the curves have been rectified it is a simple matter to construct the alignment nomogram by employing the law of duality.

The examples presented illustrate the manner in which families of curves that consist either of straight lines or curves, that can be rectified, may be represented in concise alignment nomogram form without the need for a describing algebraic equation.

In addition, the alignment nomogram provides not only an effective chart for ease of reading values of the variables, but also overcomes the difficulty of interpolation between the data curves. Moreover, *the "nomographic method" serves as a good check on the accuracy of experimental data when there is a consistent relation among the variables.* Although the illustrations are taken from a few fields, it is obvious that the method used may be applied in any technological or scientific field in which data are obtained in this form.

EXERCISES

Employ the method of graphical anamorphosis and the duality principle to construct alignment nomograms for the following data problems:

16.1
Form Stress Factor, k, for Plate in Tension

$\dfrac{r}{b}$	0.025	0.05	0.10	0.15	0.20	0.25	$\dfrac{h_1}{b}$
0.02	2.28	3.42	4.35	. .	. .	. .	
0.04	1.70	2.16	2.69	3.12	3.70	. .	
0.06	1.45	1.76	2.08	2.48	2.78	3.05	
0.10	1.22	1.43	1.67	1.96	2.18	2.33	
0.14	1.11	1.29	1.49	1.72	1.90	2.03	
0.18	1.07	1.22	1.39	1.58	1.74	1.85	
0.22	1.04	1.17	1.33	1.49	1.63	1.75	
0.26	1.04	1.15	1.29	1.43	1.56	1.67	
0.30	1.03	1.13	1.26	1.38	1.51	1.61	

See the accompanying figure.

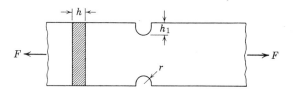

16.2
Mole Percentages of H_2O over Aqueous Solutions of NH_3

Temp.	Molal Concentration of Ammonia in the Solutions (%)									
(°F.)	0	10	20	30	40	50	60	70	80	90
40	100	14.1	4.73	1.59	0.581	0.248	0.124	0.0706	0.0395	0.0185
60	100	16.2	5.69	1.97	0.777	0.331	0.172	0.0986	0.0566	0.0251
80	100	18.5	6.89	2.45	0.978	0.444	0.230	0.130	0.0772	0.0351
100	100	21.0	7.92	3.00	1.250	0.574	0.307	0.179	0.104	0.0473
120	100	23.4	9.22	3.63	1.520	0.714	0.395	0.233	0.135	0.0619
140	100	25.8	10.50	4.28	1.860	0.906	0.501	0.297	0.175	0.0786
160	100	28.3	11.90	5.01	2.230	1.110	0.617	0.372	0.218	0.1005

Data from Perry's *Chemical Engineers Handbook*, 3rd ed., McGraw-Hill, New York, 1950, p. 171, Table 22.

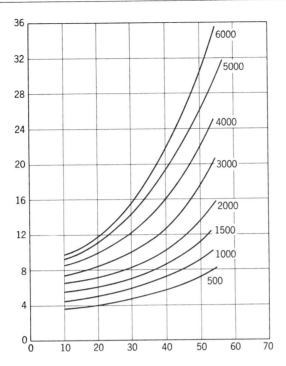

16.3   Use the concurrency chart shown above as the given information. (From Perry, *op. cit.*, p. 703, Fig. 52.)

16.4   Use the concurrency chart shown at the top of p. 204 as the given information. (From Perry, *op. cit.*, p. 551, Fig. 23.)

16.5   Use the concurrency chart shown at the bottom of p. 204 as the given information. (From Perry, *op. cit.*, p. 552, Fig. 24.)

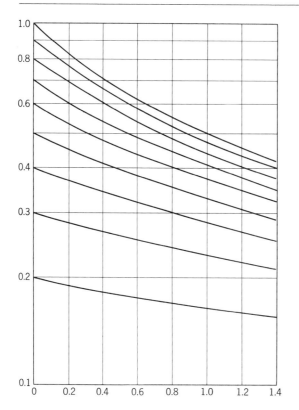

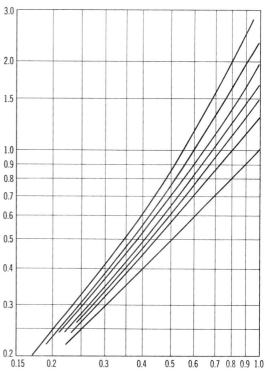

Summary of Type Forms

Geometric Method

1. $f_1(u) + f_2(v) = f_3(w)$

Scale equations:

$$X_u = m_u f_1(u)$$

$$X_v = m_v f_2(v)$$

$$X_w = \frac{m_u m_v}{m_u + m_v} f_3(w)$$

Scale location:

$$\frac{a}{b} = \frac{m_u}{m_v}$$

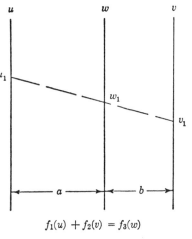

$$f_1(u) + f_2(v) = f_3(w)$$

2. $f_1(u) = f_2(v) \cdot f_3(w)$

Scale equations:

$$X_u = m_u f_1(u)$$

$$X_v = m_v f_2(v)$$

$$X_w = \frac{K}{r_1 f_3(w) + 1}$$

where $r_1 = \dfrac{m_u}{m_v}$ and K is the length of the diagonal.

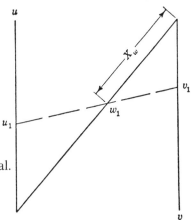

$$f_1(u) = f_2(v) \cdot f_3(w)$$

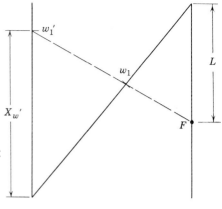

3. $f_1(u) = f_2(v) \cdot f_3(w)$

Alternative Solution—Simplified Method

To graduate the diagonal scale, first plot:

$$X_{w'} = L \frac{m_u}{m_v} f_3(w)$$

and then project to the diagonal scale by lines drawn through point F and the graduations on the temporary w-scale.

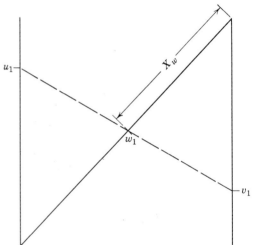

4. $f_1(u) + f_2(v) = \dfrac{f_2(v)}{f_3(w)}$

Scale equations:

$$X_u = m_u f_1(u)$$
$$X_v = m_v f_2(v)$$
$$X_w = K f_3(w)$$

Note: $m_u = m_v$.

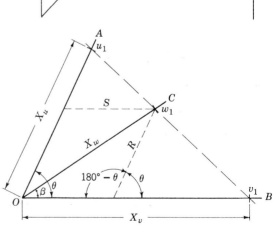

5. $\dfrac{1}{f_1(u)} + \dfrac{1}{f_2(v)} = \dfrac{1}{f_3(w)}$

Scale equations:

$$X_u = m_u f_1(u)$$
$$X_v = m_v f_2(v)$$

Location of w-scale:

$$\frac{R}{S} = \frac{m_u}{m_v}$$

Graduate w-scale by

    (a) $R = m_u f_3(w)$ and parallels to the B-axis, or
    (b) $S = m_v f_3(w)$ and parallels to the A-axis, or
    (c) $X_w = [m_u{}^2 + m_v{}^2 + 2m_u m_v \cos \theta]^{1/2} f_3(w)$.

6. $f_1(u) + f_2(v) + f_3(w) \ldots = f_4(q)$

See Type 1.

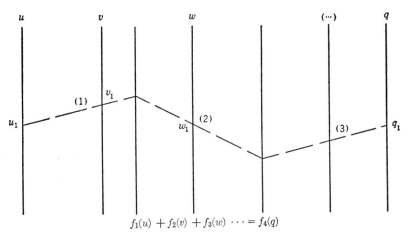

$$f_1(u) + f_2(v) + f_3(w) \cdots = f_4(q)$$

7. $f_1(u) - f_2(v) =$
$f_3(w) - f_4(q)$

Scale equations:

$$X_u = m_u f_1(u)$$
$$X_v = m_v f_2(v)$$
$$X_w = m_w f_3(w)$$
$$X_q = m_q f_4(q)$$

Note: $\dfrac{m_u}{m_w} = \dfrac{L}{L'}$

$m_u = m_v$

$m_w = m_q$

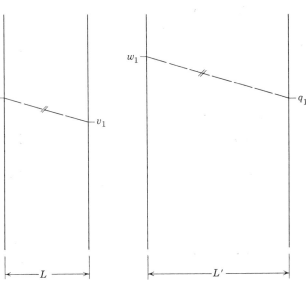

Alternative arrangement of scales.

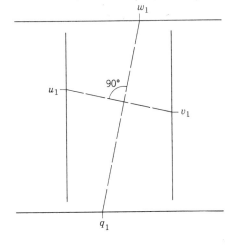

8. $\dfrac{f_1(u)}{f_2(v)} = \dfrac{f_3(w)}{f_4(q)}$

Scale equations:

$$X_u = m_u f_1(u)$$
$$X_v = m_v f_2(v)$$
$$X_w = m_w f_3(w)$$
$$X_q = m_q f_4(q)$$
$$\dfrac{m_u}{m_v} = \dfrac{m_w}{m_q}$$

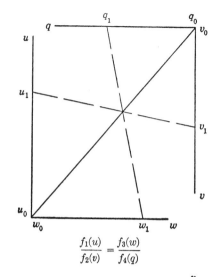

$$\dfrac{f_1(u)}{f_2(v)} = \dfrac{f_3(w)}{f_4(q)}$$

9. $f_1(u) + f_2(v) = \dfrac{f_3(w)}{f_4(q)}$

Scale equations:

$$X_u = m_u f_1(u)$$
$$X_v = m_v f_2(v)$$
$$X_w = m_w f_3(w)$$
$$m_u = m_v$$

$$X_q = m_q f_4(q) \text{ where } m_q = \dfrac{K m_w}{m_u}$$

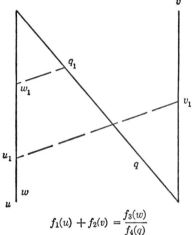

$$f_1(u) + f_2(v) = \dfrac{f_3(w)}{f_4(q)}$$

10. $f_1(u) + f_2(v) = \dfrac{f_3(w)}{f_4(q)}$

Same as in Type 9. Alternative form of chart shown at right.

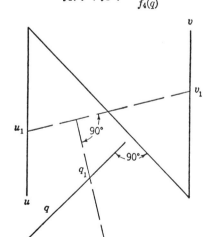

11. $f_1(u) + f_2(v)f_3(w) = f_4(w)$

Scale equations:

$$X_u = m_u f_1(u)$$

$$X_v = m_v f_2(v)$$

$$X_w = \frac{K m_u f_3(w)}{m_u f_3(w) + m_v}$$

$$Y_w = \frac{m_u m_v f_4(w)}{m_u f_3(w) + m_v}$$

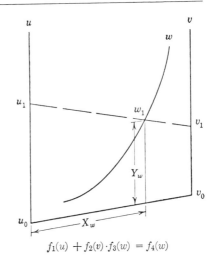

$$f_1(u) + f_2(v) \cdot f_3(w) = f_4(w)$$

12. $f_1(u) = f_2(v) \cdot f_3(w)$

Circular Nomogram

$$\tan \theta = m_v f_2(v)$$

$$\tan \phi = m_w f_3(w)$$

$$m_u = m_v \cdot m_w$$

$$\frac{X_u}{2R - X_u} = m_u f_1(u)$$

or $\qquad X_u = \dfrac{2R \left[m_u f_1(u) \right]}{1 + \left[m_u f_1(u) \right]}$

where R is the radius of the circle.

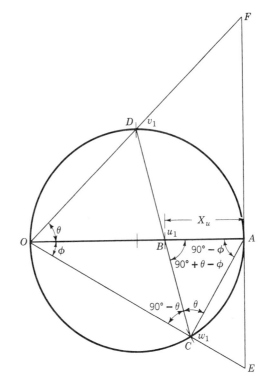

Determinant Method

1. $f_1(u) + f_2(v) = f_3(w)$

$$\begin{array}{ccc} (x) & (y) & \\ 0 & m_u f_1(u) & 1 \\ 1 & m_v f_2(v) & 1 \\ \dfrac{m_u}{m_u + m_v} & \dfrac{m_u m_v}{m_u + m_v} f_3(w) & 1 \end{array} = 0$$

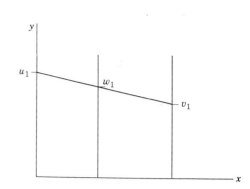

2. $f_1(u) = f_2(v) \cdot f_3(w)$

$$\begin{array}{ccc} (x) & (y) & \\ 0 & m_u f_1(u) & 1 \\ 1 & -m_v f_2(v) & 1 \\ \dfrac{m_u f_3(w)}{m_u f_3(w) + m_v} & 0 & 1 \end{array} = 0$$

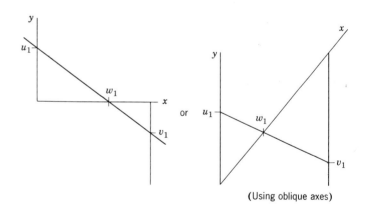

(Using oblique axes)

3. $\dfrac{1}{f_1(u)} + \dfrac{1}{f_2(v)} = \dfrac{1}{f_3(w)}$

$$\begin{array}{ccc} (x) & (y) & \\ m_u f_1(u) & 0 & 1 \\ m_u f_3(w) & m_v f_3(w) & 1 \\ 0 & m_v f_2(v) & 1 \end{array} = 0$$

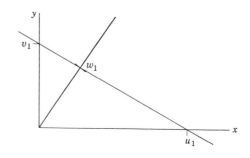

4. $f_1(u) + f_2(v) \cdot f_3(w) = f_4(w)$

$$
\begin{vmatrix}
& (x) & & (y) & \\
& 0 & & m_y f_1(u) & 1 \\
& 1 & & m_y f_2(v) & 1 \\
& \dfrac{m_y f_3(w)}{m_y f_3(w) + m_v} & & \dfrac{m_u m_v}{m_y f_3(w) + m_v} & \dfrac{f_4(w)}{1}
\end{vmatrix} = 0
$$

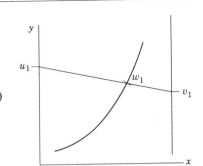

5. $\dfrac{1}{f_1(u)} + \dfrac{f_4(w)}{f_2(v)} = \dfrac{1}{f_3(w)}$

$$
\begin{vmatrix}
(x) & (y) & \\
m_y f_1(u) & 0 & 1 \\
0 & m_y f_2(v) & 1 \\
m_y f_3(w) & m_y f_4(w) & 1
\end{vmatrix} = 0
$$

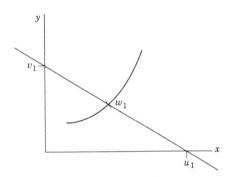

6. $f_2(v)[f_5(w) - f_1(u)] + f_4(w)[f_1(u) - f_3(v)] = 0$

$$
\begin{vmatrix}
(x) & (y) & \\
0 & m_y f_1(u) & 1 \\
m_y f_2(v) & m_y f_3(w) & 1 \\
m_y f_4(w) & m_y f_5(w) & 1
\end{vmatrix} = 0
$$

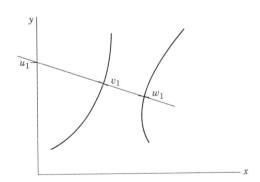

7. $f_1(u)[f_4(v) - f_6(w)] + f_3(v)[f_6(w) - f_2(u)] + f_5(w)[f_2(u) - f_4(v)] = 0$

$\quad\quad (x) \quad\quad\quad (y)$

$$\begin{vmatrix} m_u f_1(u) & m_v f_2(u) & 1 \\ m_u f_3(v) & m_v f_4(v) & 1 \\ m_u f_5(w) & m_v f_6(w) & 1 \end{vmatrix} = 0$$

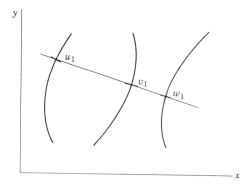

Index to Appendix Nomograms

Appendix

The following nomograms are useful examples of applications to engineering, science, business, statistics, food technology, medicine, etc.

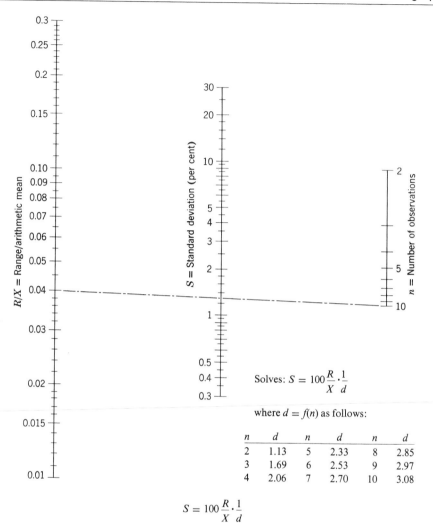

$$S = 100 \frac{R}{X} \cdot \frac{1}{d}$$

where S = standard deviation in per cent;

R = range (difference between high and low readings);

X = arithmetic mean;

d = deviation factor, a function of the number of observations, n (see chart).

Determination of the standard deviation for a set of test data is further facilitated by means of the accompanying nomogram. Use of the nomogram is illustrated by the following example: Ten consecutive readings of the acceleration time for a machine averaged 5 sec. The range was 0.2 sec. What is the standard deviation, S, and how may the acceleration be specified? Connecting R/X = 0.2/5, or 0.04, on the chart with n = 10 yields S = 1.3%. The machine is capable of accelerating to speed in 5 sec within the probable 99.7% limits for three standard deviations ± 3S, or 3.9%.

Figure 1A. Standard deviation values for small samples. (W. E. Stalmuth; Courtesy *Design News*.)

Test n units. If the first failure occurs in H hours the probability, W, that no more than $K\%$ of a large future lot will fail before H hours is found by drawing a line from the n-value to the K-value and reading off the W-value.

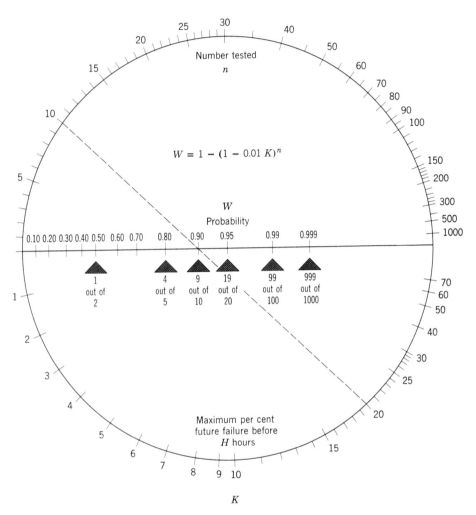

$$W = 1 - (1 - 0.01\ K)^n$$

Example: Ten units are tested. First unit fails after 1178 hr. The chances are 9 out of 10 that no more than 20% of a large lot of future units will fail before 1178 hr. ($n = 10$, $K = 20$, draw line to find $W = 0.90$.)

Figure 2A. Life test nomogram. (Courtesy E. C. Varnum; Barber-Colman Co.) Reference: L. B. Harris, "On a Limiting Case for the Distribution of Exceedances, with an Application to Life-Testing," *Annals of Mathematical Statistics,* Vol. 23, No. 2, June 1952.

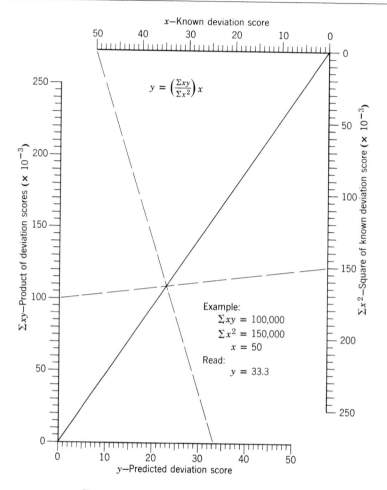

Figure 3A. Regression line for predicting scores.

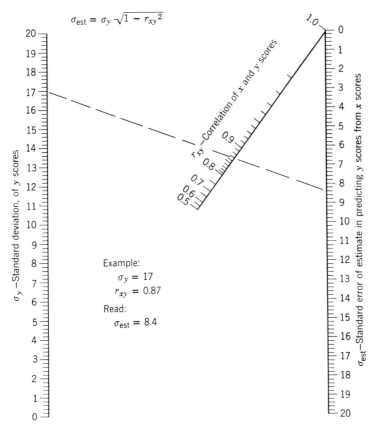

Figure 4A. Standard error of estimate in predicting *y*-scores from *x*-scores.

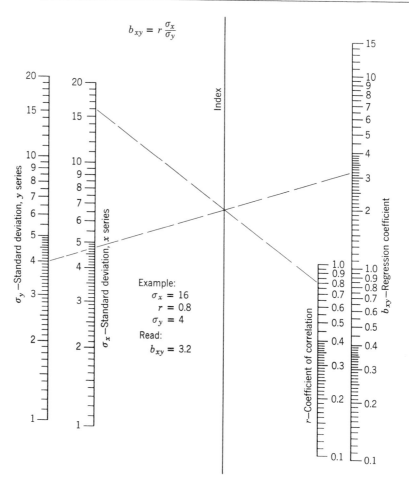

Figure 5A. Regression coefficient.

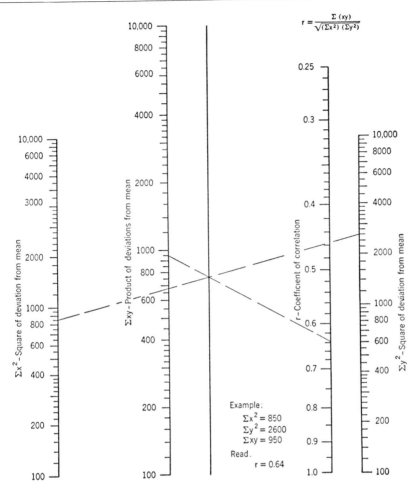

Figure 6A. Coefficient of correlation.

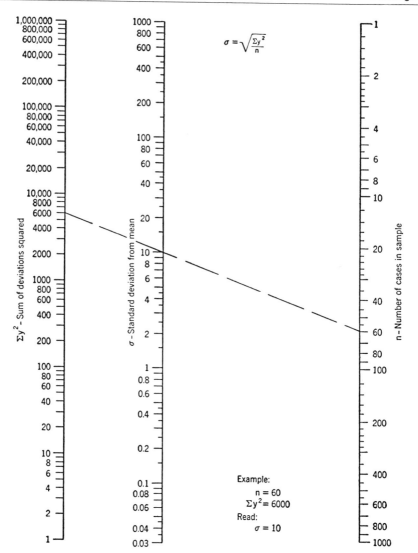

Figure 7A. Standard deviation of a set of scores.

$$\sigma_1{}^2 = \frac{\Sigma x_1{}^2}{N_1} - \bar{x}_1{}^2 \qquad\qquad \sigma_2{}^2 = \frac{\Sigma x_2{}^2}{N_2} - \bar{x}_2{}^2$$

$$N = N_1 = N_2$$

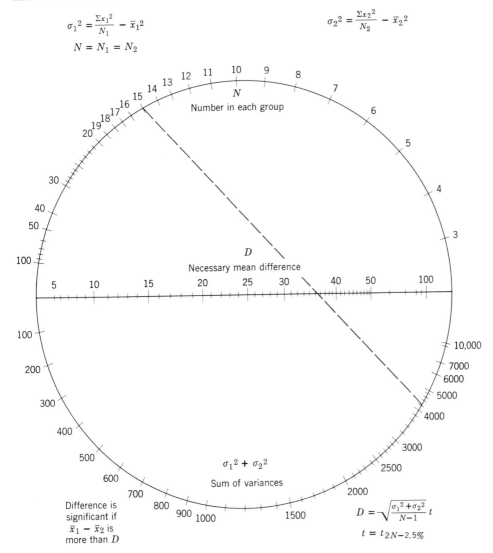

Example: One group of data which consists of 15 items has a variance of 1444. Another group of 15 items is found to have a variance of 2809.

Solution: Since the sum of the two variances is 4253, a line is drawn as shown in the nomogram from $N = 15$ to 4253 on the lower scale. This gives the necessary mean difference as 35.7. If the averages of the two differ by more than 35.7, the difference is significant.

Figure 8A. Nomogram for evaluating test data. (Courtesy E. C. Varnum; Barber-Colman Có.)

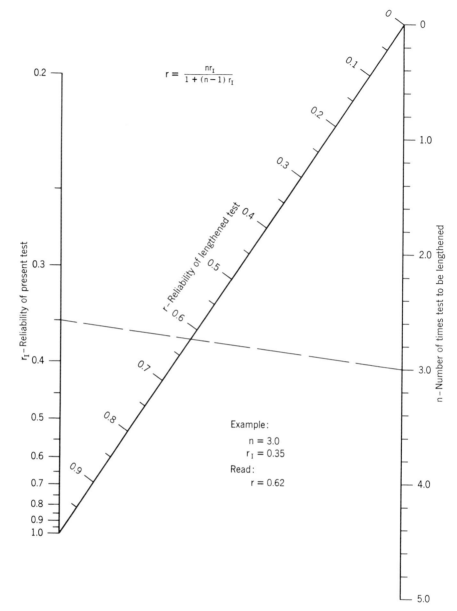

Figure 9A. Spearman-Brown formula for reliability of lengthened test.

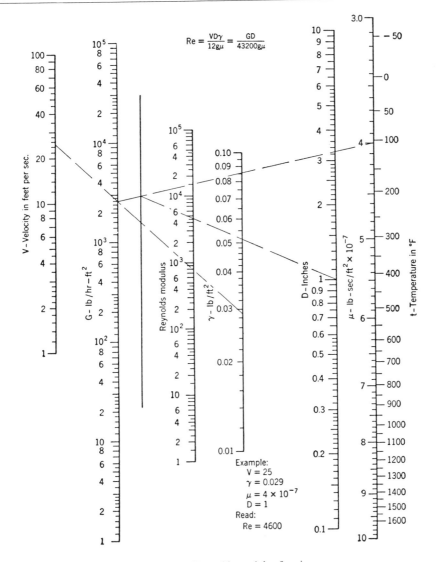

Figure 10A. Reynolds modulus for air.

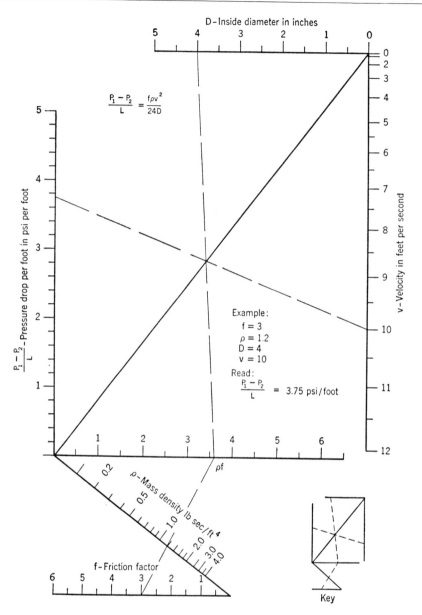

Figure 11A. Pressure drop in pipe line.

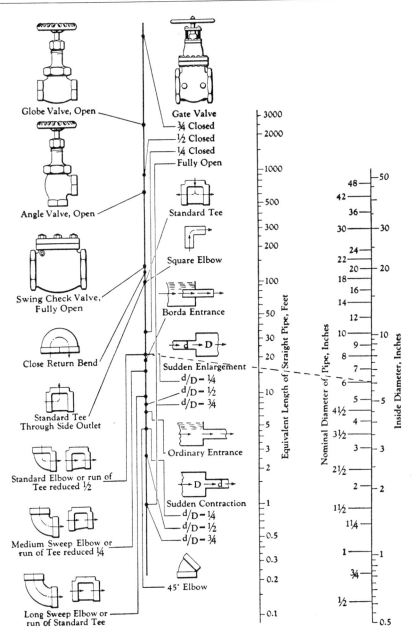

Figure 12A. Resistance of valves and fittings to flow of fluids. (Courtesy Crane Co.)

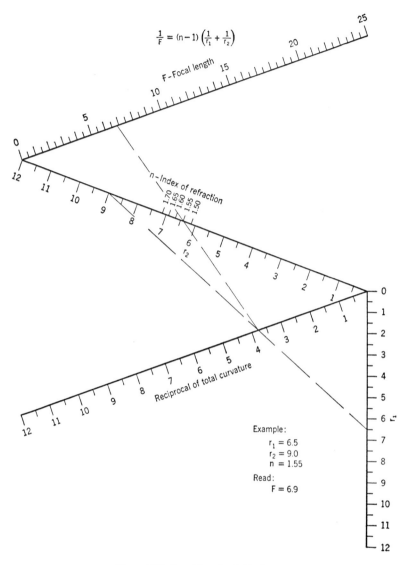

$$\frac{1}{F} = (n-1)\left(\frac{1}{r_1} + \frac{1}{r_2}\right)$$

F–Focal length

n–Index of refraction

r_2

Reciprocal of total curvature

r_1

Example:
  $r_1 = 6.5$
  $r_2 = 9.0$
  $n = 1.55$

Read:
  $F = 6.9$

Figure 13A. Focal length of thin lenses.

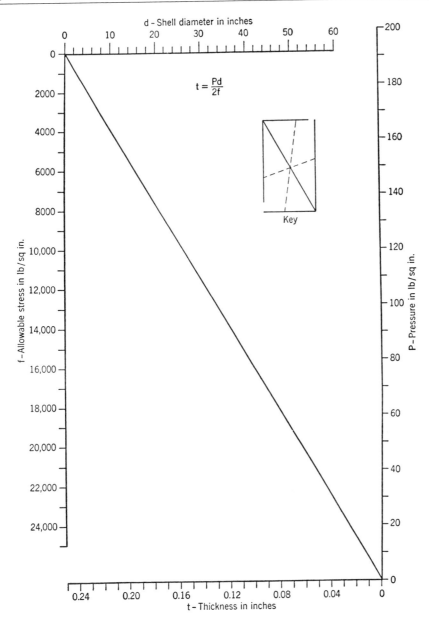

Figure 14A. Required shell thickness for various fluid pressures.

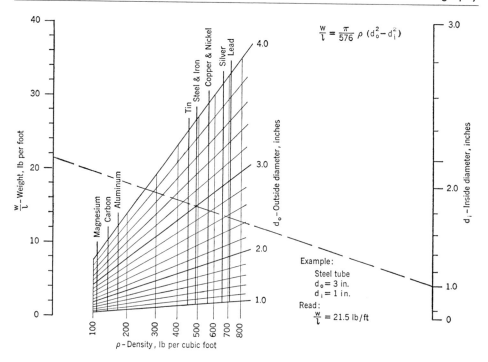

Figure 15A. Weight of tubing.

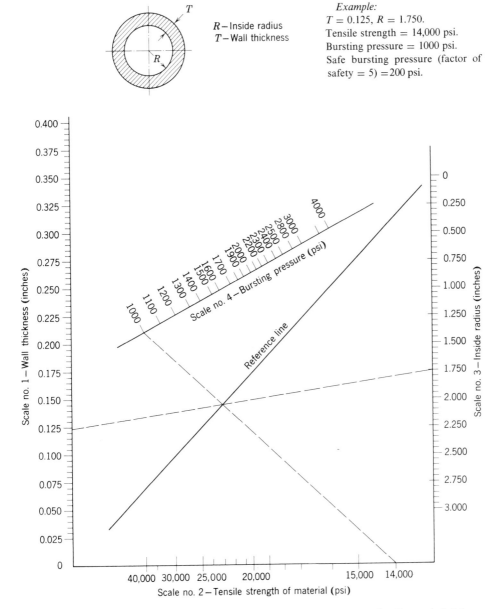

Example:
$T = 0.125$, $R = 1.750$.
Tensile strength = 14,000 psi.
Bursting pressure = 1000 psi.
Safe bursting pressure (factor of safety = 5) = 200 psi.

To use the nomogram: Locate wall thickness T on scale 1 and the inside radius R on scale 3. Join these two points with a straight line. With a straightedge, line up the tensile strength on scale 2 with the point of intersection of the first line drawn with the reference line, and read the bursting pressure on scale 4. Divide this bursting pressure by an adequate factor of safety to determine a safe bursting pressure. (Note—if the tensile strength is over 40,000 psi, divide by the factor of safety on scale 2 and read the safe bursting pressure directly on scale 4.)

Figure 16A. Nomogram for finding the safe bursting pressure (in pounds per square inch) for hollow tubing. (D. E. Sweet; Courtesy *Design News.*)

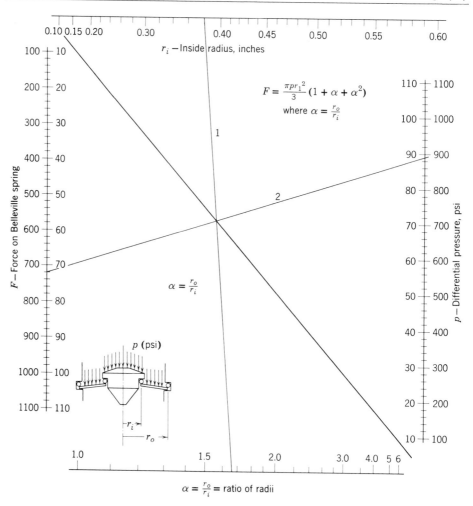

Example: Find the equivalent effective force on a Belleville spring with an inside radius, r_i, of 0.375 in., an outside radius, r_o, of 0.625 in., when the differential pressure = 90 psi.

For this case, the ratio of radii $\alpha = r_o/r_i = 1.667$. Draw line 1 from 0.375 on the top scale to 1.667 on the bottom scale. Pivot on the index line and extend line 2 from 90 psi on the right-hand scale to find the force, $F = 72.2$ lb, on the left-hand scale.

Note: Because F- and p-scales are linear, the useful range of the nomogram can be extended by using both inner scales or both outer scales together.

Figure 17A. Nomogram for finding the equivalent effective force on a Belleville spring corresponding to a uniform pressure distribution. (L. M. Majeske; Courtesy *Design News.*)

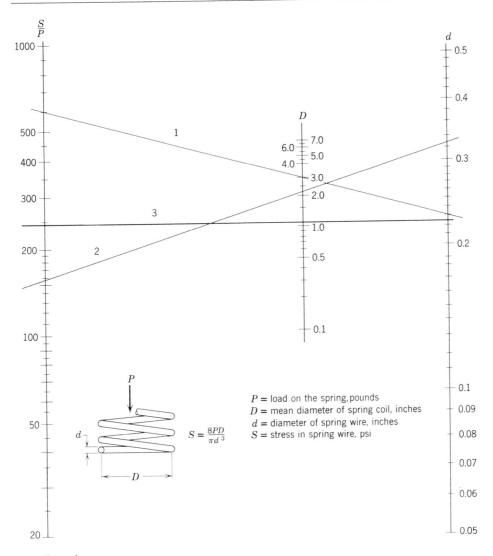

$\dfrac{S}{P}$

d

D

P = load on the spring, pounds
D = mean diameter of spring coil, inches
d = diameter of spring wire, inches
S = stress in spring wire, psi

$$S = \frac{8PD}{\pi d^3}$$

Examples

1. With $D = 3$ in., $P = 100$ lb, $S = 60,000$ psi, find wire diameter, d.

$$\frac{S}{P} = \frac{60,000}{100} = 600; \text{ from chart, } d = 0.23 \text{ in.}$$

2. With $d = 0.32$ in., $D = 2$ in., $P = 300$ lb, find the stress, S, in the spring.

From chart, $\dfrac{S}{P} = 157$; $S = 157 \times 300 = 47,000$ psi

3. What load may be used on a spring for which $S = 50,000$ psi, $D = 1$ in., $d = 0.22$ in.?

From chart, $\dfrac{S}{P} = 240$; $P = \dfrac{50,000}{240} = 208$ lb

Figure 18A. Nomogram for design of helical springs. (S. Levine; Courtesy *Design News.*)

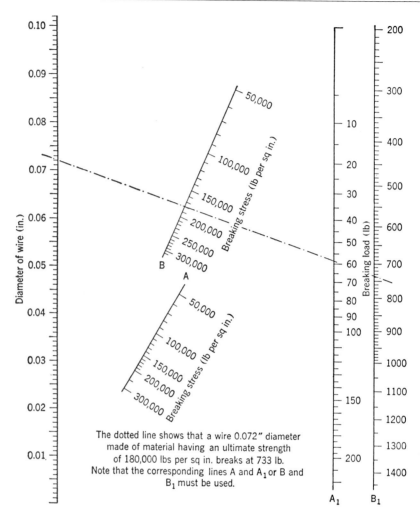

The dotted line shows that a wire 0.072″ diameter made of material having an ultimate strength of 180,000 lbs per sq in. breaks at 733 lb. Note that the corresponding lines A and A₁ or B and B₁ must be used.

Figure 19A. Breaking load of round wires. (Courtesy *Product Engineering.*)

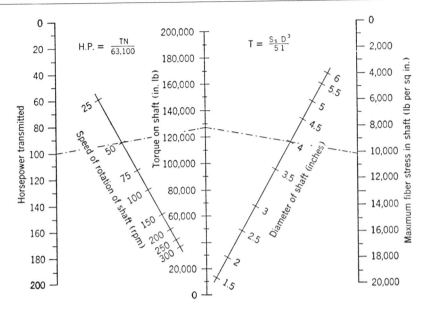

For calculating the horsepower that can be transmitted by a given shaft at a given speed, the following equation can be used:

$$\text{H.P.} = \frac{S_s D^3 N}{322,000} \tag{1}$$

This equation may be divided into two parts:

$$S_s = \frac{16T}{\pi D^3} \tag{2}$$

and

$$\text{H.P.} = \frac{TN}{63,100} \tag{3}$$

where S_s = unit shearing stress;
D = diameter;
N = revolutions per minute;
T = torque.

Manipulation of the chart is illustrated by the dashed lines. Thus, if 100 hp is to be transmitted at a speed of 50 rpm, the stress in the outer fibers of a 4-in. diameter solid shaft will be slightly in excess of 10,000 psi.

Figure 20A. Shafts for torsional strength. (Courtesy *Product Engineering.*)

Join lift on 1 to the rpm on 2, cutting 3 at pivot point. Join pivot point to total angle value on 4, extending line to give roller acceleration on 5.

For high-speed cams multiply the T and rpm scales by the same factor to sufficiently extend the rpm scale. Scales 2 and 4 completely overlap.

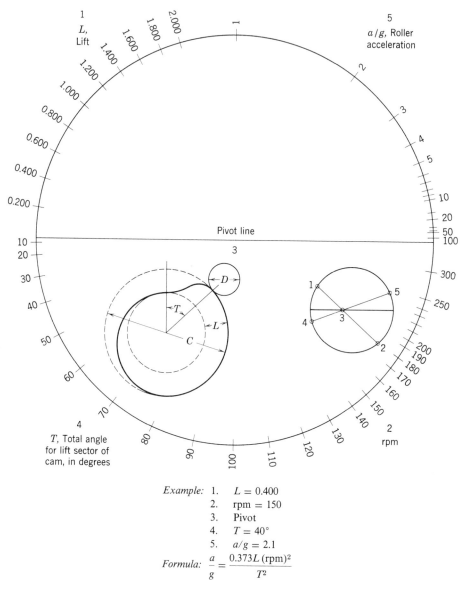

Example: 1. $L = 0.400$
2. rpm $= 150$
3. Pivot
4. $T = 40°$
5. $a/g = 2.1$

Formula: $\dfrac{a}{g} = \dfrac{0.373L\,(\text{rpm})^2}{T^2}$

Figure 21A. Nomogram for finding the roller acceleration for a uniform acceleration radial cam. (Courtesy E. C. Varnum; Barber-Colman Co.)

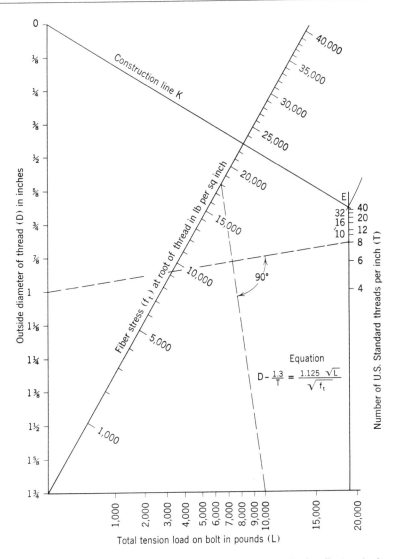

Figure 22A. Chart for determining bolt diameters. (Courtesy *Product Engineering.*)

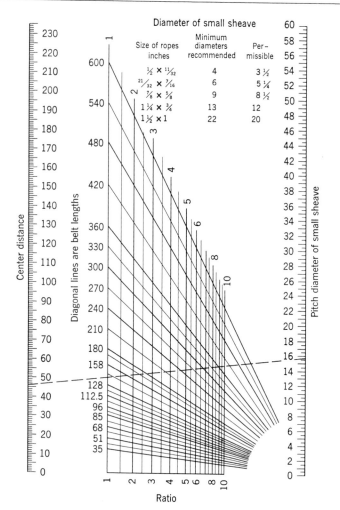

Given pitch diameter of the small sheave, center distance, and speed ratio: to find length of V-belt, place straightedge on the given points of small sheave diameter (right) and center distance (left) and note intersection with ratio line (middle). Interpolate between diagonal belt length lines to obtain desired length.

Example: Dashed line drawn between points representing small sheave diameter of 15.65 in. and center distance 46 in. intersects ratio line 2.6 at diagonal line for 180-in. belt length.

The V-belt drive consists of a driving and driven sheave, grooved for a multiplicity of belts of trapezoidal cross section. Power is transmitted by the wedging contact between the belts and grooves. At maximum load, repeated tests show an efficiency of 99% and a coefficient of friction of 1.5. V-belt drives operate, therefore, with comparatively small tension on the slack side, without slippage, and with little creep. In figuring loads, it is usually safe to take 1.5 times the torque to get the total belt pull. Manufacturer's ratings must be consulted for selection of number and size of belts for given load conditions.

A V-belt drive will usually be well proportioned when the center distance equals or is slightly greater than the large sheave diameter. On small ratios the sheaves may be operated so closely together that the sheaves almost touch each other. Maximum center distance on ½-in. belts is 17 in., except on high ratios, where 25 in. is permissible.

In the accompanying chart, the sheave diameters are the pitch diameters, measured at the midpoint of the trapezoidal section of the belt when resting in the groove.

Figure 23A. Chart for finding belt lengths, V-belt short-center drives. (Courtesy *Product Engineering.* Information courtesy Allis-Chalmers Manufacturing Co.)

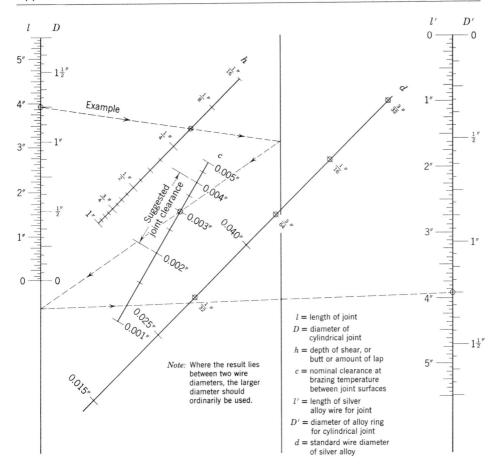

l = length of joint

D = diameter of cylindrical joint

h = depth of shear, or butt or amount of lap

c = nominal clearance at brazing temperature between joint surfaces

l' = length of silver alloy wire for joint

D' = diameter of alloy ring for cylindrical joint

d = standard wire diameter of silver alloy

Note: Where the result lies between two wire diameters, the larger diameter should ordinarily be used.

In the example illustrated, the problem is to find the proper wire diameter for a silver alloy ring to braze a cylindrical joint having these dimensions: diameter, $1\frac{1}{4}$ in.; shear depth, $\frac{3}{16}$ in.; and clearance, 0.003 in. Starting on the left axis of the chart, extend a line from the joint diameter ($1\frac{1}{4}$ in.) on the *D*-scale through the shear depth ($\frac{3}{16}$ in.) on the *h*-scale to intersect the center axis. From this point run the line back through the clearance (0.003 in.) on the *c*-scale to intersect the left-hand axis. Line up this point with the required ring diameter ($1\frac{1}{4}$ in.) on the *D'*-scale. The point where this line crosses the *d*-scale indicates that the wire diameter should be $\frac{1}{32}$ in. When the result lies between two wire sizes, the larger diameter should normally be selected.

Next, assuming you already have $\frac{3}{64}$-in. wire available, you can easily determine the minimum length of this wire needed per joint. From the intersecting point on the left-hand axis (found by using the *l*-, *h*-, and *c*-scales), extend a line through the $\frac{3}{64}$-in. mark on the *d*-scale to the *l'*-scale. The intersection on the *l'*-scale indicates that for $\frac{3}{64}$-in. wire, a $1\frac{1}{8}$-in. length would provide the proper volume of silver alloy to fill the joint. Multiplying the required length per joint by the number of joints to be brazed will give an approximate total amount of wire needed for an entire production run.

Figure 24A. Nomogram to determine diameter or length of alloy wire for brazing machined parts. (Courtesy Handy & Harman Co.)

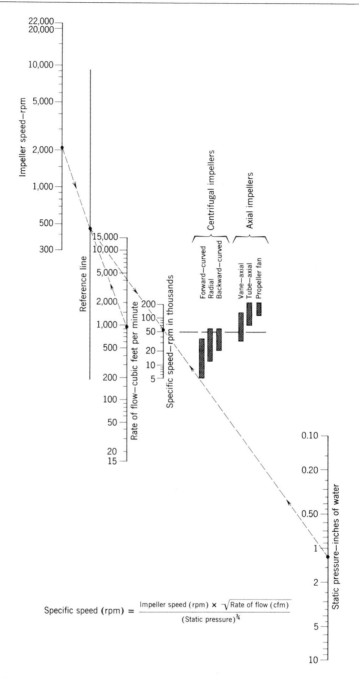

Example: Assume that the best type (or types) of impeller must be determined for a system in which $N = 2000$ rpm, $Q = 900$ cfm, and $P_s = 1.2$ in. of H_2O. A line from 2000 on the impeller speed scale to 900 on the rate of flow scale intersects the reference line as shown. A line from this point of intersection to 1.2 on the static pressure scale crosses the specific speed scale at $N_S = 50,000$ rpm. A horizontal line from 50,000 through the black columns shows that either a radial or backward-curved blower wheel or a vane-axial fan will be satisfactory. Of course, the ultimate selection of one of these three types will depend on other factors, such as space available, orientation of inlet and outlet, and cost.

Figure 25A. Specific-speed nomogram for selection of impeller type. (I. J. Roy; courtesy *Design News.*)

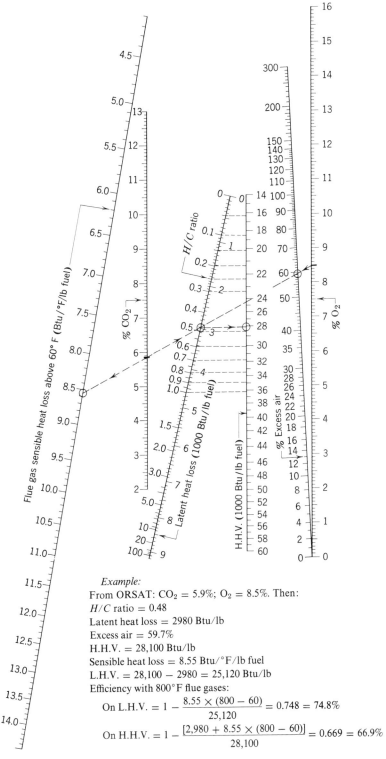

Example:

From ORSAT: $CO_2 = 5.9\%$; $O_2 = 8.5\%$. Then:

H/C ratio $= 0.48$

Latent heat loss $= 2980$ Btu/lb

Excess air $= 59.7\%$

H.H.V. $= 28,100$ Btu/lb

Sensible heat loss $= 8.55$ Btu/°F/lb fuel

L.H.V. $= 28,100 - 2980 = 25,120$ Btu/lb

Efficiency with 800°F flue gases:

$$\text{On L.H.V.} = 1 - \frac{8.55 \times (800 - 60)}{25,120} = 0.748 = 74.8\%$$

$$\text{On H.H.V.} = 1 - \frac{[2,980 + 8.55 \times (800 - 60)]}{28,100} = 0.669 = 66.9\%$$

Figure 26A. Nomogram for combustion calculations. (Mekler & Ungar; courtesy *Petroleum Refiner*.)

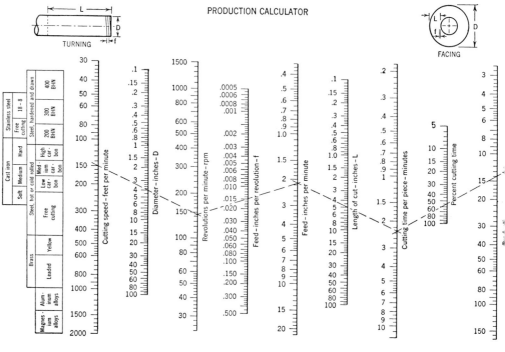

Figure 27A. Production calculator. (Courtesy Crobalt Inc., Ann Arbor, Mich.)

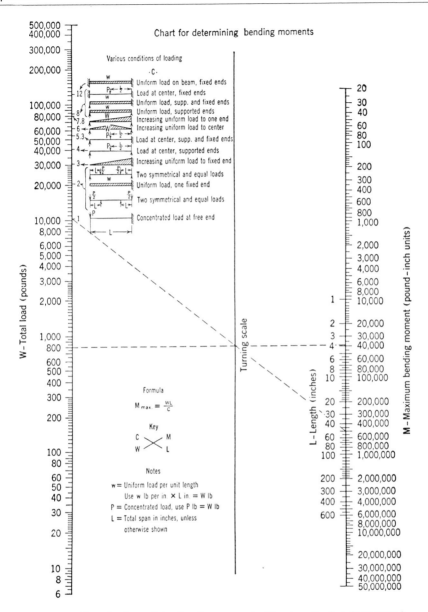

Figure 28A. Chart for determining bending moments. (Courtesy *Product Engineering.*)

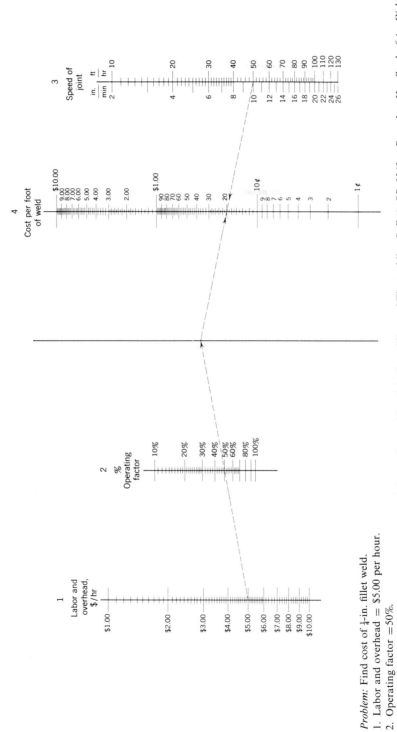

Problem: Find cost of ¼-in. fillet weld.

1. Labor and overhead = $5.00 per hour.
2. Operating factor = 50%.
3. Speed of joint = 10 in./min. (Obtain from actual time or from tables of the Jetwelding and Fleetwelding *Bulletin SB-1363* or *Procedure Handbook of Arc Welding, Section II*.)
4. Read cost = 20¢/ft. Note: This cost figure does not include electrode cost. To determine this use "pounds of electrode required per foot of joint" from above references and multiply by electrode selling price. Add this to that obtained in step 4.

Figure 29A. Nomogram to determine welding costs. (Courtesy Lincoln Electric Co.)

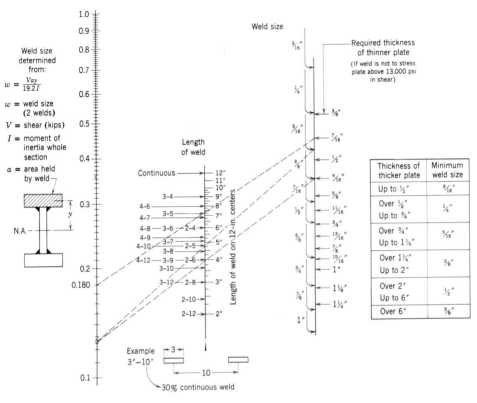

Weld size determined from:

$$w = \frac{Vay}{19.2\,I}$$

w = weld size (2 welds)

V = shear (kips)

I = moment of inertia whole section

a = area held by weld

Thickness of thicker plate	Minimum weld size
Up to ½″	³⁄₁₆″
Over ½″ Up to ¾″	¼″
Over ¾″ Up to 1¼″	⁵⁄₁₆″
Over 1¼″ Up to 2″	³⁄₈″
Over 2″ Up to 6″	½″
Over 6″	⁵⁄₈″

Figure 30A. Nomogram for size and amount of intermittent fillet welds. (Courtesy Lincoln Electric Co.)

Problem: Find weld size and center-to-center distance for the following conditions:

$$w = 0.180 \text{ continuous (found from } w = \frac{Vay}{19.2\,I})$$

plate thickness = $\frac{7}{16}$ in.
intermittent fillet weld size = $\frac{5}{16}$ in.
amount of fillet weld 3″–5″ (3″ long and 5″ centers)

Problem: $\frac{3}{8}$ ◺ 4″–12″ can be changed to
$\frac{5}{16}$ ◺ 4″–10″ or
$\frac{5}{16}$ ◺ 4.8″–12″

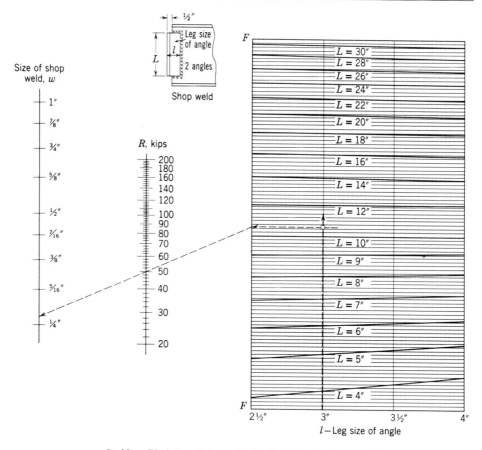

Problem: Find size of shop weld for the following frame angle:

l = 3 in. (leg size of angle);
L = 10½ in. (length of angle);
R = 50 kips (end reaction).

Read w = ⁵⁄₁₆ in. (size of shop weld).

Figure 31A. Nomogram for size of shop weld of framing angles. (Courtesy Lincoln Electric Co.)

How to use the nomograph: Place straightedge on desired values of inductance and wire size on the two vertical scales. Where curve for diameter intersects straightedge, read required number of turns on other set of curves.

Example: How many turns of no. 30 wire are required on a 0.25-in.-diameter coil form to obtain 0.7 microhenry? Run straightedge between 0.7 on left-hand vertical scale and 30 on right-hand side of right-hand vertical scale, as indicated by thin dashed line. Trace upward along 0.25-in.-diameter curve to straightedge, and read 10 turns as value of other curve passing through this intersection.

$$n = \frac{10dL + \sqrt{100d^2L^2 + 36r^3L}}{2r^2}$$

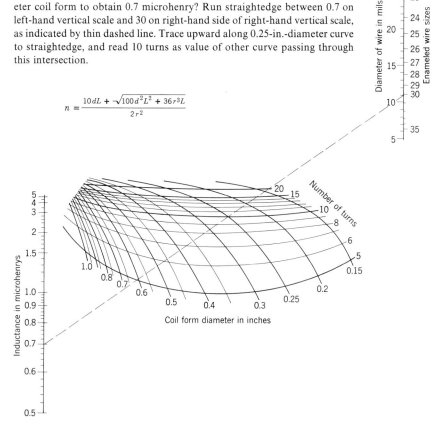

Various nomographs, charts, and calculators are available for the calculation of the inductance of coils, but most of these graphical aids do not cover the range of values of interest to the designer of coils for television, f-m, and radar i-f frequencies. This nomograph has been designed to fulfill this need. Unlike other coil nomographs, it gives in one operation the number of close-wound turns required to get a desired inductance.

The nomograph is based on a modification of H. A. Wheeler's inductance formula:[*]

$$L = \frac{r^2n^2}{9r + 10l} \text{ microhenrys} \tag{1}$$

where r is the radius of the coil in inches, l its length in inches, and n the number of turns. In close-wound coils, l is a function of n. Substitution of nd, where d is the diameter of the wire in inches in equation (1), gives an equation which can be solved for n to give

$$n = \frac{10dL + \sqrt{100d^2L^2 + 36r^3L}}{2r^2} \tag{2}$$

[*]H. A. Wheeler, "Simple Inductance Formulas for Radio Coils," *Proceedings of the Institute of Radio Engineers*, Oct. 1928, p. 1398.

Figure 32A. Nomogram for television intermediate-frequency coil design. (J. H. Felker; courtesy *Electronics.*)

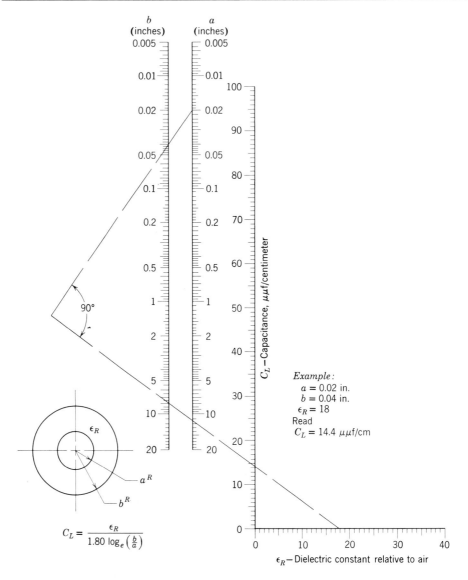

Figure 33A. Nomogram for capacitance per unit length of coaxial cable.

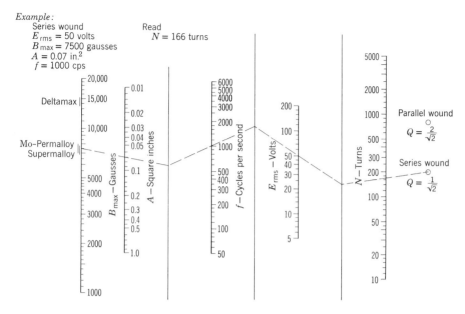

Figure 34A. Magnetic-amplifier nomogram for solving the equation $N = \dfrac{10^7\, E_{rms}\, Q}{1.29\pi B_{max} A f}$.

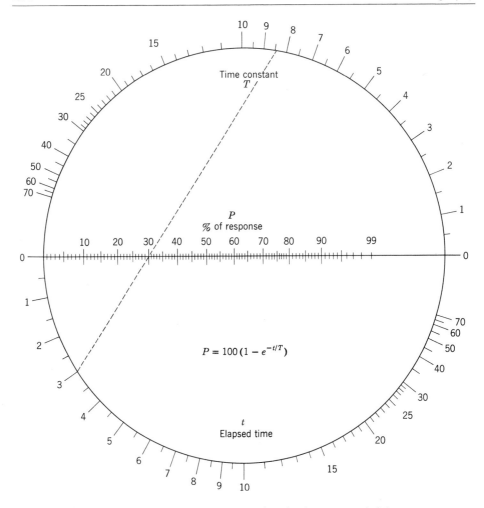

Example: If 30% of the response occurs in 3 sec, then the time constant is 8.4 sec.

The above may also be used to obtain the time constant from incomplete response data if two responses and their respective times are known: "cut and try" by assuming various maximum responses until both sets of observed data yield the same time constant.

Figure 35A. Nomogram for calculating the response of a temperature control system to a step input. (Courtesy E. C. Varnum; Barber-Colman Co.)

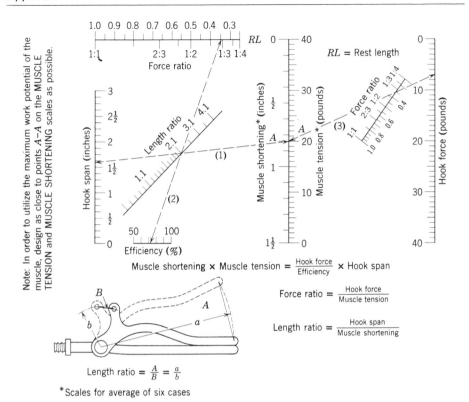

Length ratio $= \frac{A}{B} = \frac{a}{b}$

*Scales for average of six cases

For many years it has been considered logical and ideal to power an artificial hand or hook by means of voluntary contraction of residual muscles of the arm rather than by body movements such as the shoulder shrug. The problem of a durable and efficient linkage between the muscle and the moving mechanism of the prosthesis appears to be solved by the construction of a muscle tunnel. This is a surgical procedure to provide a skin-lined tunnel through the muscle, into which a pin is inserted with cables attached. Contraction of the muscle displaces the tunnel and the pin, thus transmitting force for prehension to hand or hook.

The biceps muscle tunnel is of greatest value in the below-elbow amputee. In this type of amputation the entire length of the biceps is available and provides adequate excursion to activate the prosthesis.

Example: Suppose that the muscle tension is 20 lb, the hook span 1.6 in., and the efficiency 70%. It is desired to find the force ratio, hook force, and muscle shortening. Using the nomogram, we proceed as follows:

(*a*) Join 1.6 on the hook span scale with 20 on the muscle tension scale (line 1).

(*b*) The point of intersection of line 1 with the diagonal length ratio scale is joined with 70 on the efficiency scale and extended to intersect the force ratio scale at point 0.35 (line 2).

(*c*) Point 0.35 on the *diagonal* force ratio scale is joined with 20 on the muscle tension scale (line 3).

(*d*) Read 7 lb on the hook force scale and approximately $1\frac{3}{16}$ in. on the muscle shortening scale.

Figure 36A. Design chart for artificial hook-type hand. (Below-elbow amputees.)

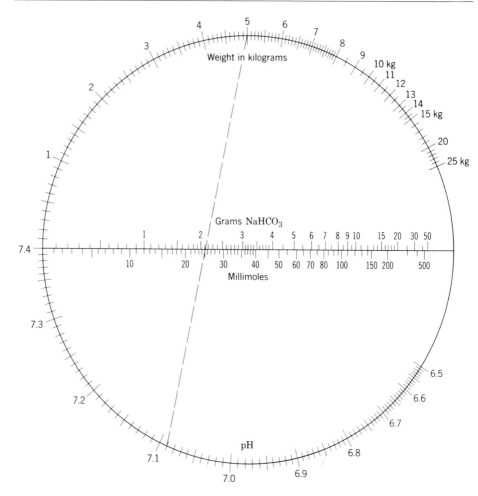

Example: A patient weighing 5 kg with a *p*H of 7.09 requires 2.1 grams or 25 millimoles of NaHCO₃.

Figure 37A. Nomogram for approximation of alkali requirements of patients in acidosis. (Courtesy: E. C. Varnum; Barber-Colman Co.) Reference: *American Journal of Clinical Pathology,* p. 426, Vol. 22, May 1952.

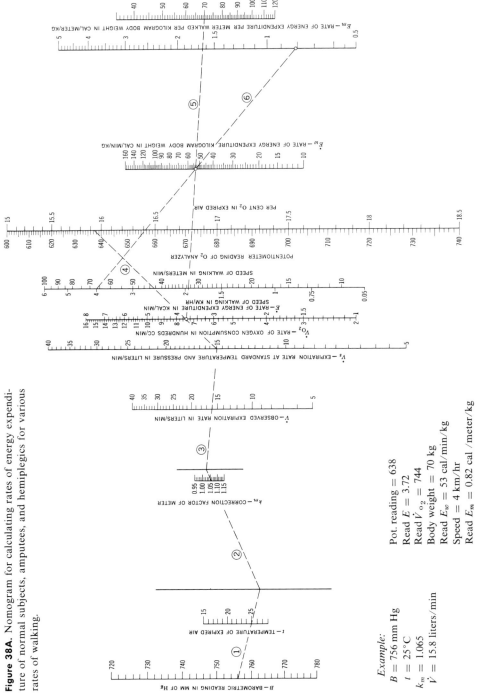

Figure 38A. Nomogram for calculating rates of energy expenditure of normal subjects, amputees, and hemiplegics for various rates of walking.

Example:

$B = 756$ mm Hg
$t = 25°C$
$k_m = 1.065$
$\dot{V} = 15.8$ liters/min

Pot. reading $= 638$
Read $E = 3.72$
Read $\dot{V}_{O_2} = 744$
Body weight $= 70$ kg
Read $E_w = 53$ cal/min/kg
Speed $= 4$ km/hr
Read $E_m = 0.82$ cal/meter/kg

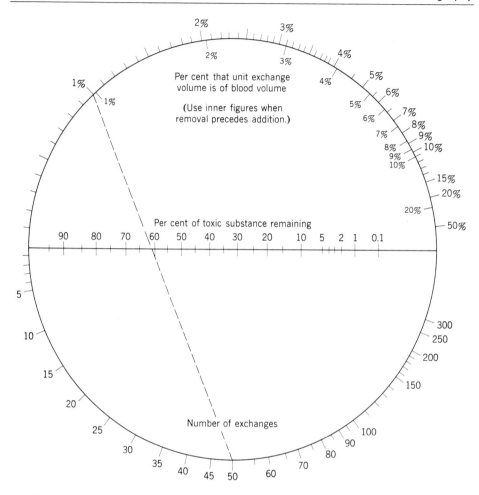

Example: Assume a blood volume of 1000 cc and that 10 cc is added and withdrawn. Then the unit exchange volume is 1% of the blood volume. After 50 exchanges, there remains 61% of an original content of toxic substance.

Figure 39A. Nomogram to determine per cent of original toxic substance remaining after several exchange transfusions. (Courtesy E. C. Varnum; Barber-Colman Co.)

Shielding Nomograms

These nomograms permit rapid estimation of the photon flux reflected from a thin object and determination of gamma-ray attenuation for a number of elements.

For the first two nomograms (Figures 40A and 41A) the photon flux I_i ($\gamma/\text{cm}^2/\text{sec}$) of energy E_i (Mev) per photon, incident upon a scatterer thin with respect to the relaxation length of the incident or scattered photon ($t<\lambda$), will scatter through an angle θ to a receiver R at distance D (cm) with an intensity I_R ($\gamma/\text{cm}^2/\text{sec}/\text{steradian}$) and energy E_R (Mev) per photon and an intensity given by:

$$I_R = N_e \sigma_D D^{-2} I_i = KI_i$$

The energy flux, ϕ_ε (Mev/cm²/sec/steradian), at R is:

$$\phi_\varepsilon = E_R I_R = PE_i KI_i$$

The scattered photon energy, E_R, is given by the Compton equation:

$$P = E_R/E_i = \left[1 + \frac{E_i}{0.51}(1 - \cos\theta) \right]^{-1}$$

The probability per electron of scattering the incident photon through angle θ is given by the Klein-Nishina equation:

$$\sigma_D = d\sigma/d\Omega = (P - P^2\sin^2\theta + P^3)r_e^2/2$$

where the classical electron radius $r_e = 2.82 \times 10^{-13}$ cm and σ_D is in cm²/steradian per electron. One must multiply by the number of electrons in the scattering medium, $N_e = 6.02 \times 10^{23}$ MZ/A, to get the total scattering probability.

Large objects must be subdivided into pieces of such size that I_i and θ can be assumed constant over each region of subdivision. Each region is then considered to be a point scatterer defining a new set of parameters M, D, and θ, and the scattered intensities from all subdivisions are summed.

If small values of M are used, K may go off-scale; in this case N_e can be multiplied by a convenient factor of 10 and K divided by the same factor to obtain the corrected value of K.

In the gamma-ray attenuation nomogram (Figure 42A) the plot of μ_m versus Z facilitates interpolation to any atomic number and energy. However, complete tables of μ_m from 0.5 to 6 Mev for all elements are still unavailable. Energies greater than 6 Mev have been neglected since for these energies and for $Z = 30$–94, μ_m is defined quite well by the 6-Mev curve, the locus of minimum absorption coefficient. This is generally used for shielding calculations for any energy above 6 Mev. For $Z = 1$–29, μ_m determined from the chart is slightly high for energies greater than 6 Mev.

The nomogram can be used to convert μ_m to the linear absorption coefficient, μ, by multiplying by the density of the shield material, ρ. If μ is connected to the shield thickness, x, the shield attenuation factor for a point source with unit build-up, e^{-b}, is obtained ($b = \mu x$). The approximate build-up factor, B, for most elements, but not lead, up to 3 Mev is $1 + b$ and for lead over the same range $1 + \frac{1}{2}b$. The corrected attenuation factor is $B \times e^{-b}$.

Source strength ($\gamma/\text{cm}^2/\text{sec}$) for an infinite plane source is approximately $\lambda/2 \times Q_v$, where Q_v is the specific activity (γ/cm^3) of the source material. If μ is determined for the source gamma ray, λ can be read on the adjacent scale.

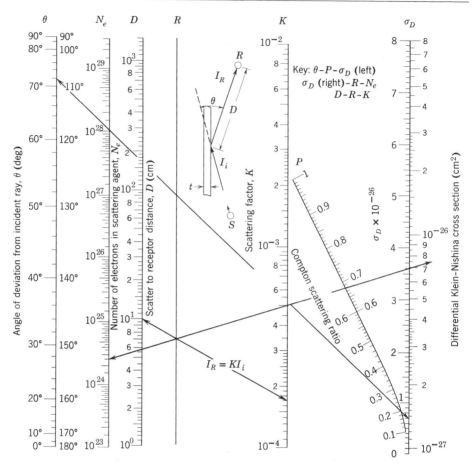

Figure 40A. Nomogram for gamma-ray scattering from thin scatterers. Reference: *Radiological Health Handbook,* January 1957.

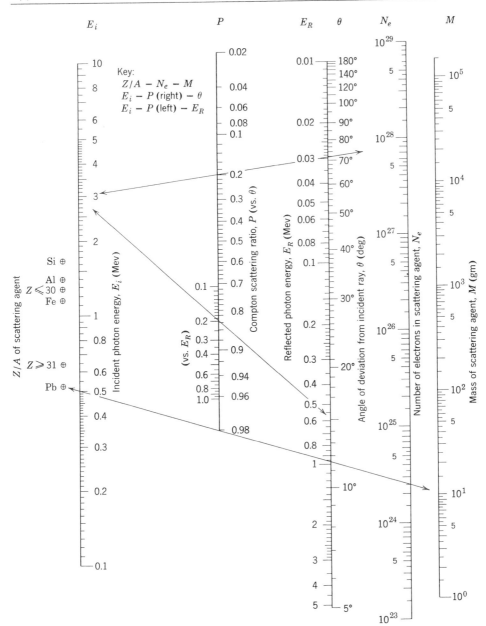

Example: Pb scatterer, M = 10 gm; therefore N_e = 2.4 × 10²⁴. An incident photon of E_i = 3 Mev scatters to θ = 72°; therefore P = 0.2, E_R = 0.6 Mev, and σ_d = 0.7 × 10²⁶ cm²/e/steradian. At D = 10 cm, K = 1.7 × 10⁻⁴ and I_R = 1.7 × 10⁻⁴ I_i or ϕ_ε = 0.2 × 3 × 1.7 × 10⁻⁴ I_i Mev/cm²/sec.

Figure 41A. Nomogram for gamma-ray scattering from thin scatterers. Reference: *Radiological Health Handbook*, January 1957.

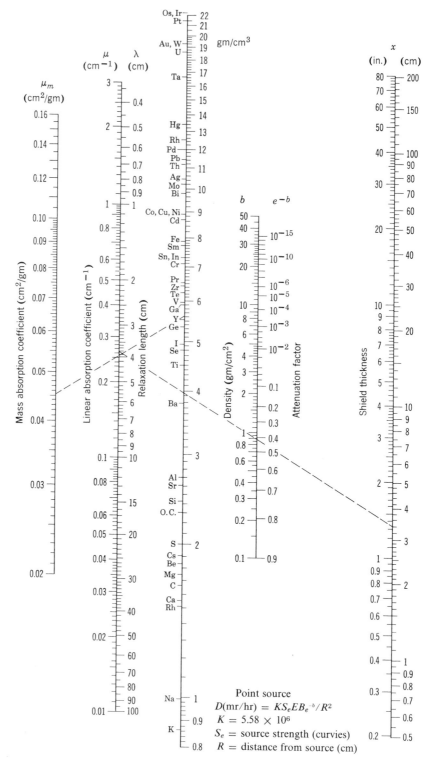

Figure 42A. Nomogram for gamma-ray attenuation. Reference: *Radiological Health Handbook,* January 1957.

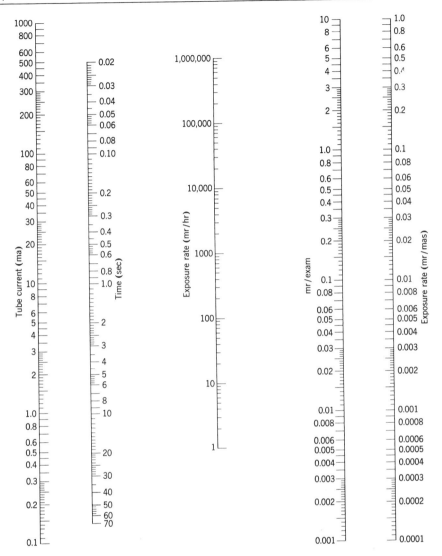

Examples of Use

(r stands for roentgens, mr for milliroentgens, and mas for milliampere-seconds.)

Example 1

Given: Exposure rate 1080 mr/hr
            Time of exposure 1 sec

Find: Total exposure

Solution: Place a straightedge connecting 1 sec, in second column, with 1080 mr/hr, in third
            column.
                     Read from fourth column: Total exposure = 0.3 mr

Example 2

Given: Tube current in the problem above is 50 ma

Find: Exposure rate in mr/mas

Solution: Place straightedge connecting 50 ma in first column, and 1080 mr/hr in third column.
                     Read from fifth column: Exposure rate = 0.006 mr/mas

Figure 43A. Nomogram for X-ray exposure–exposure rate relationship. Reference: *Radiological Health Handbook,* January 1957. (Figure prepared by P. J. Valaers, U. S. Public Health Service.)

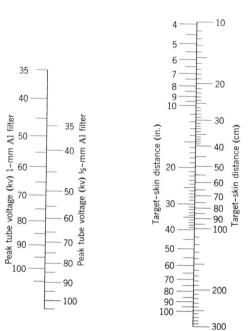

Rotating anode.
Full-wave rectification.
Equivalent inherent filtration 0.5-mm Al.

Example of Use

(r stands for roentgens, mr for milliroentgens,
and mas for milliampere-seconds.)

Diagnostic Fluoroscope

Given: Peak tube kilovoltage 75 kvp
                Tube current 3 ma
                External filtration 1 mm Al
                Target-skin distance 15 in.
Find: Dosage rate in air, in r/min
Solution: Place a straightedge connecting 75 kvp with 1 mm Al, in first column, with 15 in.
           target-skin distance, in second column.
                    Read from third column: Dosage rate in air = 55 mr/mas
           Time = 1 min = 60 sec
           Current = 3 ma
           Mas/min = 3 × 60 = 180 mas/min
           Dosage rate in air = (55 mr/mas) × (180 mas/min)
                             = 9900
                             = 9.9 r/min

The nomogram in its present form can be used directly for many different types of X-ray machines which have added filters of 0.5- or 1.0-mm Al. For added filter of 1.5-mm Al, the dosage rate will be approximately 11% less than the values given for 1.0-mm Al for 65 kv to 105 kv. The roentgen dose in air at the skin given by the nomogram should be correct, for a given machine, to within ±25%. In all cases the dosage rate is given in air at the skin.

Figure 44A. Nomogram for dosage rate determinations in diagnostic roentgenology. Reference: *Radiological Health Handbook,* January 1957.

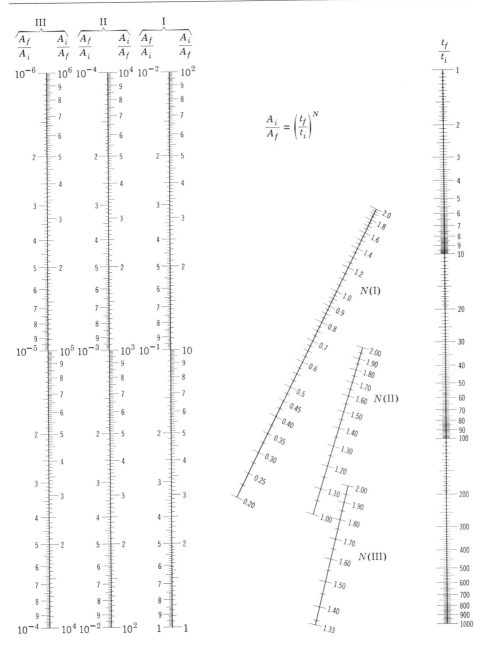

$$\frac{A_i}{A_f} = \left(\frac{t_f}{t_i}\right)^N$$

A symbolizes the activity; t, the time; and subscripts i and f, the initial and final conditions.

Example: $\dfrac{A_i}{A_f} = 250$

$\dfrac{t_f}{t_i} = 100$

Join these values on the II scales and read $N = 120$ on the corresponding II scale.

Figure 45A. Nomograph for the decay of gross fission product activities. (Courtesy U. S. Naval Radiological Defense Laboratory, San Francisco.)

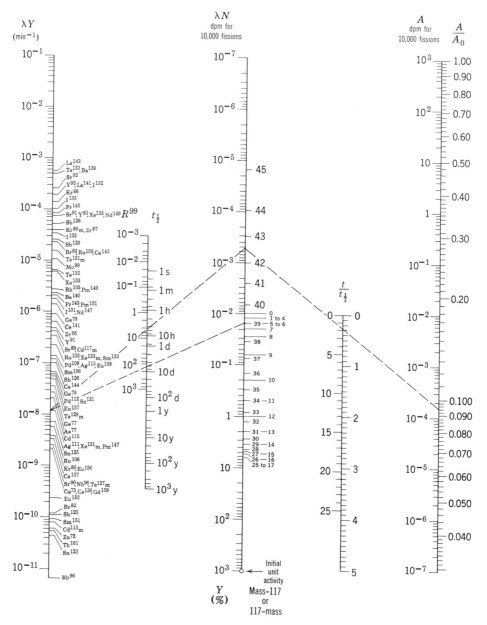

In problems dealing with the radiochemical analysis of fission product mixtures, calculations of fission yields and activities of product nuclides are involved.

Questions which may arise are: What is the activity of a certain product nuclide at various times after fission? The measured activity of an isolated product corresponds to how many atoms produced in fission? What was the fission yield?

Information may be desired about the resulting fission yield curve: Is it similar to that of thermal neutron fission of U^{235}? Did fractionation of the elements occur in sampling?

This nomogram supplies that sort of information. It plots the relationships for various product nuclides among:

1. Thermal neutron fission yield from U^{235} in terms of deviation in mass units from the point of symmetrical fission (M-117 or 117-M).

2. Half-life.

3. Fission yield in thermal neutron fission of $U^{235} \times$ decay constant.

4. R value—defined as $\dfrac{\text{fission yield of nuclide in sample}}{\text{fission yield of reference nuclide in sample}} \div$

$\dfrac{U^{235} \text{ thermal neutron fission yield of nuclide}}{U^{235} \text{ thermal neutron fission yield of reference nuclide}}$. The reference nuclide is chosen so that the yield in sample and U^{235} is the same.

5. "Initial activity" produced in 10,000 fissions.

6. Decay time expressed in number of half-lives $(t/t_{1/2})$.

7. Remaining activity from 10,000 fissions.

Example: A fission product sample is taken for radiochemical analysis of 7.6 d Ag^{111}. For this isotope 117-M $= 6$. A line from 6 on the M-117 scale through 7.6 d on the $t_{1/2}$ scale gives $Y\lambda$ in min^{-1}. The value of $Y\lambda$ for Ag^{111} (and all important appropriate nuclides of half-life greater than 60 m) is conveniently indicated on the right side of the $Y\lambda$ scale. A reference nuclide, Mo^{99}, is separated from the same sample. A comparison of the ratio of the activities of Ag^{111} to Mo^{99} shows that it is 4.61 times greater than the corresponding activity ratio for U^{235} fission at the same time after fission. A line from Ag^{111} through 4.61 on the R value scale shows that the 111 chain production corresponded to an initial 5.3×10^{-4} dpm of Ag^{111} activity per 10,000 fissions. If the activity of the Ag^{111} is measured 12.4 days after fission, or 1.63 half-lives thereafter, there will remain 1.7×10^{-4} dpm per 10,000 fissions.

To find on the A/A_o scale the fraction of activity remaining after a certain number of half-lives, draw a line from the initial unit activity point on the bottom of the middle scale through $t/t_{1/2}$.

Figure 46A. Nomogram for radioactivity in gross fission product analyses. (Courtesy U. S. Naval Radiological Defense Laboratory, San Francisco.)

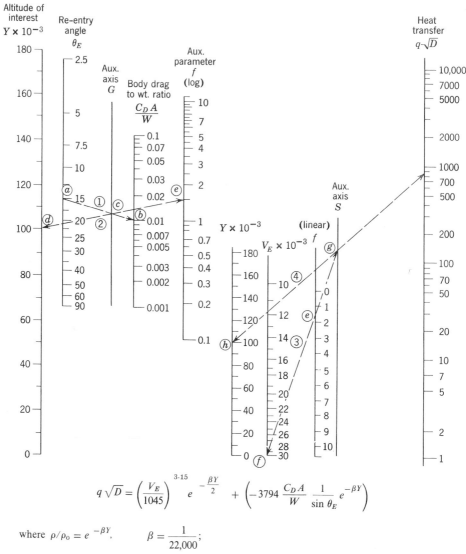

$$q\sqrt{D} = \left(\frac{V_E}{1045}\right)^{3.15} e^{-\frac{\beta Y}{2}} + \left(-3794 \frac{C_D A}{W} \frac{1}{\sin\theta_E} e^{-\beta Y}\right)$$

where $\rho/\rho_0 = e^{-\beta Y}$, $\beta = \dfrac{1}{22,000}$;

$\dfrac{C_D A}{W}$ = drag to weight parameter for the body in feet² per pound;

Y = altitude in feet;

θ_E = angle between horizontal and missile direction at re-entry;

V_E = re-entry velocity in feet per second.

Example: If the velocity, re-entry angle, drag to weight characteristics, and altitude of interest are known, the heat transfer at the stagnation point may be arrived at by drawing four lines as indicated. The first two points located are the re-entry angle, θ_E, and the body drag to weight parameter, $C_D A/W$. Connecting these points gives a point on the auxiliary axis, G. Choosing an altitude for the computation on Y and drawing a line through the point on G yields a point on the auxiliary parameter line, f(log). This point is then transferred to f(linear), where it is used with a point on the re-entry velocity axis, V_E, to obtain a point on the auxiliary axis, S. The point on S is used with the altitude point on the Y-axis to obtain the desired heat transfer value, q/D.

Figure 47A. Re-entry heat transfer nomogram. (Courtesy Convair Division, General Dynamics.) Reference: Convair Scientific Research Laboratory Research Note 15, "A Nomograph for Stagnation Point Heat Transfer Rate during Hypersonic Ballistic Re-Entry," Mary F. Roming, March 1958.

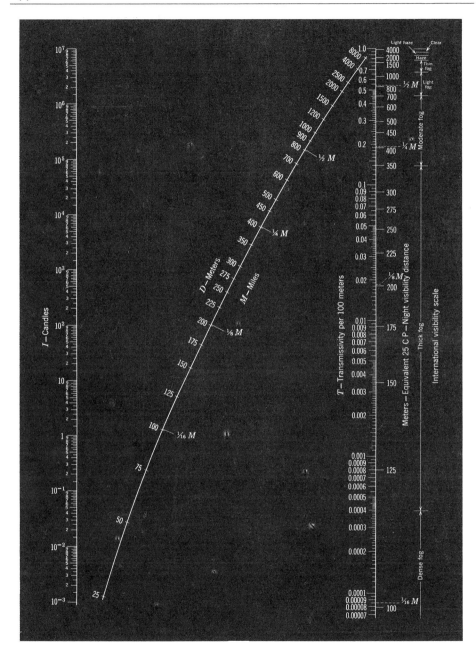

Visibility of signal lights for various candlepowers and transmissivities as calculated by Allard's law $I = E_0 D^2 T^{-D}$

where I = candlepower of signal light;
E_0 = threshold illumination = 0.002 hm C (night);
D = distance, hectometers;
T = transmissivity per 100 meters (hectometers).

Figure 48A. Nomogram for visibility of signal lights—night. (Courtesy Civil Aeronautics Administration.)

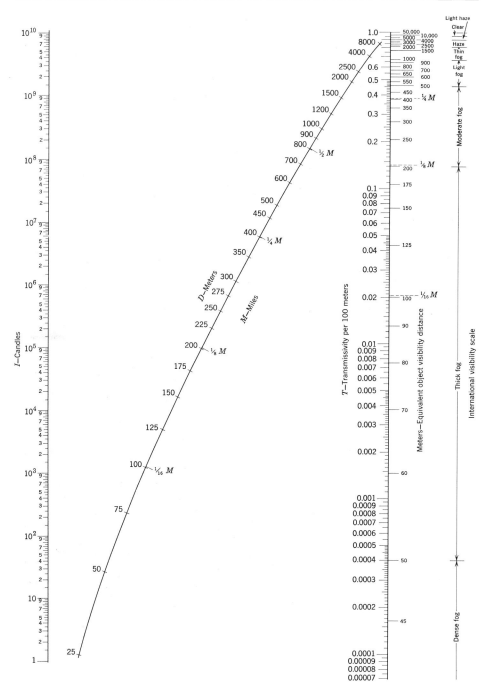

Visibility of signal lights for various candlepowers and transmissivities as calculated by Allard's law $I = E_0 D^2 T^{-D}$

where I = candle powers of signal light;
    E_0 = threshold illumination = 2 hm C (day);
    D = distance, hectometers;
    T = transmissivity per 100 meters (hectometers).

Equivalent object visibility distance calculated by formula $T^d = 0.02$.

Figure 49A. Nomogram for visibility of signal lights—daylight. (Courtesy Civil Aeronautics Administration.)

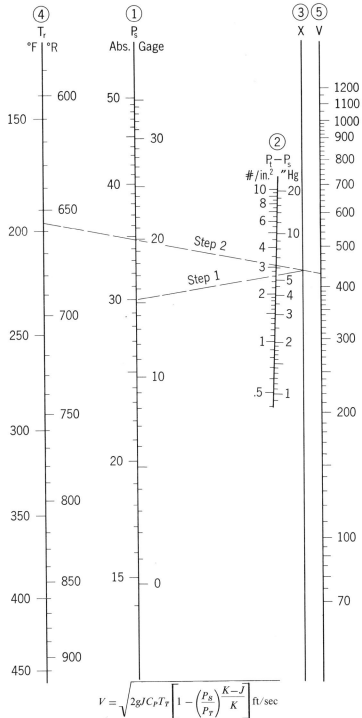

$$V = \sqrt{2gJC_PT_T\left[1 - \left(\frac{P_S}{P_T}\right)^{\frac{K-J}{K}}\right]} \text{ ft/sec}$$

where $g = 32.17$ ft/sec²; $J = 778$ ft-lb/Btu; $K = 1.4$; $C_P = 0.24$ Btu/°F/lb air;
$T_T = $ stagnation temperature in degrees Rankine;
$P_T = $ stagnation pressure $\Big\}$ in pounds per square inch absolute or similar units.
$P_S = $ static pressure

Example. Given: $P_S = 30.0$ lb/in.² abs., $P_T - P_S = 2.6$ lb/in.², $T_T = 196°$F. Connect 30.0 on scale 1 to 2.6 on scale 2 and note point X on scale 3. Connect this point with 196 on scale 4 and read answer on scale 5, $V = 429$ ft/sec.

Figure 50A. Nomogram for solving the Pitot tube formula for compressible fluids. (Courtesy Consolidated Vultee Aircraft Corp.)

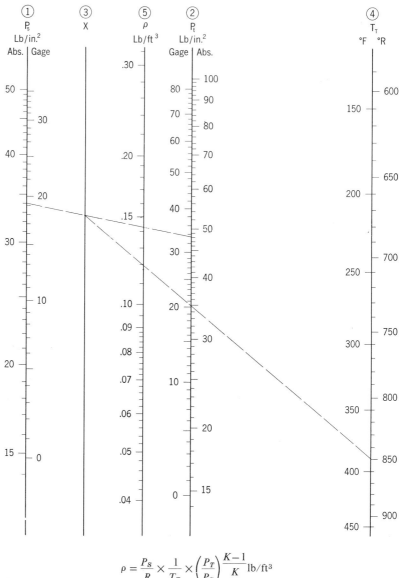

$$\rho = \frac{P_S}{R} \times \frac{1}{T_T} \times \left(\frac{P_T}{P_S}\right)^{\frac{K-1}{K}} \text{lb/ft}^3$$

where R = 53.3 ft-lb/°F/lb of air; K = 1.4 (for air);
$\quad T_T$ = stagnation temperature in degrees Rankenè;
$\quad P_T$ = stagnation pressure $\Big\}$ in similar units.
$\quad P_S$ = static pressure

Example. Given: P_S = 34.0 lb/in.² abs., P_T = 48.0 lb/in.² abs., T_T = 850°R. Connect 34.0 on scale 1 to 48.0 on scale 2 and thus locate point X on scale 3. Connect point X with 850 on scale 4 and read answer, ρ = 0.1195, on scale 5.

Figure 51A. Nomogram for solving density of fluid in a Pitot tube traverse. (Courtesy Consolidated Vultee Aircraft Co.)

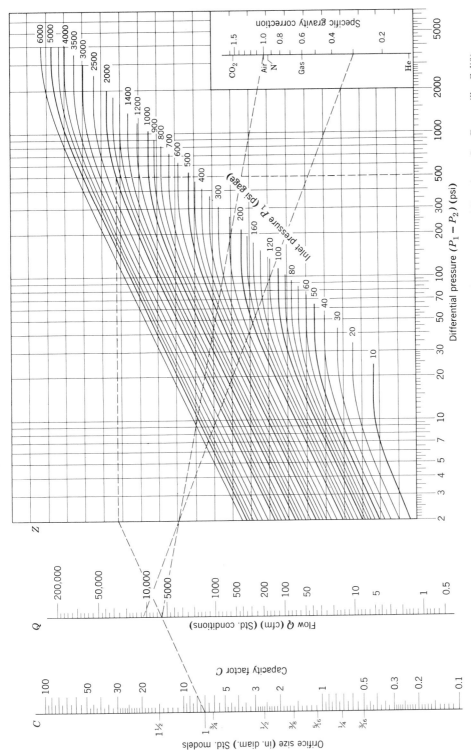

Figure 52A. Nomogram to determine regulator capacities for use on air or gas. (Courtesy Grove Valve and Regulator Co., Emeryville, Calif.)

Example for Figure 52A:
Inlet pressure P_1 = 2000 psi gage
Outlet pressure P_2 = 1500 psi gage
1-in. orifice, C = 7.0
Specific gravity = 0.3
Answer: Q = 11,100 cfm

How to Use the Capacity Chart, Figure 52A

1. Determine the following quantities:
(a) Minimum expected inlet pressure at the regulator in psi gage, taking into account pipeline drop if appreciable.
(b) Minimum expected differential pressure (inlet pressure minus outlet pressure).
2. On the chart locate the curve corresponding to the minimum inlet pressure and the point on the differential pressure scale, corresponding to the minimum differential pressure. From the point on the differential pressure scale, follow a vertical line to the point of intersection with the inlet pressure curve, then follow a horizontal line to the intersection with line Z.
3. Locate the orifice size of the regulator being considered on line C. Using a straightedge draw a line through orifice size on line C and point on line Z previously located. The intersection with scale Q gives the rated capacity of the regulator under the above conditions in cubic feet of free air per minute (standard conditions 60° and 14.7 psi atmospheric pressure).
4. If the fluid is gas other than air the flow must be corrected for specific gravity. To accomplish this draw a line from the value of Q determined above through 1.0 on the specific gravity correction scale. Using the intersection with line Z as a turning point, draw a line through the value of specific gravity of the gas being considered. The intersection of this line with scale Q will give the rated capacity in cubic feet per minute of free gas.

The capacity given by this chart is the rated capacity to insure good regulation and also represents a conservative average value to include all regulators listed in the company's catalog. The actual maximum flow with valve blocked wide open would be from 30% to 70% greater than this value.

The capacity chart is based on the regulator pipe size being larger than the orifice size which is true with all standard models.

The use of single-seated valve construction causes a slight variation in reduced pressure control when the initial pressure varies over a wide range. The table indicates the amount of pressure in the outlet line for each 100 lb of pressure variation in the initial pressure.

| | Valve size (in. diam.) | | | | | | | |
	$\frac{3}{16}$	$\frac{1}{4}$	$\frac{5}{16}$	$\frac{3}{8}$	$\frac{1}{2}$	$\frac{3}{4}$	1	$1\frac{1}{2}$
Series 200	0.6	1.0	1.7	2.4	4.4			
Series 300		0.3	0.5	0.7	1.3	3.0	5.4	
Series 400				0.3	0.5	1.2	2.0	4.8

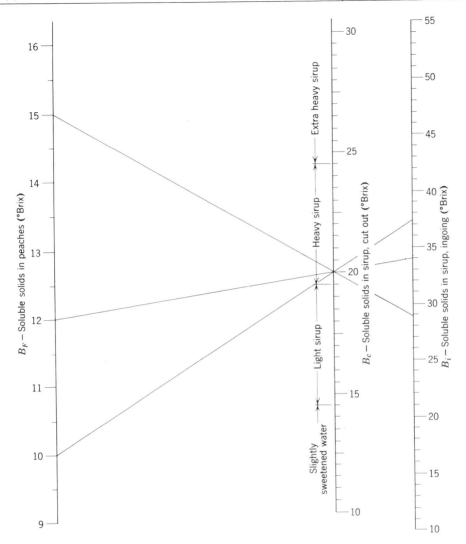

Figure 53A. Nomogram for calculating ingoing strength of sirup for clingstone peaches in no. $2\frac{1}{2}$ cans.

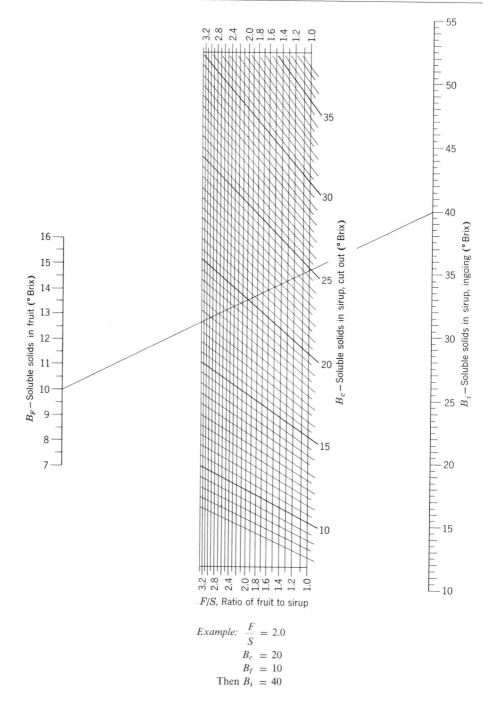

Figure 54A. Nomogram for calculating relation between sirup strength and fruit solids content for various ratios of weight of fruit to sirup.

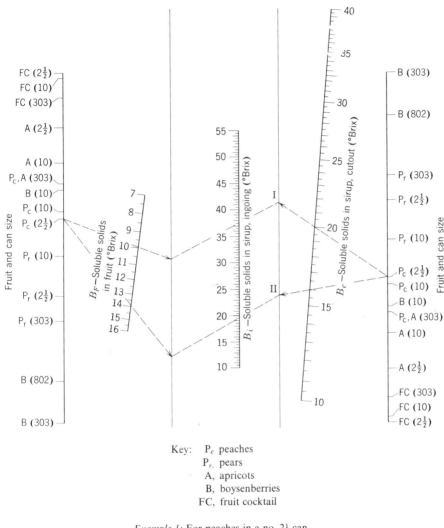

Key: P_c   peaches
        P_r. pears
        A, apricots
        B, boysenberries
        FC, fruit cocktail

Example 1: For peaches in a no. 2½ can.
If $B_F = 10$ and $B_c = 20$, read: $B_i = 37.3$.
Example 2: For peaches in a no. 2½ can.
If $B_F = 10$ and $B_c = 14$, read: $B_i = 19.4$.

Figure 55A. Nomogram for calculating ingoing degrees Brix of sirup for different fruit in cans of various size.

$V_n = Cv^n + FrA_{\overline{n}|} =$ bond present value
C = bond redemption or disposal price in dollars
F = bond face or par value = fixed at $1000.00
r = bond rate per interest period in per cent
$V^n = I/(I + i)^n$, $A_{\overline{n}|} = (I - v^n)/i$
i = bond investment rate per period in per cent
n = number of interest periods

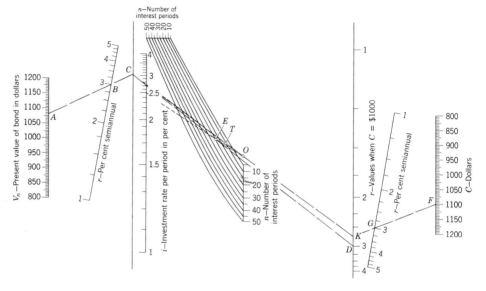

Example 1

Find the yield on a 10-yr, 6% bond, interest payable semiannually, redeemable at $1000 par value, and having a present value of $1080.

Solution:

(a) Connect points A and B and locate point C.

(b) Connect points C and D. Line CD intersects curve $n = 20$ (20 semiannual periods) at point E.

(c) Connect points O and E and read 2.5% on the i-scale. This value, 2.5%, is the semiannual rate of return, or the yield is 5% per year.

Example 2

The bond in Example 1 was held 5 yr and the value of the bond at that time was $1100. What was the yield?

Solution:

(a) Locate point C as before.

(b) Connect points F and G and locate point K. Line CK intersects the curve $n = 10$ at point T.

(c) Join O and T and read 2.8% on the i-scale. The annual yield is $2 \times 2.8\%$ or 5.6%.

Figure 56A. Nomogram for computing bond values.

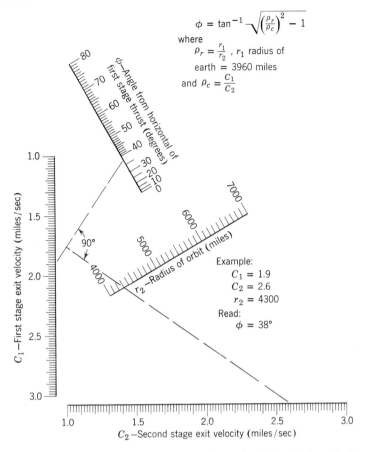

$$\phi = \tan^{-1}\sqrt{\left(\frac{\rho_r}{\rho_c}\right)^2 - 1}$$

where

$\rho_r = \frac{r_1}{r_2}$, r_1 radius of

earth = 3960 miles

and $\rho_c = \frac{C_1}{C_2}$

Example:

$C_1 = 1.9$

$C_2 = 2.6$

$r_2 = 4300$

Read:

$\phi = 38°$

Figure 57A. Nomogram for optimum direction angle, ϕ, from horizontal of first-stage thrust (launch direction); for the case $\rho_c \leqq \rho_r$.

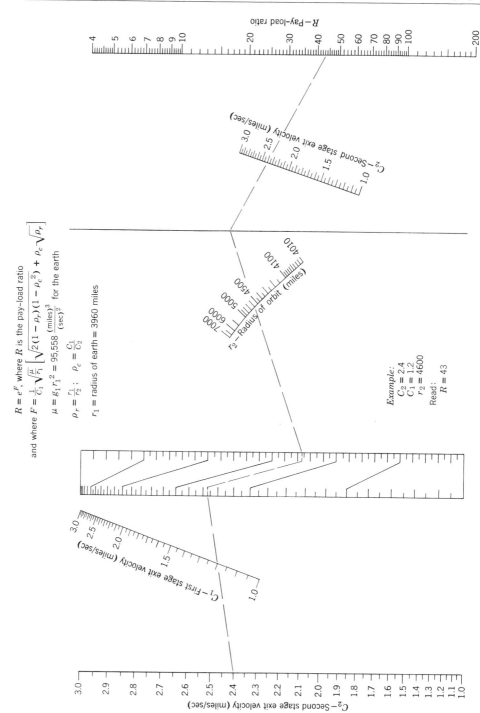

$R = e^F$, where R is the pay-load ratio

and where $F = \frac{1}{C_1}\sqrt{\frac{\mu}{r_1}}\left[\sqrt{2(1 - \rho_r)(1 - \rho_c{}^2)} + \rho_c\sqrt{\rho_r}\right]$

$\mu = g_1 r_1{}^2 = 95{,}558\ \frac{(miles)^3}{(sec)^{\frac{1}{2}}}$ for the earth

$\rho_r = \frac{r_1}{r_2};\ \ \rho_c = \frac{C_1}{C_2}$

r_1 = radius of earth = 3960 miles

Example:
$C_2 = 2.4$
$C_1 = 1.2$
$r_2 = 4600$
Read:
$R = 43$

Figure 58A. Nomogram for optimum pay-load ratio, R, for the case $\rho_c \leqq \rho_r$.

Earth Satellite Problem for Figure 58A

It is required to place a given pay load into a circular orbit of a specified radius by means of a two-stage "all fuel" rocket with *minimum* fuel consumption. It is assumed that the earth is nonrotating and spherically symmetrical; that both stages burn instantaneously, one at the surface of the earth and the second at satellite altitude; and that flight is in vacuum. The pay-load ratio (ratio of total propellant mass to pay-load mass) is expressed by

$$R = e^F \tag{1}$$

where

$$F = \frac{1}{C_1} \sqrt{\frac{\mu}{r_1}} \left[\sqrt{2 (1 - \rho_r)(1 - \rho_c{}^2)} + \rho_c \sqrt{\rho_r} \right]$$

and

$$\phi = \tan^{-1} \sqrt{\frac{\rho_r{}^2}{\rho_c} - 1} = \begin{array}{l} \text{direction angle from horizontal of first} \\ \text{stage thrust (launch direction)} \end{array} \tag{2}$$

for the case $\rho_c \leqq \rho_r$.

The two nomograms, Figures 57A and 58A, solve equations (2) and (1) respectively very quickly for the launch angle, ϕ, and the optimum pay-load ratio, R.

Selected Bibliography

The following list of books on nomography provides adequate reading for those who are interested in further study of the subject.

Encyclopédie des Sciences Mathématiques, Tome I, Vol. 4, Gauthier-Villars, Paris, 1908.

M. D'OCAGNE, *Traité de Nomographie,* 2nd Ed., Gauthier-Villars, Paris, 1921.

R. SOREAU, *Nomographie,* 2nd Ed., 2 Vols., Chiron, Paris, 1921.

P. WERKMEISTER, *Das Entwerfen, von graphischen Rechentafeln,* J. Springer, Berlin, 1923.

R. SCHWERDT, *Lehrbuch der Nomographie,* J. Springer, Berlin, 1924.

JOHN B. PEDDLE, *The Construction of Graphical Charts,* McGraw-Hill Book Co., New York, 1910.

CARL RUNGE, *Graphical Methods,* Lemcke and Buechner, New York, 1912.

JOSEPH LIPKA, *Graphical and Mechanical Computation,* John Wiley & Sons, New York, 1918.

S. BRODETSKY, *First Course in Nomography,* G. Bell and Sons, London, 1920, 2nd Ed., 1925.

W. N. ROSE, *Line Charts for Engineers,* E. P. Dutton and Co., New York, 1923.

L. I. HEWES and H. L. SEWARD, *Design of Diagrams for Engineering Formulas,* McGraw-Hill Book Co., New York, 1923.

W. J. KEARTON and GEORGE WOOD, *Alignment Charts for Engineers and Students,* J. B. Lippincott Co., Philadelphia, 1924.

G. W. SWETT, *Construction of Alignment Charts,* John Wiley & Sons, New York, 1928.

H. J. ALLCOCK and J. R. JONES, *The Nomogram,* Pitman Publishing Corp., New York, 1932.

C. O. MACKEY, *Graphical Solutions,* 2nd Ed., John Wiley & Sons, New York, 1936.

F. T. MAVIS, *The Construction of Nomographic Charts,* International Textbook Co., Scranton, Pa., 1939.

M. KRAITCHIK, *Alignment Charts,* D. Van Nostrand Co., New York, 1944.

A. S. LEVENS, *Nomography,* John Wiley & Sons, New York, 1948.

M. V. PENTKOWSKI, *Nomographie,* Akademie-Verlag, Berlin, 1953.

D. S. DAVIS, *Nomography and Empirical Equations,* Reinhold Publishing Corp., New York, 1955.

A. GIET, *Abacs or Nomograms,* Philosophical Library, New York, 1956.

LASCU BAL and FRANCISC RADO, *Lectii de Nomografie,* Editura Teknica, Bucuresti, 1956.

Table 1

NATURAL TRIGONOMETRIC FUNCTIONS

Angles	Sines	Cosines	Tangents	Cotangents	Angles
0° 00′	.0000	1.0000	.0000	∞	90° 00′
10	.0029	1.0000	.0029	343.77	50
20	.0058	1.0000	.0058	171.89	40
30	.0087	1.0000	.0087	114.59	30
40	.0116	.9999	.0116	85.940	20
50	.0145	.9999	.0145	68.750	10
1° 00′	.0175	.9998	.0175	57.290	89° 00′
10	.0204	.9998	.0204	49.104	50
20	.0233	.9997	.0233	42.964	40
30	.0262	.9997	.0262	38.188	30
40	.0291	.9996	.0291	34.368	20
50	.0320	.9995	.0320	31.242	10
2° 00′	.0349	.9994	.0349	28.636	88° 00′
10	.0378	.9993	.0378	26.432	50
20	.0407	.9992	.0407	24.542	40
30	.0436	.9990	.0437	22.904	30
40	.0465	.9989	.0466	21.470	20
50	.0494	.9988	.0495	20.206	10
3° 00′	.0523	.9986	.0524	19.081	87° 00′
10	.0552	.9985	.0553	18.075	50
20	.0581	.9983	.0582	17.169	40
30	.0610	.9981	.0612	16.350	30
40	.0640	.9980	.0641	15.605	20
50	.0669	.9978	.0670	14.924	10
4° 00′	.0698	.9976	.0699	14.301	86° 00′
10	.0727	.9974	.0729	13.727	50
20	.0756	.9971	.0758	13.197	40
30	.0785	.9969	.0787	12.706	30
40	.0814	.9967	.0816	12.251	20
50	.0843	.9964	.0846	11.826	10
5° 00′	.0872	.9962	.0875	11.430	85° 00′
10	.0901	.9959	.0904	11.059	50
20	.0929	.9957	.0934	10.712	40
30	.0958	.9954	.0963	10.385	30
40	.0987	.9951	.0992	10.078	20
50	.1016	.9948	.1022	9.7882	10
6° 00′	.1045	.9945	.1051	9.5144	84° 00′
10	.1074	.9942	.1080	9.2553	50
20	.1103	.9939	.1110	9.0098	40
30	.1132	.9936	.1139	8.7769	30
40	.1161	.9932	.1169	8.5555	20
50	.1190	.9929	.1198	8.3450	10
7° 00′	.1219	.9925	.1228	8.1443	83° 00′
10	.1248	.9922	.1257	7.9530	50
20	.1276	.9918	.1287	7.7704	40
30	.1305	.9914	.1317	7.5958	30
40	.1334	.9911	.1346	7.4287	20
50	.1363	.9907	.1376	7.2687	10
Angles	Cosines	Sines	Cotangents	Tangents	Angles

Table 1 *(continued)*

NATURAL TRIGONOMETRIC FUNCTIONS

Angles	Sines	Cosines	Tangents	Cotangents	Angles
8° 00′	.1392	.9903	.1405	7.1154	82° 00′
10	.1421	.9899	.1435	6.9682	50
20	.1449	.9894	.1465	6.8269	40
30	.1478	.9890	.1495	6.6912	30
40	.1507	.9886	.1524	6.5606	20
50	.1536	.9881	.1554	6.4348	10
9° 00′	.1564	.9877	.1584	6.3138	81° 00′
10	.1593	.9872	.1614	6.1970	50
20	.1622	.9868	.1644	6.0844	40
30	.1650	.9863	.1673	5.9758	30
40	.1679	.9858	.1703	5.8707	20
50	.1708	.9853	.1733	5.7694	10
10° 00′	.1736	.9848	.1763	5.6713	80° 00′
10	.1765	.9843	.1793	5.5764	50
20	.1794	.9838	.1823	5.4845	40
30	.1822	.9833	.1853	5.3955	30
40	.1851	.9827	.1883	5.3093	20
50	.1880	.9822	.1914	5.2257	10
11° 00′	.1908	.9816	.1944	5.1446	79° 00′
10	.1937	.9811	.1974	5.0658	50
20	.1965	.9805	.2004	4.9894	40
30	.1994	.9799	.2035	4.9152	30
40	.2022	.9793	.2065	4.8430	20
50	.2051	.9787	.2095	4.7729	10
12° 00′	.2079	.9781	.2126	4.7046	78° 00′
10	.2108	.9775	.2156	4.6382	50
20	.2136	.9769	.2186	4.5736	40
30	.2164	.9763	.2217	4.5107	30
40	.2193	.9757	.2247	4.4494	20
50	.2221	.9750	.2278	4.3897	10
13° 00′	.2250	.9744	.2309	4.3315	77° 00′
10	.2278	.9737	.2339	4.2747	50
20	.2306	.9730	.2370	4.2193	40
30	.2334	.9724	.2401	4.1653	30
40	.2363	.9717	.2432	4.1126	20
50	.2391	.9710	.2462	4.0611	10
14° 00′	.2419	.9703	.2493	4.0108	76° 00′
10	.2447	.9696	.2524	3.9617	50
20	.2476	.9689	.2555	3.9136	40
30	.2504	.9681	.2586	3.8667	30
40	.2532	.9674	.2617	3.8208	20
50	.2560	.9667	.2648	3.7760	10
15° 00′	.2588	.9659	.2679	3.7321	75° 00′
10	.2616	.9652	.2711	3.6891	50
20	.2644	.9644	.2742	3.6470	40
30	.2672	.9636	.2773	3.6059	30
40	.2700	.9628	.2805	3.5656	20
50	.2728	.9621	.2836	3.5261	10
Angles	Cosines	Sines	Cotangents	Tangents	Angles

Table 1 *(continued)*

NATURAL TRIGONOMETRIC FUNCTIONS

Angles	Sines	Cosines	Tangents	Cotangents	Angles
16° 00′	.2756	.9613	.2867	3.4874	74° 00′
10	.2784	.9605	.2899	3.4495	50
20	.2812	.9596	.2931	3.4124	40
30	.2840	.9588	.2962	3.3759	30
40	.2868	.9580	.2994	3.3402	20
50	.2896	.9572	.3026	3.3052	10
17° 00′	.2924	.9563	.3057	3.2709	73° 00′
10	.2952	.9555	.3089	3.2371	50
20	.2979	.9546	.3121	3.2041	40
30	.3007	.9537	.3153	3.1716	30
40	.3035	.9528	.3185	3.1397	20
50	.3062	.9520	.3217	3.1084	10
18° 00′	.3090	.9511	.3249	3.0777	72° 00′
10	.3118	.9502	.3281	3.0475	50
20	.3145	.9492	.3314	3.0178	40
30	.3173	.9483	.3346	2.9887	30
40	.3201	.9474	.3378	2.9600	20
50	.3228	.9465	.3411	2.9319	10
19° 00′	.3256	.9455	.3443	2.9042	71° 00′
10	.3283	.9446	.3476	2.8770	50
20	.3311	.9436	.3508	2.8502	40
30	.3338	.9426	.3541	2.8239	30
40	.3365	.9417	.3574	2.7980	20
50	.3393	.9407	.3607	2.7725	10
20° 00′	.3420	.9397	.3640	2.7475	70° 00′
10	.3448	.9387	.3673	2.7228	50
20	.3475	.9377	.3706	2.6985	40
30	.3502	.9367	.3739	2.6746	30
40	.3529	.9356	3772	2.6511	20
50	.3557	.9346	.3805	2.6279	10
21° 00′	.3584	.9336	.3839	2.6051	69° 00′
10	.3611	.9325	.3872	2.5826	50
20	.3638	.9315	.3906	2.5605	40
30	.3665	.9304	.3939	2.5386	30
40	.3692	.9293	.3973	2.5172	20
50	.3719	.9283	.4006	2.4960	10
22° 00′	.3746	.9272	.4040	2.4751	68° 00′
10	.3773	.9261	.4074	2.4545	50
20	.3800	.9250	.4108	2.4342	40
30	.3827	.9239	.4142	2.4142	30
40	.3854	.9228	.4176	2.3945	20
50	.3881	.9216	.4210	2.3750	10
23° 00′	.3907	.9205	.4245	2.3559	67° 00′
10	.3934	.9194	.4279	2.3369	50
20	.3961	.9182	.4314	2.3183	40
30	.3987	.9171	.4348	2.2998	30
40	.4014	.9159	.4383	2.2817	20
50	.4041	.9147	.4417	2.2637	10
Angles	Cosines	Sines	Cotangents	Tangents	Angles

Table 1 *(continued)*

Natural Trigonometric Functions

Angles	Sines	Cosines	Tangents	Cotangents	Angles
24° 00′	.4067	.9135	.4452	2.2460	66° 00′
10	.4094	.9124	.4487	2.2286	50
20	.4120	.9122	.4522	2.2113	40
30	.4147	.9100	.4557	2.1943	30
40	.4173	.9088	.4592	2.1775	20
50	.4200	.9075	.4628	2.1609	10
25° 00′	.4226	.9063	.4663	2.1445	65° 00′
10	.4253	.9051	.4699	2.1283	50
20	.4279	.9038	.4734	2.1123	40
30	.4305	.9026	.4770	2.0965	30
40	.4331	.9013	.4806	2.0809	20
50	.4358	.9001	.4841	2.0655	10
26° 00′	.4384	.8988	.4877	2.0503	64° 00′
10	.4410	.8975	.4913	2.0353	50
20	.4436	.8962	.4950	2.0204	40
30	.4462	.8949	.4986	2.0057	30
40	.4488	.8936	.5022	1.9912	20
50	.4514	.8923	.5059	1.9768	10
27° 00′	.4540	.8910	.5095	1.9626	63° 00′
10	.4566	.8897	.5132	1.9486	50
20	.4592	.8884	.5169	1.9347	40
30	.4617	.8870	.5206	1.9210	30
40	.4643	.8857	.5243	1.9074	20
50	.4669	.8843	.5280	1.8940	10
28° 00′	.4695	.8829	.5317	1.8807	62° 00′
10	.4720	.8816	.5354	1.8676	50
20	.4746	.8802	.5392	1.8546	40
30	.4772	.8788	.5430	1.8418	30
40	.4797	.8774	.5467	1.8291	20
50	.4823	.8760	.5505	1.8165	10
29° 00′	.4848	.8746	.5543	1.8040	61° 00′
10	.4874	.8732	.5581	1.7917	50
20	.4899	.8718	.5619	1.7796	40
30	.4924	.8704	.5658	1.7675	30
40	.4950	.8689	.5696	1.7556	20
50	.4975	.8675	.5735	1.7437	10
30° 00′	.5000	.8660	.5774	1.7321	60° 00′
10	.5025	.8646	.5812	1.7205	50
20	.5050	.8631	.5851	1.7090	40
30	.5075	.8616	.5890	1.6977	30
40	.5100	.8601	.5930	1.6864	20
50	.5125	.8587	.5969	1.6753	10
31° 00′	.5150	.8572	.6009	1.6643	59° 00′
10	.5175	.8557	.6048	1.6534	50
20	.5200	.8542	.6088	1.6426	40
30	.5225	.8526	.6128	1.6319	30
40	.5250.	.8511	.6168	1.6212	20
50	.5275	.8496	.6208	1.6107	10
Angles	Cosines	Sines	Cotangents	Tangents	Angles

Table 1 *(continued)*

NATURAL TRIGONOMETRIC FUNCTIONS

Angles	Sines	Cosines	Tangents	Cotangents	Angles
32° 00′	.5299	.8480	.6249	1.6003	58° 00′
10	.5324	.8465	.6289	1.5900	50
20	.5348	.8450	.6330	1.5798	40
30	.5373	.8434	.6371	1.5697	30
40	.5398	.8418	.6412	1.5597	20
50	.5422	.8403	.6453	1.5497	10
33° 00′	.5446	.8387	.6494	1.5399	57° 00′
10	.5471	.8371	.6536	1.5301	50
20	.5495	.8355	.6577	1.5204	40
30	.5519	.8339	.6619	1.5108	30
40	.5544	.8323	.6661	1.5013	20
50	.5568	.8307	.6703	1.4919	10
34° 00′	.5592	.8290	.6745	1.4826	56° 00′
10	.5616	.8274	.6787	1.4733	50
20	.5640	.8258	.6830	1.4641	40
30	.5664	.8241	.6873	1.4550	30
40	.5688	.8225	.6916	1.4460	20
50	.5712	.8208	.6959	1.4370	10
35° 00′	.5736	.8192	.7002	1.4281	55° 00′
10	.5760	.8175	.7046	1.4193	50
20	.5783	.8158	.7089	1.4106	40
30	.5807	.8141	.7133	1.4019	30
40	.5831	.8124	.7177	1.3934	20
50	.5854	.8107	.7221	1.3848	10
36° 00′	.5878	.8090	.7265	1.3764	54° 00′
10	.5901	.8073	.7310	1.3680	50
20	.5925	.8056	.7355	1.3597	40
30	.5948	.8039	.7400	1.3514	30
40	.5972	.8021	.7445	1.3432	20
50	.5995	.8004	.7490	1.3351	10
37° 00′	.6018	.7986	.7536	1.3270	53° 00′
10	.6041	.7969	.7581	1.3190	50
20	.6065	.7951	.7627	1.3111	40
30	.6088	.7934	.7673	1.3032	30
40	.6111	.7916	.7720	1.2954	20
50	.6134	.7898	.7766	1.2876	10
38° 00′	.6157	.7880	.7813	1.2799	52° 00′
10	.6180	.7862	.7860	1.2723	50
20	.6202	.7844	.7907	1.2647	40
30	.6225	.7826	.7954	1.2572	30
40	.6248	.7808	.8002	1.2497	20
50	.6271	.7790	.8050	1.2423	10
39° 00′	.6293	.7771	.8098	1.2349	51° 00′
10	.6316	.7753	.8146	1.2276	50
20	.6338	.7735	.8195	1.2203	40
30	.6361	.7716	.8243	1.2131	30
40	.6383	.7698	.8292	1.2059	20
50	.6406	.7679	.8342	1.1988	10
Angles	Cosines	Sines	Cotangents	Tangents	Angles

Table 1 *(continued)*

NATURAL TRIGONOMETRIC FUNCTIONS

Angles	Sines	Cosines	Tangents	Cotangents	Angles
40° 00′	.6428	.7660	.8391	1.1918	50° 00′
10	.6450	.7642	.8441	1.1847	50
20	.6472	.7623	.8491	1.1778	40
30	.6494	.7604	.8541	1.1708	30
40	.6517	.7585	.8591	1.1640	20
50	.6539	.7566	.8642	1.1571	10
41° 00′	.6561	.7547	.8693	1.1504	49° 00′
10	.6583	.7528	.8744	1.1436	50
20	.6604	.7509	.8796	1.1369	40
30	.6626	.7490	.8847	1.1303	30
40	.6648	.7470	.8899	1.1237	20
50	.6670	.7451	.8952	1.1171	10
42° 00′	.6691	.7431	.9004	1.1106	48° 00′
10	.6713	.7412	.9057	1.1041	50
20	.6734	.7392	.9110	1.0977	40
30	.6756	.7373	.9163	1.0913	30
40	.6777	.7353	.9217	1.0850	20
50	.6799	.7333	.9271	1.0786	10
43° 00′	.6820	.7314	.9325	1.0724	47° 00′
10	.6841	.7294	.9380	1.0661	50
20	.6862	.7274	.9435	1.0599	40
30	.6884	.7254	.9490	1.0538	30
40	.6905	.7234	.9545	1.0477	20
50	.6926	.7214	.9601	1.0416	10
44° 00′	.6947	.7193	.9657	1.0355	46° 00′
10	.6967	.7173	.9713	1.0295	50
20	.6988	.7153	.9770	1.0235	40
30	.7009	.7133	.9827	1.0176	30
40	.7030	.7112	.9884	1.0117	20
50	.7050	.7092	.9942	1.0058	10
45° 00′	.7071	.7071	1.0000	1.0000	45° 00′
Angles	Cosines	Sines	Cotangents	Tangents	Angles

Table 2

COMMON LOGARITHMS

N	0	1	2	3	4	5	6	7	8	9
10	0000	0043	0086	0128	0170	0212	0253	0294	0334	0374
11	0414	0453	0492	0531	0569	0607	0645	0682	0719	0755
12	0792	0828	0864	0899	0934	0969	1004	1038	1072	1106
13	1139	1173	1206	1239	1271	1303	1335	1367	1399	1430
14	1461	1492	1523	1553	1584	1614	1644	1673	1703	1732
15	1761	1790	1818	1847	1875	1903	1931	1959	1987	2014
16	2041	2068	2095	2122	2148	2175	2201	2227	2253	2279
17	2304	2330	2355	2380	2405	2430	2455	2480	2504	2529
18	2553	2577	2601	2625	2648	2672	2695	2718	2742	2765
19	2788	2810	2833	2856	2878	2900	2923	2945	2967	2989
20	3010	3032	3054	3075	3096	3118	3139	3160	3181	3201
21	3222	3243	3263	3284	3304	3324	3345	3365	3385	3404
22	3424	3444	3464	3483	3502	3522	3541	3560	3579	3598
23	3617	3636	3655	3674	3692	3711	3729	3747	3766	3784
24	3802	3820	3838	3856	3874	3892	3909	3927	3945	3962
25	3979	3997	4014	4031	4048	4065	4082	4099	4116	4133
26	4150	4166	4183	4200	4216	4232	4249	4265	4281	4298
27	4314	4330	4346	4362	4378	4393	4409	4425	4440	4456
28	4472	4487	4502	4518	4533	4548	4564	4579	4594	4609
29	4624	4639	4654	4669	4683	4698	4713	4728	4742	4757
30	4771	4786	4800	4814	4829	4843	4857	4871	4886	4900
31	4914	4928	4942	4955	4969	4983	4997	5011	5024	5038
32	5051	5065	5079	5092	5105	5119	5132	5145	5159	5172
33	5185	5198	5211	5224	5237	5250	5263	5276	5289	5302
34	5315	5328	5340	5353	5366	5378	5391	5403	5416	5428
35	5441	5453	5465	5478	5490	5502	5514	5527	5539	5551
36	5563	5575	5587	5599	5611	5623	5635	5647	5658	5670
37	5682	5694	5705	5717	5729	5740	5752	5763	5775	5786
38	5798	5809	5821	5832	5843	5855	5866	5877	5888	5899
39	5911	5922	5933	5944	5955	5966	5977	5988	5999	6010
40	6021	6031	6042	6053	6064	6075	6085	6096	6107	6117
41	6128	6138	6149	6160	6170	6180	6191	6201	6212	6222
42	6232	6243	6253	6263	6274	6284	6294	6304	6314	6325
43	6335	6345	6355	6365	6375	6385	6395	6405	6415	6425
44	6435	6444	6454	6464	6474	6484	6493	6503	6513	6522
45	6532	6542	6551	6561	6571	6580	6590	6599	6609	6618
46	6628	6637	6646	6656	6665	6675	6684	6693	6702	6712
47	6721	6730	6739	6749	6758	6767	6776	6785	6794	6803
48	6812	6821	6830	6839	6848	6857	6866	6875	6884	6893
49	6902	6911	6920	6928	6937	6946	6955	6964	6972	6981
50	6990	6998	7007	7016	7024	7033	7042	7050	7059	7067
51	7076	7084	7093	7101	7110	7118	7126	7135	7143	7152
52	7160	7168	7177	7185	7193	7202	7210	7218	7226	7235
53	7243	7251	7259	7267	7275	7284	7292	7300	7308	7316
54	7324	7332	7340	7348	7356	7364	7372	7380	7388	7396

Table 2 *(continued)*

COMMON LOGARITHMS

N	0	1	2	3	4	5	6	7	8	9
55	7404	7412	7419	7427	7435	7443	7451	7459	7466	7474
56	7482	7490	7497	7505	7513	7520	7528	7536	7543	7551
57	7559	7566	7574	7582	7589	7597	7604	7612	7619	7627
58	7634	7642	7649	7657	7664	7672	7679	7686	7694	7701
59	7709	7716	7723	7731	7738	7745	7752	7760	7767	7774
60	7782	7789	7796	7803	7810	7818	7825	7832	7839	7846
61	7853	7860	7868	7875	7882	7889	7896	7903	7910	7917
62	7924	7931	7938	7945	7952	7959	7966	7973	7980	7987
63	7993	8000	8007	8014	8021	8028	8035	8041	8048	8055
64	8062	8069	8075	8082	8089	8096	8102	8109	8116	8122
65	8129	8136	8142	8149	8156	8162	8169	8176	8182	8189
66	8195	8202	8209	8215	8222	8228	8235	8241	8248	8254
67	8261	8267	8274	8280	8287	8293	8299	8306	8312	8319
68	8325	8331	8338	8344	8351	8357	8363	8370	8376	8382
69	8388	8395	8401	8407	8414	8420	8426	8432	8439	8445
70	8451	8457	8463	8470	8476	8482	8488	8494	8500	8506
71	8513	8519	8525	8531	8537	8543	8549	8555	8561	8567
72	8573	8579	8585	8591	8597	8603	8609	8615	8621	8627
73	8633	8639	8645	8651	8657	8663	8669	8675	8681	8686
74	8692	8698	8704	8710	8716	8722	8727	8733	8739	8745
75	8751	8756	8762	8768	8774	8779	8785	8791	8797	8802
76	8808	8814	8820	8825	8831	8837	8842	8848	8854	8859
77	8865	8871	8876	8882	8887	8893	8899	8904	8910	8915
78	8921	8927	8932	8938	8943	8949	8954	8960	8965	8971
79	8976	8982	8987	8993	8998	9004	9009	9015	9020	9025
80	9031	9036	9042	9047	9053	9058	9063	9069	9074	9079
81	9085	9090	9096	9101	9106	9112	9117	9122	9128	9133
82	9138	9143	9149	9154	9159	9165	9170	9175	9180	9186
83	9191	9196	9201	9206	9212	9217	9222	9227	9232	9238
84	9243	9248	9253	9258	9263	9269	9274	9279	9284	9289
85	9294	9299	9304	9309	9315	9320	9325	9330	9335	9340
86	9345	9350	9355	9360	9365	9370	9375	9380	9385	9390
87	9395	9400	9405	9410	9415	9420	9425	9430	9435	9440
88	9445	9450	9455	9460	9465	9469	9474	9479	9484	9489
89	9494	9499	9504	9509	9513	9518	9523	9528	9533	9538
90	9542	9547	9552	9557	9562	9566	9571	9576	9581	9586
91	9590	9595	9600	9605	9609	9614	9619	9624	9628	9633
92	9638	9643	9647	9652	9657	9661	9666	9671	9675	9680
93	9685	9689	9694	9699	9703	9708	9713	9717	9722	9727
94	9731	9736	9741	9745	9750	9754	9759	9763	9768	9773
95	9777	9782	9786	9791	9795	9800	9805	9809	9814	9818
96	9823	9827	9832	9836	9841	9845	9850	9854	9859	9863
97	9868	9872	9877	9881	9886	9890	9894	9899	9903	9908
98	9912	9917	9921	9926	9930	9934	9939	9943	9948	9952
99	9956	9961	9965	9969	9974	9978	9983	9987	9991	9996

Table 3

HYPERBOLIC OR NAPERIAN LOGARITHMS

No.	H. Log.	No.	H. Log.	No.	H. Log.	No.	H. Log.	No.	H. Log.
1.00	0.0000								
1.01	0.0099	1.51	0.4121	2.01	0.6981	2.51	0.9203	3.01	1.1019
1.02	0.0198	1.52	0.4187	2.02	0.7031	2.52	0.9243	3.02	1.1053
1.03	0.0296	1.53	0.4253	2.03	0.7080	2.53	0.9282	3.03	1.1086
1.04	0.0392	1.54	0.4318	2.04	0.7129	2.54	0.9322	3.04	1.1119
1.05	0.0488	1.55	0.4383	2.05	0.7178	2.55	0.9361	3.05	1.1151
1.06	0.0583	1.56	0.4447	2.06	0.7227	2.56	0.9400	3.06	1.1184
1.07	0.0677	1.57	0.4511	2.07	0.7275	2.57	0.9439	3.07	1.1216
1.08	0.0770	1.58	0.4574	2.08	0.7324	2.58	0.9478	3.08	1.1249
1.09	0.0862	1.59	0.4637	2.09	0.7372	2.59	0.9517	3.09	1.1282
1.10	0.0953	1.60	0.4700	2.10	0.7419	2.60	0.9555	3.10	1.1314
1.11	0.1044	1.61	0.4762	2.11	0.7467	2.61	0.9594	3.11	1.1346
1.12	0.1133	1.62	0.4824	2.12	0.7514	2.62	0.9632	3.12	1.1378
1.13	0.1222	1.63	0.4886	2.13	0.7561	2.63	0.9670	3.13	1.1410
1.14	0.1310	1.64	0.4947	2.14	0.7608	2.64	0.9708	3.14	1.1442
1.15	0.1398	1.65	0.5008	2.15	0.7655	2.65	0.9746	3.15	1.1474
1.16	0.1484	1.66	0.5068	2.16	0.7701	2.66	0.9783	3.16	1.1506
1.17	0.1570	1.67	0.5128	2.17	0.7747	2.67	0.9821	3.17	1.1537
1.18	0.1655	1.68	0.5188	2.18	0.7793	2.68	0.9858	3.18	1.1569
1.19	0.1740	1.69	0.5247	2.19	0.7839	2.69	0.9895	3.19	1.1600
1.20	0.1823	1.70	0.5306	2.20	0.7885	2.70	0.9933	3.20	1.1632
1.21	0.1906	1.71	0.5365	2.21	0.7930	2.71	0.9969	3.21	1.1663
1.22	0.1988	1.72	0.5423	2.22	0.7975	2.72	1.0006	3.22	1.1694
1.23	0.2070	1.73	0.5481	2.23	0.8020	2.73	1.0043	3.23	1.1725
1.24	0.2151	1.74	0.5539	2.24	0.8065	2.74	1.0080	3.24	1.1756
1.25	0.2231	1.75	0.5596	2.25	0.8109	2.75	1.0116	3.25	1.1787
1.26	0.2311	1.76	0.5653	2.26	0.8154	2.76	1.0152	3.26	1.1817
1.27	0.2390	1.77	0.5710	2.27	0.8198	2.77	1.0188	3.27	1.1848
1.28	0.2469	1.78	0.5766	2.28	0.8242	2.78	1.0225	3.28	1.1878
1.29	0.2546	1.79	0.5822	2.29	0.8286	2.79	1.0260	3.29	1.1909
1.30	0.2624	1.80	0.5878	2.30	0.8329	2.80	1.0296	3.30	1.1939
1.31	0.2700	1.81	0.5933	2.31	0.8372	2.81	1.0332	3.31	1.1969
1.32	0.2776	1.82	0.5988	2.32	0.8416	2.82	1.0367	3.32	1.1999
1.33	0.2852	1.83	0.6043	2.33	0.8458	2.83	1.0403	3.33	1.2030
1.34	0.2927	1.84	0.6098	2.34	0.8502	2.84	1.0438	3.34	1.2060
1.35	0.3001	1.85	0.6152	2.35	0.8544	2.85	1.0473	3.35	1.2090
1.36	0.3075	1.86	0.6206	2.36	0.8587	2.86	1.0508	3.36	1.2119
1.37	0.3148	1.87	0.6259	2.37	0.8629	2.87	1.0543	3.37	1.2149
1.38	0.3221	1.88	0.6313	2.38	0.8671	2.88	1.0578	3.38	1.2179
1.39	0.3293	1.89	0.6366	2.39	0.8713	2.89	1.0613	3.39	1.2208
1.40	0.3365	1.90	0.6419	2.40	0.8755	2.90	1.0647	3.40	1.2238
1.41	0.3436	1.91	0.6471	2.41	0.8796	2.91	1.0682	3.41	1.2267
1.42	0.3507	1.92	0.6523	2.42	0.8838	2.92	1.0716	3.42	1.2296
1.43	0.3577	1.93	0.6575	2.43	0.8879	2.93	1.0750	3.43	1.2326
1.44	0.3646	1.94	0.6627	2.44	0.8920	2.94	1.0784	3.44	1.2355
1.45	0.3716	1.95	0.6678	2.45	0.8961	2.95	1.0818	3.45	1.2384
1.46	0.3784	1.96	0.6729	2.46	0.9002	2.96	1.0852	3.46	1.2413
1.47	0.3853	1.97	0.6780	2.47	0.9042	2.97	1.0886	3.47	1.2442
1.48	0.3920	1.98	0.6831	2.48	0.9083	2.98	1.0919	3.48	1.2470
1.49	0.3988	1.99	0.6881	2.49	0.9123	2.99	1.0953	3.49	1.2499
1.50	0.4055	2.00	0.6931	2.50	0.9163	3.00	1.0986	3.50	1.2528

Table 3 *(continued)*

HYPERBOLIC OR NAPERIAN LOGARITHMS

No.	H. Log.	No.	H. Log.	No.	H. Log.	No.	H. Log.	No.	H. Log.
3.51	1.2556	4.01	1.3888	4.51	1.5063	5.01	1.6114	5.51	1.7066
3.52	1.2585	4.02	1.3913	4.52	1.5085	5.02	1.6134	5.52	1.7084
3.53	1.2613	4.03	1.3938	4.53	1.5107	5.03	1.6154	5.53	1.7102
3.54	1.2641	4.04	1.3962	4.54	1.5129	5.04	1.6174	5.54	1.7120
3.55	1.2669	4.05	1.3987	4.55	1.5151	5.05	1.6194	5.55	1.7138
3.56	1.2698	4.06	1.4012	4.56	1.5173	5.06	1.6214	5.56	1.7156
3.57	1.2726	4.07	1.4036	4.57	1.5195	5.07	1.6233	5.57	1.7174
3.58	1.2754	4.08	1.4061	4.58	1.5217	5.08	1.6253	5.58	1.7192
3.59	1.2782	4.09	1.4085	4.59	1.5239	5.09	1.6273	5.59	1.7210
3.60	1.2809	4.10	1.4110	4.60	1.5261	5.10	1.6292	5.60	1.7228
3.61	1.2837	4.11	1.4134	4.61	1.5282	5.11	1.6312	5.61	1.7246
3.62	1.2865	4.12	1.4159	4.62	1.5304	5.12	1.6332	5.62	1.7263
3.63	1.2892	4.13	1.4183	4.63	1.5326	5.13	1.6351	5.63	1.7281
3.64	1.2920	4.14	1.4207	4.64	1.5347	5.14	1.6371	5.64	1.7299
3.65	1.2947	4.15	1.4231	4.65	1.5369	5.15	1.6390	5.65	1.7317
3.66	1.2975	4.16	1.4255	4.66	1.5390	5.16	1.6409	5.66	1.7334
3.67	1.3002	4.17	1.4279	4.67	1.5412	5.17	1.6429	5.67	1.7352
3.68	1.3029	4.18	1.4303	4.68	1.5433	5.18	1.6448	5.68	1.7370
3.69	1.3056	4.19	1.4327	4.69	1.5454	5.19	1.6467	5.69	1.7387
3.70	1.3083	4.20	1.4351	4.70	1.5476	5.20	1.6487	5.70	1.7405
3.71	1.3110	4.21	1.4375	4.71	1.5497	5.21	1.6506	5.71	1.7422
3.72	1.3137	4.22	1.4398	4.72	1.5518	5.22	1.6525	5.72	1.7440
3.73	1.3164	4.23	1.4422	4.73	1.5539	5.23	1.6544	5.73	1.7457
3.74	1.3191	4.24	1.4446	4.74	1.5560	5.24	1.6563	5.74	1.7475
3.75	1.3218	4.25	1.4469	4.75	1.5581	5.25	1.6582	5.75	1.7492
3.76	1.3244	4.26	1.4493	4.76	1.5602	5.26	1.6601	5.76	1.7509
3.77	1.3271	4.27	1.4516	4.77	1.5623	5.27	1.6620	5.77	1.7527
3.78	1.3297	4.28	1.4540	4.78	1.5644	5.28	1.6639	5.78	1.7544
3.79	1.3324	4.29	1.4563	4.79	1.5665	5.29	1.6658	5.79	1.7561
3.80	1.3350	4.30	1.4586	4.80	1.5686	5.30	1.6677	5.80	1.7579
3.81	1.3376	4.31	1.4609	4.81	1.5707	5.31	1.6696	5.81	1.7596
3.82	1.3403	4.32	1.4633	4.82	1.5728	5.32	1.6715	5.82	1.7613
3.83	1.3429	4.33	1.4656	4.83	1.5748	5.33	1.6734	5.83	1.7630
3.84	1.3455	4.34	1.4679	4.84	1.5769	5.34	1.6752	5.84	1.7647
3.85	1.3481	4.35	1.4702	4.85	1.5790	5.35	1.6771	5.85	1.7664
3.86	1.3507	4.36	1.4725	4.86	1.5810	5.36	1.6790	5.86	1.7681
3.87	1.3533	4.37	1.4748	4.87	1.5831	5.37	1.6808	5.87	1.7699
3.88	1.3558	4.38	1.4770	4.88	1.5851	5.38	1.6827	5.88	1.7716
3.89	1.3584	4.39	1.4793	4.89	1.5872	5.39	1.6845	5.89	1.7733
3.90	1.3610	4.40	1.4816	4.90	1.5892	5.40	1.6864	5.90	1.7750
3.91	1.3635	4.41	1.4839	4.91	1.5913	5.41	1.6882	5.91	1.7766
3.92	1.3661	4.42	1.4861	4.92	1.5933	5.42	1.6901	5.92	1.7783
3.93	1.3686	4.43	1.4884	4.93	1.5953	5.43	1.6919	5.93	1.7800
3.94	1.3712	4.44	1.4907	4.94	1.5974	5.44	1.6938	5.94	1.7817
3.95	1.3737	4.45	1.4929	4.95	1.5994	5.45	1.6956	5.95	1.7834
3.96	1.3762	4.46	1.4951	4.96	1.6014	5.46	1.6974	5.96	1.7851
3.97	1.3788	4.47	1.4974	4.97	1.6034	5.47	1.6993	5.97	1.7867
3.98	1.3813	4.48	1.4996	4.98	1.6054	5.48	1.7011	5.98	1.7884
3.99	1.3838	4.49	1.5019	4.99	1.6074	5.49	1.7029	5.99	1.7901
4.00	1.3863	4.50	1.5041	5.00	1.6094	5.50	1.7047	6.00	1.7918

Table 3 *(continued)*

HYPERBOLIC OR NAPERIAN LOGARITHMS

No.	H. Log.	No.	H. Log.	No.	H. Log.	No.	H. Log.	No.	H. Log.
6.01	1.7934	6.51	1.8733	7.01	1.9473	7.51	2.0162	8.01	2.0807
6.02	1.7951	6.52	1.8749	7.02	1.9488	7.52	2.0176	8.02	2.0819
6.03	1.7967	6.53	1.8764	7.03	1.9502	7.53	2.0189	8.03	2.0832
6.04	1.7984	6.54	1.8779	7.04	1.9516	7.54	2.0202	8.04	2.0844
6.05	1.8001	6.55	1.8795	7.05	1.9530	7.55	2.0215	8.05	2.0857
6.06	1.8017	6.56	1.8810	7.06	1.9544	7.56	2.0229	8.06	2.0869
6.07	1.8034	6.57	1.8825	7.07	1.9559	7.57	2.0242	8.07	2.0882
6.08	1.8050	6.58	1.8840	7.08	1.9573	7.58	2.0255	8.08	2.0894
6.09	1.8066	6.59	1.8856	7.09	1.9587	7.59	2.0268	8.09	2.0906
6.10	1.8083	6.60	1.8871	7.10	1.9601	7.60	2.0281	8.10	2.0919
6.11	1.8099	6.61	1.8886	7.11	1.9615	7.61	2.0295	8.11	2.0931
6.12	1.8116	6.62	1.8901	7.12	1.9629	7.62	2.0308	8.12	2.0943
6.13	1.8132	6.63	1.8916	7.13	1.9643	7.63	2.0321	8.13	2.0956
6.14	1.8148	6.64	1.8931	7.14	1.9657	7.64	2.0334	8.14	2.0968
6.15	1.8165	6.65	1.8946	7.15	1.9671	7.65	2.0347	8.15	2.0980
6.16	1.8181	6.66	1.8961	7.16	1.9685	7.66	2.0360	8.16	2.0992
6.17	1.8197	6.67	1.8976	7.17	1.9699	7.67	2.0373	8.17	2.1005
6.18	1.8213	6.68	1.8991	7.18	1.9713	7.68	2.0386	8.18	2.1017
6.19	1.8229	6.69	1.9006	7.19	1.9727	7.69	2.0399	8.19	2.1029
6.20	1.8245	6.70	1.9021	7.20	1.9741	7.70	2.0412	8.20	2.1041
6.21	1.8262	6.71	1.9036	7.21	1.9755	7.71	2.0425	8.21	2.1054
6.22	1.8278	6.72	1.9051	7.22	1.9769	7.72	2.0438	8.22	2.1066
6.23	1.8294	6.73	1.9066	7.23	1.9782	7.73	2.0451	8.23	2.1078
6.24	1.8310	6.74	1.9081	7.24	1.9796	7.74	2.0464	8.24	2.1090
6.25	1.8326	6.75	1.9095	7.25	1.9810	7.75	2.0477	8.25	2.1102
6.26	1.8342	6.76	1.9110	7.26	1.9824	7.76	2.0490	8.26	2.1114
6.27	1.8358	6.77	1.9125	7.27	1.9838	7.77	2.0503	8.27	2.1126
6.28	1.8374	6.78	1.9140	7.28	1.9851	7.78	2.0516	8.28	2.1138
6.29	1.8390	6.79	1.9155	7.29	1.9865	7.79	2.0528	8.29	2.1150
6.30	1.8405	6.80	1.9169	7.30	1.9879	7.80	2.0541	8.30	2.1163
6.31	1.8421	6.81	1.9184	7.31	1.9892	7.81	2.0554	8.31	2.1175
6.32	1.8437	6.82	1.9199	7.32	1.9906	7.82	2.0567	8.32	2.1187
6.33	1.8453	6.83	1.9213	7.33	1.9920	7.83	2.0580	8.33	2.1199
6.34	1.8469	6.84	1.9228	7.34	1.9933	7.84	2.0592	8.34	2.1211
6.35	1.8485	6.85	1.9242	7.35	1.9947	7.85	2.0605	8.35	2.1223
6.36	1.8500	6.86	1.9257	7.36	1.9961	7.86	2.0618	8.36	2.1235
6.37	1.8516	6.87	1.9272	7.37	1.9974	7.87	2.0631	8.37	2.1247
6.38	1.8532	6.88	1.9286	7.38	1.9988	7.88	2.0643	8.38	2.1258
6.39	1.8547	6.89	1.9301	7.39	2.0001	7.89	2.0656	8.39	2.1270
6.40	1.8563	6.90	1.9315	7.40	2.0015	7.90	2.0669	8.40	2.1282
6.41	1.8579	6.91	1.9330	7.41	2.0028	7.91	2.0681	8.41	2.1294
6.42	1.8594	6.92	1.9344	7.42	2.0041	7.92	2.0694	8.42	2.1306
6.43	1.8610	6.93	1.9359	7.43	2.0055	7.93	2.0707	8.43	2.1318
6.44	1.8625	6.94	1.9373	7.44	2.0069	7.94	2.0719	8.44	2.1330
6.45	1.8641	6.95	1.9387	7.45	2.0082	7.95	2.0732	8.45	2.1342
6.46	1.8656	6.96	1.9402	7.46	2.0096	7.96	2.0744	8.46	2.1353
6.47	1.8672	6.97	1.9416	7.47	2.0109	7.97	2.0757	8.47	2.1365
6.48	1.8687	6.98	1.9430	7.48	2.0122	7.98	2.0769	8.48	2.1377
6.49	1.8703	6.99	1.9445	7.49	2.0136	7.99	2.0782	8.49	2.1389
6.50	1.8718	7.00	1.9459	7.50	2.0149	8.00	2.0794	8.50	2.1401

Table 3 *(continued)*

HYPERBOLIC OR NAPERIAN LOGARITHMS

No.	H. Log.	No.	H. Log.	No.	H. Log.	No.	H. Log.	No.	H. Log.
8.51	2.1412	9.01	2.1983	9.51	2.2523	10.25	2.3273	41	3.7136
8.52	2.1424	9.02	2.1994	9.52	2.2534	10.50	2.3514	42	3.7377
8.53	2.1436	9.03	2.2006	9.53	2.2544	10.75	2.3749	43	3.7612
8.54	2.1448	9.04	2.2017	9.54	2.2555	11.00	2.3979	44	3.7842
8.55	2.1459	9.05	2.2028	9.55	2.2565	11.25	2.4204	45	3.8067
8.56	2.1471	9.06	2.2039	9.56	2.2576	11.50	2.4423	46	3.8286
8.57	2.1483	9.07	2.2050	9.57	2.2586	11.75	2.4638	47	3.8501
8.58	2.1494	9.08	2.2061	9.58	2.2597	12.00	2.4849	48	3.8712
8.59	2.1506	9.09	2.2072	9.59	2.2607	12.25	2.5055	49	3.8918
8.60	2.1518	9.10	2.2083	9.60	2.2618	12.50	2.5257	50	3.9120
8.61	2.1529	9.11	2.2094	9.61	2.2628	12.75	2.5455	51	3.9318
8.62	2.1541	9.12	2.2105	9.62	2.2638	13.00	2.5649	52	3.9512
8.63	2.1552	9.13	2.2116	9.63	2.2649	13.25	2.5840	53	3.9703
8.64	2.1564	9.14	2.2127	9.64	2.2659	13.50	2.6027	54	3.9890
8.65	2.1576	9.15	2.2138	9.65	2.2670	13.75	2.6210	55	4.0073
8.66	2.1587	9.16	2.2148	9.66	2.2680	14.00	2.6391	56	4.0254
8.67	2.1599	9.17	2.2159	9.67	2.2690	14.25	2.6568	57	4.0431
8.68	2.1610	9.18	2.2170	9.68	2.2701	14.50	2.6741	58	4.0604
8.69	2.1622	9.19	2.2181	9.69	2.2711	14.75	2.6912	59	4.0775
8.70	2.1633	9.20	2.2192	9.70	2.2721	15.00	2.7081	60	4.0943
8.71	2.1645	9.21	2.2203	9.71	2.2732	15.50	2.7408	61	4.1109
8.72	2.1656	9.22	2.2214	9.72	2.2742	16.00	2.7726	62	4.1271
8.73	2.1668	9.23	2.2225	9.73	2.2752	16.50	2.8034	63	4.1431
8.74	2.1679	9.24	2.2235	9.74	2.2762	17.00	2.8332	64	4.1589
8.75	2.1691	9.25	2.2246	9.75	2.2773	17.50	2.8622	65	4.1744
8.76	2.1702	9.26	2.2257	9.76	2.2783	18.00	2.8904	66	4.1897
8.77	2.1713	9.27	2.2268	9.77	2.2793	18.50	2.9178	67	4.2047
8.78	2.1725	9.28	2.2279	9.78	2.2803	19.00	2.9444	68	4.2195
8.79	2.1736	9.29	2.2289	9.79	2.2814	19.50	2.9704	69	4.2341
8.80	2.1748	9.30	2.2300	9.80	2.2824	20.00	2.9957	70	4.2485
8.81	2.1759	9.31	2.2311	9.81	2.2834	21	3.0445	71	4.2627
8.82	2.1770	9.32	2.2322	9.82	2.2844	22	3.0910	72	4.2767
8.83	2.1782	9.33	2.2332	9.83	2.2854	23	3.1355	73	4.2905
8.84	2.1793	9.34	2.2343	9.84	2.2865	24	3.1781	74	4.3041
8.85	2.1804	9.35	2.2354	9.85	2.2875	25	3.2189	75	4.3175
8.86	2.1815	9.36	2.2364	9.86	2.2885	26	3.2581	76	4.3307
8.87	2.1827	9.37	2.2375	9.87	2.2895	27	3.2958	77	4.3438
8.88	2.1838	9.38	2.2386	9.88	2.2905	28	3.3322	78	4.3567
8.89	2.1849	9.39	2.2396	9.89	2.2915	29	3.3673	79	4.3694
8.90	2.1861	9.40	2.2407	9.90	2.2925	30	3.4012	80	4.3820
8.91	2.1872	9.41	2.2418	9.91	2.2935	31	3.4340	82	4.4067
8.92	2.1883	9.42	2.2428	9.92	2.2946	32	3.4657	84	4.4308
8.93	2.1894	9.43	2.2439	9.93	2.2956	33	3.4965	86	4.4543
8.94	2.1905	9.44	2.2450	9.94	2.2966	34	3.5264	88	4.4773
8.95	2.1917	9.45	2.2460	9.95	2.2976	35	3.5553	90	4.4998
8.96	2.1928	9.46	2.2471	9.96	2.2986	36	3.5835	92	4.5218
8.97	2.1939	9.47	2.2481	9.97	2.2996	37	3.6109	94	4.5433
8.98	2.1950	9.48	2.2492	9.98	2.3006	38	3.6376	96	4.5643
8.99	2.1961	9.49	2.2502	9.99	2.3016	39	3.6636	98	4.5850
9.00	2.1972	9.50	2.2513	10.00	2.3026	40	3.6889	100	4.6052

Index

295